MOLLUSCS

BIOLOGICAL SCIENCES

Editor

PROFESSOR H. MUNRO FOX

M.A., F.R.S.

Emeritus Professor of Zoology
in the University of London

MOLLUSCS

J. E. MORTON
D.Sc.

Professor of Zoology,
Auckland University, New Zealand

HUTCHINSON UNIVERSITY LIBRARY

LONDON

HUTCHINSON & CO. (*Publishers*) LTD
178–202 Great Portland Street, London, W.1

London Melbourne Sydney
Auckland Bombay Toronto
Johannesburg New York

★

First published 1958
2nd edition 1963
3rd edition 1964

*This book has been set in Times New Roman,
printed in Great Britain on Antique Wove paper
by The Anchor Press, Ltd., and bound by Wm.
Brendon & Son Ltd., both of Tiptree, Essex.*

To

E. F. M.
(*in gratam memoriam*)

and

R. B. M.

CONTENTS

8 CONTENTS

PREFACE

There has been no general book on malacology written in England for forty-five years. This is a surprising fact, for in that time the Mollusca have suffered no lack of study. They have been the favourites of collectors and skilled amateur naturalists, and today form the experimental material of physiologists, neurologists, geneticists and biochemists. Molluscs are easily caught, patient of observation and wonderfully diverse in their adaptations. In particular, students of molluscs have been interested in what is now called 'functional morphology', though it was surely the aim of good zoologists in all ages to study structure with an eye to the working of the live animal, and to bring to the laboratory a knowledge of the animal's ecology and behaviour in the field.

I have attempted in this book to describe the evolution of the various functions of the molluscan body, and the organs responsible for them, and to say something of the relationships within the various classes of the phylum. There is today a very rich literature of the Mollusca, and even in an introductory book some things have had to be taken for granted. Many generic names have been introduced, as far as possible British, and there has been little space to characterize each of these examples in detail. It is hoped that the beginner will be able to profit from this book; but he will get most from it if he is already acquainted with the names of some common shells, or has, better still, dissected one of the molluscs described in elementary courses.

This work is not a detailed anatomical study, as such information is hardly lacking in various books and memoirs already. The selection of material has a personal bias, though to some extent it is justified by the outlook of present-day work. It is especially regretted that some of the smaller groups have had to be squeezed to narrow dimensions, and that more could not be said here about the conchological aspects of the molluscs. But where there was an opportunity to mention new facts or put old facts in a new light, I have frequently done this, rather than recall examples already familiar.

The classification of molluscs is bound to be complicated and I hope I have not made it needlessly so. It was outside the scope of this book to propound any formal or detailed classification. Instead, I have introduced with each chapter as much classification as seemed to be needed, and—as the argument proceeds—have tried to show the value of a natural classification in working use. In the three summing-up chapters the classification is examined in more detail. It is particularly hoped that the simplified Classification of Recent Mollusca (pp. 213-14) may help to smooth the reader's path. The detailed classification (Appendix 1) is in general that of Thiele, though recent knowledge has made some alterations really necessary. Appendix 1 goes down to the main families, and gives the modern prominence to the super-family (or *stirps*), as the largest unit in which natural relationships and evolution can generally be interpreted in detail.

Lack of direct reference in the text does not diminish my debt of gratitude to many authors, as will appear at once from the literature list. Here, some indication of the contents of papers is given, and—as the list had to be short—reference is made as far as possible to reviewing articles, and those which themselves give good summaries of literature.

There are many people for whose help I am grateful, earliest of all Dr. A. W. B. Powell, Assistant Director of Auckland Museum, N.Z., whose unsurpassed field and taxonomic knowledge of the molluscs and superb Shell Gallery, gave me my first interest in this group as a boy. From Dr. D. Atkins, Dr. A. M. Bidder, Dr. L. R. Cox, F.R.S., Dr. J. E. Forrest, Mr. N. A. Holme, the late Prof. J. H. Orton, F.R.S., Mr. G. Owen, Dr. H. E. Quick, Dr. W. J. Rees, Prof. J. E. Smith, F.R.S., and Dr. Gunnar Thorson I have had great kindness and help.

And to three workers especially, Professor C. M. Yonge, F.R.S., Professor Alastair Graham and Dr. Vera Fretter, I share with all students of the Mollusca a great debt. By their published papers and personal kindness they have helped me more than I can fully realize; and it is my hope that this book, for all its shortcomings, may do justice to some of the things I have learned from them.

July 1958   J. E. M.

I

INTRODUCTION AND GENERAL FEATURES

IT IS not difficult to recognize a mollusc. One looks first for a hard shell, a soft body and a slippery skin. The usual term 'shellfish' is too narrow, however, to include slugs and squids, and there is indeed no English vernacular name taking in the whole phylum Mollusca. In essentials molluscs are one of the most compact groups of animals; but there can be few phyla that show such wide diversity imposed on such a uniform plan. Most molluscs have no internal skeleton, and no stereotyped pattern, as in a segmented worm or a jointed arthropod. There is no standard molluscan shape, and in an evolutionary sense molluscs are plastic material. The outlines of the body are freely altered as new habits are acquired and new structures are needed. Though there are many exceptions, most molluscs are slow-moving and confined to rather special habitats. They bear the adaptive stamp of the environment in a far more obvious way than more active animals that can move about widely.

Molluscs range from limpets clinging to the rocks, to snails which crawl or dig or swim, to bivalves which anchor or burrow or bore, to cephalopods which torpedo through the water or lurk watchfully on the bottom. They penetrate all habitats: the abysses of the sea, coral reefs, mudflats, deserts and forests, rivers, lakes and under ground. They may become hidden as parasites in the interior of other animals. They feed on every possible food and vary in size from giant squids and clams to little snails a millimetre long. In number of species, the Mollusca are the second phylum to the Arthropoda: it is almost impossible to assess accurately the total of species—probably about 80,000, as compared with eight times as many insects but only half as many vertebrates. Three-quarters of the molluscs are gastropods, with about 1650 genera. The

lamellibranchs come next with 420. Third in numbers, but greatest
in size, are the cephalopods, with 150 genera.

There are six classes of molluscs, and it is hard for any definition to take account of all their variations. In this book we shall
survey the Mollusca from an evolutionary and adaptive point of
view, and try to recognize the trends running through the history of
each class. As others have done before, we must first present our own
concept of the early, primitive mollusc. The idea of an 'archimollusc' is a favourite and well-worked one. We have already had
archetypal snails, with conical shells poised at rakish angles, and
strange pelagic molluscs—half nautilus and half veliger. The danger
is that in mixing genealogical ideas with morphology our archetype
may become like an heraldic animal—a lowest common multiple of
incompatible organs.

A possible early mollusc has been reconstructed in Fig. 1A. It is
a slow-moving animal, with a low conical shell and a broad creeping
surface. It probably lived on a firm substratum in shallow inshore
waters. The molluscan body has two well-marked regions. The
anterior and lower part is firm and muscular and normally lies outside the shell, though it can be wholly retracted into it. This part is
sometimes known as the 'head-foot'. Though it has no common
name it is a real structural entity in all molluscs. It primitively forms
a flat foot on which the animal crawls by muscular waves, and a
head carrying a short snout bearing the mouth, and with eyes and
tentacles. The second part of the body is dorsal and posterior, and
never leaves the shell. It forms a soft, thin-walled visceral mass,
entirely non-muscular. Attached to the visceral mass, and hanging
freely from it, is a wide skirt called the mantle or pallium. This lines
the whole of the shell, which is secreted by its interior and free
margin. A large space lies between the mantle and the sides of the
body. It is deepest behind, where it is known as the *mantle cavity* or
pallial cavity, morphologically 'outside' the body, and forming—
like the shell—one of the leading features of the Mollusca.

The head-foot, though covered with cilia and mucous cells,
works chiefly by the action of muscles. The visceral mass and the
pallial cavity at this early stage rely most on the action of mucus and
cilia. The mollusc is thus divided into separate muscular and ciliary
components. The muscular animal is responsible for locomotion,

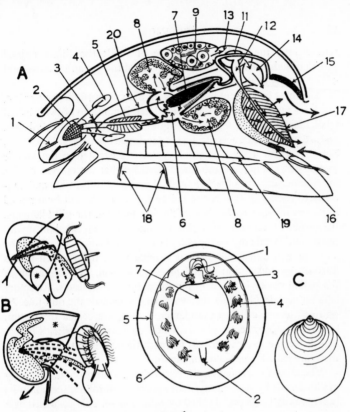

FIG. 1

A Schematic view of an ideal early mollusc, in side view. 1) jaws in buccal cavity, 2) radula on odontophore, 3) nerve ring, 4) salivary glands, 5) oesophageal glands, 6) stomach, 7) protostyle with food string, 8) paired digestive diverticula, 9) gonad, 11) ventricle and intestine, 12) left auricle, 13) pericardium, 14) left renal organ, 15) hypobranchial gland, 16) osphradium, 17) ctenidium (showing currents), 18) epipodial tentacles, 19) pedal nerve cords, 20) pallial nerve cords. (Certain structures, such as the organs of the head and the nerve cords, are turned so as to appear slightly in dorsal view, and the digestive diverticula have been displaced from their respective left and right positions.)

B Veliger of *Patella* before and after torsion, showing the relation of the asymmetrical shell muscle to the gut, and the movement in position of the mantle cavity, during the passage of the visceral mass through 180°.

* Mantle cavity.

C Simplified sketch of *Neopilina galatheae*, in ventral view, and (right) the shell in dorsal view on a smaller scale. 1) mouth, 2) anus, 3) palp-like appendages, 4) paired gill-like organs, 5) mantle, 6) shell rim, 7) foot.

retreat into the shell and capture of food; the ciliary animal carries out almost all the other functions of the gut and viscera, and of the organs in the pallial cavity.

The most prominent mantle organs are a pair of gills or *ctenidia*, one lying at either side of the cavity. Each is made up of two rows of triangular leaflets or *filaments* lying at either side of a central axis. Quite complicated tracts of cilia are developed upon the gill filaments. Some of these draw a respiratory water current into the mantle cavity, others intercept unwanted particles that the current carries in. A water current enters the pallial cavity at either side and ventrally to each gill. It is tested before it reaches the gill by a pallial sense organ—the *osphradium*. Filtering between the gill filaments, the currents meet near the dorsal mid-line, where an exhalant stream passes backwards out of the pallial cavity. In the line of exit lies the anus, and at either side of it is a renal pore, from which passes nitrogenous waste, and genital products as well. The sanitation of the pallial cavity is an early preoccupation of molluscs. Rejectory cilia on the gill filaments throw off waste towards the mid-line. As well as mucous cells on the filaments, there are beside the rectum two very large mucous glands which consolidate particles before they leave the cavity. Perhaps inappropriately, from their position, these are called *hypobranchial glands*.

The mouth is carried on the snout close to the ground. The early mollusc feeds by rasping up small particles and raking them into its buccal cavity by an organ called the *odontophore*. This is worked by a complex of small muscles and is a unique feature of the molluscs. It forms a broad tongue covered with a chitinous membrane, the *radula*, bearing very numerous teeth. The odontophore is alternately spread out and licked over the substratum and then withdrawn, taking its load of food into the mouth like a scoop. Mucus is provided by small 'salivary' glands and by the wall of the oesophagus. A series of small food boluses passes down the gut, bound into a continuous mucous rope as they go. The stomach of the early mollusc[132] is rather complicated. The food rope, as it passes in, becomes continuous with a stiff mucous rod which projects into the stomach from the intestine and is continuously rotated by cilia. This rod has been called the 'protostyle' and forms a windlass which helps to draw in the food from the oesophagus. As the string is rotated on the protostyle it is swept repeatedly over the ciliated wall of the stomach. Particles detached from it are here graded for size by the ridges of a *ciliary sorting area*. Small nutritive particles at length pass into one of the paired openings of the *digestive diverticula*, leading to the tubules of the bulky digestive gland. Here they are phagocytosed and digested within the cells. Coarser particles are plastered on to the protostyle or by-pass it into the intestine. Pieces of the rod itself are nipped off by muscular contractions at the far end and moulded into faeces as they pass back to the rectum.

The early mollusc is shown in Fig. 1A as having a heart consisting of a median ventricle and two lateral auricles. Into each auricle blood passes directly from the gill of the same side, and from the ventricle it is sent to the whole body by closed arteries. The true *coelom* is a very small space, just large enough to provide a pericardium round the heart, and to form a gonadial cavity in front of the pericardium. These two spaces communicate, and the eggs and sperms shed from the wall of the gonad pass into the pericardium. They are removed by paired *coelomoducts* which open into the mantle cavity, and these ducts have glandular walls which extract nitrogenous waste from the blood. In addition, the pericardial wall is itself excretory. Protonephridia with flame cells are found in molluscs only in some embryos; the permanent excretory organs are always open coelomoducts.

Most of the space round the viscera is not coelomic, but is filled with venous blood which drains there after transport round the body. This blood-filled space reaches into the spongy muscular meshwork of the head and foot, and may be referred to as a *haemocoele*, though this is a rather imprecise term. There is no evidence that the molluscan haemocoele was formed, as it is in Arthropoda, by true blood vessels encroaching on a large coelom. At all events, where the annelids and lower worms make use of coelomic fluid as a hydroskeleton, the molluscs employ the great volume of blood in the haemal spaces. This forms a malleable 'haemoskeleton' that can be manipulated by the muscles of the body wall. By appropriate shifting of blood the mollusc performs startling changes of shape. The foot is dilated, the proboscis extended or the whole head region enlarged as the animal expands from the shell.

A year ago (1957) such a description of the early molluscan

pericardial organs would have been accepted by almost everyone. We should have said that molluscs were never in their history segmented, that the pericardium and gonocoele were probably all the coelom they had ever developed, and that the gills, auricles and coelomoducts were primitively in one pair. We now know something of a new living mollusc which gives us a glimpse of an earlier condition. Till 1957 the Class Monoplacophora were known only as limpet-like fossils from the Cambrian to the Devonian. A living monoplacophoran has now been discovered by Dr. Henning Lemche of the Danish Galathea Expedition from a depth of 5000 metres off the Pacific Coast of Mexico.[121] This species—*Neopilina galatheae* (Fig. 1c)—has a flat, saucer-shaped shell, up to 4 cm. long, with a ventral foot, a mouth in front and the anus behind. Gills lie in shallow grooves between the mantle skirt and the foot, and these number five pairs! And more remarkable, the auricles, coelomoducts and possibly the gonads too are multiplied in the same way. The muscles attaching the animal to the shell are also metameric— eight on each side (some fossil shells show intermediate numbers of muscle scars). The genital products are shed directly through the coelomoducts and the sexes are separate. The animal is a detritus feeder and the gut has a small radula, a style sac and a long intestine. We can but wait impatiently for a full description of *Neopilina*. But already this fine discovery raises many questions as to the sort of ancestors that gave rise to the molluscs. Perhaps the larger number of gills and pericardial organs was widespread before their number was ultimately fixed at one pair.

We have no account yet of the nervous system of *Neopilina*; but in those early molluscs we know, e.g. the Amphineura, this is extremely simple—it hardly rises above flatworm level. The central portion is a ring surrounding the oesophagus, formed by a dorsal *cerebral* and a ventral *labial commissure*. Two pairs of parallel cords run back from this ring, *pleural cords* lying laterally and innervating the organs in the mantle cavity, and *pedal cords* running along the foot. Cross connections link these cords in ladder fashion. The cords themselves are studded with nerve cells, but the only neurones organized at this stage into ganglia are those of the buccal ganglia which control the odontophore. For the rest, apart from the muscles that withdraw it into the shell, the early mollusc is a slow-working creature, with little fast nervous control. Mucus and cilia serve most of its needs. The muscular parts are the buccal mass and the foot, but the general dominance of nerve and muscle is yet to come.

Sense organs are distributed at the points most exposed to stimuli. The paired tentacles on the head are tactile and probably gustatory. Eyes are formed by simple pigmented retinal cups. Small otocysts are embedded in the foot at the base of the nerve ring. An osphradium lies—as we have seen—at the base of each gill, forming a pallial sense testing the entering water current. Around the base of the foot runs an *epipodium*, a fringe like a false mantle, bearing delicate tentacles that come in contact with the substratum. They are probably both chemosensitive and tactile.

Fertilization is external. The eggs have no protective capsules and little yolk. They hatch after spiral cleavage into top-shaped *trochophore* larvae, with a ring of cilia, very like the larvae of annelid worms. A further larval organ soon appears, a wheel-shaped *velum*, fringed with long cilia. A foot develops upon the ventral side and a shell-gland near the lower pole soon secretes a horny larval shell.

No living mollusc is quite like this ideal ancestor. With the primitive Monoplacophora, there are six classes of living Mollusca, and each has emphasized in a different way certain of the features offered by the early form.

The six classes are:

1. The Monoplacophora.
2. The Amphineura—containing the chitons or coat-of-mail shells (Polyplacophora), together with two groups of aberrant deeper water forms, without shells (Aplacophora).
3. The Gastropoda—the largest and most diverse class, containing the spirally coiled snails, flat-shelled limpets, shell-less nudibranchs and terrestrial snails and slugs.
4. The Scaphopoda—a small class with only a few genera, typified by *Dentalium*, the elephant's tusk shell.
5. The Lamellibranchia—a much larger group including the shellfish with two valves such as mussels, oysters and clams.
6. The Cephalopoda—the most active and specialized of molluscs, with a chambered shell as in *Nautilus*, an internal shell as in squids and cuttlefish, or no shell at all as in octopods.

Though a small group, the Amphineura includes two very distinct subclasses. The chitons (Polyplacophora) are among the least altered of living molluscs but the other subclass (Aplacophora) is very specialized, itself made up of two groups, each containing aberrant worm-like molluscs that have lost the shell.

The Aplacophora (Fig. 2B) are non-littoral, but live in moderate depths to abyssal waters.[99] One series, the Chaetodermomorpha, feeds on organic muds and ooze; the other, the Neomeniomorpha, lives suctorially on the tissues of gorgonians and hydroids. In all species the body is covered by the shell-less mantle, in which are embedded minute calcareous spicules. The Neomeniomorpha have a narrow ventral pedal groove which is lacking in Chaetodermomorpha. Both groups are at first unlikely to be taken for molluscs, but they have several characteristics that stamp them as such beyond doubt—a simple radula in the buccal cavity, and a small posterior mantle cavity with an elementary gill or a true ctenidium. They are placed with the Amphineura because the internal anatomy, especially the nervous and excretory systems, hides some very archaic molluscan features. There are twenty-four genera of Neomeniomorpha (three British) and two of Chaetodermomorpha.

The Polyplacophora—including the chitons or coat-of-mail shells—have many of the features of our early primitive molluscs (Fig. 2A). They are flattened like limpets and the body is closely applied to the ground by the foot. The head and mouth are anterior, the anus posterior. The shell is divided into eight transverse plates, lying across the back. Round the margin of these and fitting closely to the ground runs a scaly or fleshy girdle. A chiton is thus adapted for clinging tightly to irregular surfaces. When detached it protects itself by rolling up like a woodlouse. The close-fitting habit has led to great modification of the mantle cavity. This now reaches forward to the head, as narrow side grooves lying between the girdle and the foot. The gills are no longer paired, but are secondarily multiplied into two long series, extending further forward until in higher chitons they reach the head. An inward passage for a water current can be made by temporarily lifting the girdle at any point. The pallial

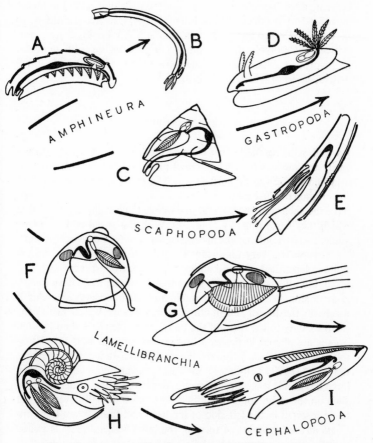

FIG. 2. The radiation of the five classes of the Mollusca (Monopla-cophora omitted)

The examples chosen are: Amphineura: A *Chiton* and B *Chaeto-derma*; Gastropoda: C *Trochus* and D *Doris*; Scaphopoda: E *Dentalium*; Lamellibranchia: F *Nucula* and G *Gari*; Cephalo-poda: H *Nautilus* and I *Sepia*. All the sketches are diagrammatic and severely simplified.

current, after bathing the gills, passes out behind with the faeces and excretory products.[208] The internal organs, such as the digestive, nervous and reproductive systems, remain on the whole very primitive. The Polyplacophora are a compact group with uniform, herbivorous habits. They include some six families with forty-three genera, seven of which are British.

THE GASTROPODA

As well as being the largest class of molluscs, the Gastropoda are easily the most varied. They crawl primitively by a flattened foot attached to the ventral surface which in many ways keeps close to the original mollusc pattern. Most gastropods, including the earliest, have the shell and the visceral mass coiled in a right-handed spiral which they carry dorsally (Fig. 2c). With this spiral coiling, many students have confused the process called *torsion* of the visceral mass.

Torsion is a very important event in gastropod history, and is quite independent of spiral coiling; some gastropods are not coiled at all, but all gastropods—at some time in phylogeny—have undergone torsion. We must try to explain how torsion occurs and what it means in the life of the mollusc. It is a change which brings the mantle cavity to the front of the body, while the visceral and pallial organs are altered in position by twisting through 180° in relation to the head and foot. From the diagram in Fig. 1B it can be seen that the mantle cavity before torsion faces backwards and ventrally. The larva has at this stage an asymmetric retractor muscle attached to the shell on the right, some of whose fibres sweep dorsally over the gut to be inserted in the left side of the head and foot. When this contracts at the beginning of torsion, the bulky visceral mass is pulled over from above towards the left. It is slung round the left side of the animal to a ventral position, and the mantle cavity at the same time moves up the right until it is dorsal and faces forwards.[58] Everything behind the 'neck'—which is the actual site of twisting—is thus reversed in position. Thus the gill, auricle and kidney that were at first left are now right, and *vice versa*. At the point of twisting, the two long nerve connectives running to the viscera are crossed in a figure of eight.

Torsion is a drastic process that would be impossible during adult growth. Yet in the larvae of *Acmaea* and *Trochus* its first stages through 90° take only a few hours, as the visceral mass is slung over to its new position by contraction of the asymmetric muscle. Later stages of torsion are added by asymmetric growth of the larva.

What is the value of torsion? More controversy has been devoted to the adaptive explanation of this change than to any other point of molluscan biology. The theory most favoured today and involving fewest improbabilities is Garstang's.[88] He held that torsion first took place as a larval mutation, of little direct use in the adult. Before torsion, when the veliger retreated from predators into its shell, the posterior mantle cavity could receive the head and velum only after the foot was already inside. With the mantle cavity to the front, the sensitive parts were no longer exposed; the head and velum could withdraw first, followed by the foot and later an operculum to seal the aperture. Such an explanation of torsion serves well enough if we are thinking of predators of medium size like chaetognaths or stinging coelenterates. But what of larger fish, such as herrings and mackerel, which must be the heaviest eaters of larvae and may swallow hundreds of veligers at one draught?

It is doubtful, too, whether the needs of the adult should be ruled out so completely. The initial value of torsion to the larva is obvious. But the pallial cavity is such a commanding feature of the adult that it cannot be an indifferent matter whether it opens in front or behind. In a freely moving gastropod it would seem moreover highly advantageous that the mantle cavity should be at the advancing end. This would convert it from primarily a cloaca with gills into an organ in sensitive touch with the environment of the head. As the animal orients by the sense organs of the head and makes continual small adjustments of position, the pallial opening would be so placed as to make immediate contact with every slight change of surroundings. The gills could now be bathed by undisturbed water from in front of the animal, and the osphradium continuously could sample the environment into which the animal was moving.[139]

After torsion, the anus lay in front and the animal could not conveniently grow longer. The viscera, including the loop of the gut, began to bulge in a dorsal hump, which could in turn be disposed most compactly by spiral coiling. In most living gastropods, the viscera have thus formed a helicoid, right-handed spiral. As the penultimate whorl of the spiral bulges into the right side of the mantle cavity, a new asymmetry is produced there and one set of pallial organs tends to be reduced and lost. To this we shall return later.

In one whole sub-class of gastropods, the Opisthobranchia (Fig. 2D), the shell and mantle cavity are reduced or wholly lost. Torsion and spiral coiling disappear with them and the body is re-organized on bilateral lines in the shape of a slug. Gastropods have also rivalled the cephalopods in producing pelagic swimmers—such as heteropods and pteropods. One sub-class—the Pulmonata—has become terrestrial, replacing the gill by a vascular lung.

THE SCAPHOPODA

The tusk shells are burrowing molluscs with a tapered shell, as if the conical cap of the early mollusc had been produced upwards into a slender tube open at either end (Fig. 2E). The shell projects obliquely from the sand, the broad end lying deepest and containing the head and foot. The foot is plug-shaped and can be extended and plunged into the sand, drawing the animal down by subsequent contraction. The head bears several bunches of slender retractile tentacles called *captacula*. These reach into the substratum to pick up foraminifera and very small molluscs that adhere to their expanded tips. The buccal mass has a large strong radula, and the stomach is simple, with paired digestive diverticula.

The mantle forms a complete tube, and the pallial cavity, on the ventral side of the body, runs right through the shell. Both inward and outward ciliary currents pass through the posterior end. There is no gill, respiration taking place through transverse folds in the lining of the mantle.[203] The blood circulates in a system of rudimentary sinuses, with merely a contractile portion near the anus serving as a heart. A pericardium is lacking, but there is a pair of small renal organs opening at either side of the anus. The sexes are separate, and there is a large median gonad, discharging its gametes through the right renal organ.[118]

The lamellibranchs or bivalves are in some ways the most highly modified of all the molluscs (Fig. 2G). They have completely lost the head, the buccal mass and the radula. They are a rather more uniform class than the Gastropoda, and the great majority are ciliary feeders with extreme development of the gills. The mantle cavity is much larger than in other molluscs and has quite dominated lamellibranch evolution. Two symmetrical mantle flaps enclose the whole body, and these secrete right and left shell valves hinged in the dorsal line. The shell can be tightly closed by the *adductor muscles*, which are the shell retractors of the early mollusc rearranged to run directly between the valves.

With few exceptions all lamellibranchs are sedentary. Some of them remain anchored to the substratum, or firmly cemented, as with oysters. Those that burrow do so by the use of the foot, which is usually a compressed muscular tongue that can be elongated and thrust forward in the substratum to haul the animal behind it.

The lamellibranch gills remain paired, and each consists of two plate-like *demibranchs* hanging in the mantle cavity at either side of the foot. In most bivalves their filaments have become bent back upon themselves like a V, so that each of the demibranchs is double and composed of two flat *lamellae*. The cilia of the gill draw a powerful water current into the mantle cavity; a typical lamellibranch filters thirty to sixty times its own volume of water in a hour. As the water passes between the filaments, food particles are held back by straining cilia and are carried forward by other cilia in mucous strings towards the mouth. Here they are carefully graded for size by ciliated labial palps before being ingested. Cilia and mucus are just as important in the gut as in the mantle cavity. The stomach is extremely elaborate, with large ciliary sorting areas and a long rotating style. Specialized as they are in the pallial and digestive organs, the bivalves are much less so in the reproductive, circulatory and excretory systems. These are but little altered in plan from those of early molluscs.

The pallial and visceral organs having developed at the expense of the head, most of the sense organs have quite withdrawn from the

23

anterior end. The margin of the mantle is now the site of contact with the environment, and develops abundant tactile organs and in some cases, as in the scallops, eyes as well.

The Protobranchia—typified by the British *Nucula*—are the earliest of the bivalves and they make the transition from more primitive molluscs easier to understand (Fig. 2F). Here the foot still has its flat sole. The gills, while already large, do not yet dominate the mantle cavity but lie in the primitive posterior position. Their filaments remain triangular. The largest pallial organs in *Nucula* are the labial palps, which lie behind the mouth, and these—rather than the gills—collect the food. They are prolonged into grooved tentacles or *palp proboscides*, which can be protruded from the shell to collect deposits from the substratum by ciliary action.

THE CEPHALOPODA

The Cephalopoda are not only the most elaborately evolved molluscs, but are entitled to pride of place among all the invertebrates. They are almost all fast-moving carnivores, and either pelagic or at least much more independent of the bottom than other molluscs. The class is named from the close union of the head with the foot, which has become much sub-divided to produce two new types of organ. First there is a series of prehensile tentacles which have spread completely around the head so that the mouth now lies at their centre. In primitive *Nautilus* (Fig. 2H) these tentacles are small and very numerous. In higher cephalopods (Fig. 2I) they form a set of eight or ten muscular arms, bearing long rows of suckers. The octopods have eight long arms equally developed, and the cuttlefish and squids a circlet of eight short arms and two long tentacular arms.

The second organ developed from part of the foot is a muscular spout or *funnel* lying behind the head at the posterior side of the animal, where the mantle cavity is situated. This controls the exit of water from the mantle cavity and produces a strong jet which is used in swimming. In its proper orientation, the body of a modern cephalopod is elongated dorso-ventrally, the ventral surface carrying the mouth surrounded by the tentacles, and the opposite end—

blunt or pointed—being dorsal. In normal swimming, the posterior surface, with the funnel, is the lowermost, and the anterior surface is carried above.

The shell plays only a subsidiary role in modern cephalopods, being internal or even lost. Most extinct cephalopods however—as well as the ancient living *Nautilus*—have a large external shell. This is closely coiled in a plane spiral with the hump carried dorsally, and is divided by septa into successive chambers filled with gas. They are quite closed off from the animal, which occupies only the last one, and by their lightness they confer buoyancy.

In the modern cephalopods—where the shell is internal—the visceral hump is covered by a muscular mantle, giving the body a rounded or a streamlined contour. In squids the aboral end is tipped by a pair of fins, and in cuttlefish these run along the sides of the body. The ciliary functions of the early mollusc are now assumed by muscles. The mantle cavity contains two gills, but these are no longer ciliated and water is pumped in and out by strong contractions of the muscular mantle. With the loss of the external shell the whole mantle can freely contract, and jet propulsion is the characteristic means of locomotion. In deeper-water forms the swimming function may be taken over by the pulsations of a web running between the arms.

The most prominent sense organs of cephalopods are the eyes, which reach a perfection found nowhere else in the invertebrates. The brain is very elaborate too. The nerve centres of the primitive mollusc are concentrated within a cartilage head capsule, and the cephalopods have acquired many of the higher functions of the brain as found in vertebrates. Speed, alertness and large size are the key-notes of the Cephalopoda. Like the bivalves they have concentrated with great success upon one possible molluscan pattern. Yet such are the differences between, for example, a clam and a squid that it is hard to realize that the resources of one phylum have made both of them possible.

From what ancestors are molluscs descended? And how are they related to other phyla? The spiral cleavage of the egg and the trochophore larva link them with that broad division of the Metazoa that includes the unsegmented flatworms and the segmented annelids. Fashions in the derivation of molluscs have changed as new information has come to light and old facts have been viewed in different ways. Most theories have postulated some worm-like bottom-dwelling ancestor; only Naef—with his special interest in cephalopods—has suggested a pelagic origin. The oldest view—from the high Victorian era of phylogeny—was advocated by Ray Lankester and championed by Pelseneer. Molluscs were held to be derived from segmented annelids that had already acquired a full coelom. By a process, which Lankester called 'phleboedesis', enlarged blood spaces encroached on the coelom and reduced it to its molluscan dimensions. Garstang's principle of *paedomorphosis*, or 'escape from specialization' by attainment of sexual maturity in a larval condition, has brought some much-needed support to the annelid theory.[88] It would make the molluscs neotenic annelids that had lost their segmentation by dropping off the original adult stages from their life history. The trochophore larva becomes thus the last point of contact between these two phyla.

In recent times there has been a reaction from this view. Many have felt that annelids and molluscs were fundamentally unlike, and that the paedomorphosis theory glanced over big difficulties altogether too lightly. They looked for the ancestors of molluscs among the early Turbellaria, which Hadzi now regards as the stemming point of all the phyla of Metazoa. As Professor Graham has recently shown,[97] the molluscs and the turbellarians have an impressive list of resemblances, some of them admittedly no more than unspecialized features held in common. Both are ciliated externally, and either glide by cilia or creep by a ventral muscular wave. Molluscs possess mucous glands and turbellarians have comparable cells called 'rhabdites'. Neither show any trace of lateral limb-like outgrowths, or of cuticle or setae. Both groups—it was thought—were without trace of segmentation (nobody knew of *Neopilina* then!). In both

26

turbellarians and molluscs we find intracellular digestion, very un-
common in any other higher phyla. The nervous system shows
elementary beginnings in both phyla, a ring with longitudinal cords
and few or no distinct ganglia. There are complex genital ducts in
Turbellaria, none at all in early Mollusca; yet—in contrast with
Annelida—we shall find some evidence that early molluscs were,
like turbellarians, hermaphrodite. Finally, while no turbellarian has
a coelom, the molluscs have acquired just enough of one to receive
the genital products and, as circulation improved, to contain the
heart. Flatworms excrete from their spongy parenchyma by flame
cells; molluscs lose these and drain the pericardium by coelomoducts.

The dramatic discovery of *Neopilina*,* a living monoplacophoran,
with five serial pairs of gill-like organs, auricles, coelomoducts and
perhaps gonads, will again tip the balance in favour of annelid
relationships. Numbers of questions spring up at once. What is the
condition of the coelom and the nervous system in Monoplacophora? Were all the Molluscs once fundamentally metameric
animals? Was there ever a total segmentation involving the foot?
And would such segmentation if established necessarily require an
annelid origin?

Taken together, two such ancient forms as *Neopilina* with five
pairs of palliopericardial organs, and *Nautilus* with two pairs (p. 84),
may challenge all our existing views. With greater knowledge of
Neopilina we shall be able to look back further into molluscan
origins than was ever dreamed possible. Of all the living fossils we
could have desired to see, many zoologists would unhesitatingly
have made such a mollusc as this their first choice.

See Appendix 2, p. 219.

II

EXTERNAL FORM AND HABITS—
GASTROPODA

A TYPICAL snail owes its outward shape to the shell and the flattened foot. The shell forms a cone coiled in a helical spiral, and its lowest and widest coil is the spacious body whorl, into which the animal can retreat. The foot is drawn in last, and in the first sub-class of gastropods, the Prosobranchia, the aperture is usually sealed by an operculum, a horny or calcareous plate borne on the back of the foot. In the limpets, however, the animal never emerges from the shell, there is no operculum and the foot is permanently attached to the ground. The shell is here a flattened cone, drawn down upon the animal by a circle of muscles arising from the foot. In more active prosobranchs the head and foot are attached to the viscera by a narrow 'waist'. They can be quickly withdrawn into the shell by the columellar muscle, springing from the foot and attached to the axial pillar of the shell.

The foot is held to the ground by a viscid mucus. Its sole is ciliated and some smaller snails glide along merely by cilia working through the mucous layer as in some flatworms. Tiny marine snails, such as Rissoidae, may haul themselves through the water with a mucous thread secreted from the pedal gland. Most gastropods however creep by a succession of continuous waves of muscular contraction passing over the sole from behind.[122] As these waves travel forward, short transverse bands of the sole are successively contracted and lifted from the ground. These parts move forward with reduced resistance while the snail as a whole stays fixed by the rest of the sole. As release from adhesion passes forwards over the foot, its whole length is eventually advanced. The length of one 'step'

28

is the difference in length when contracted and expanded of that portion of the foot which is off the ground at any one time. The wave being continuous, no discrete steps can generally be seen. A single wave travels along the foot of *Helix pomatia* in thirty seconds, and the waves follow in close succession, different species having different wave lengths compared to the total length of the foot. Lissmann has shown that *Haliotis* and *Pomatias* develop alternating waves on the two sides of the foot. They show a sort of bipedal forward stepping, one side moving and the corresponding part of the other side staying fixed.

Some pulmonates, such as many Ellobiidae, have the foot permanently divided into anterior and posterior halves by a transverse groove. A few, like *Helix dupetithousi*, can increase their speed by a form of 'gallop', raising and advancing the front half of the foot, after which the back part glides up behind. But even here a rhythm of shorter waves seems to be imposed on the longer rhythm of the gallop.[158]

The locomotion of gastropods is most like that of turbellarians. Both snails and many flatworms crawl by a muscular wave, which— on kinetic grounds—must run forwards. The expanded parts of the foot stay fixed with mucus and the contracted zone is in forward motion. When an earthworm crawls—by contrast—forward movement is obtained by elongation. It is the contracted areas that remain fixed by setae, and the wave of contraction passes backwards.

PROSOBRANCHIA

The prosobranchs are immensely varied in structure, and the architecture of their shells usually has an obvious adaptive meaning. Shell shape is almost always a poor guide to natural relationships and there are certain types of shell we shall find repeatedly in each of the three orders which make up this sub-class. These orders are the Archaeogastropoda, the oldest and least specialized; the Mesogastropoda, the largest order of molluscs, and particularly diverse in mode of life; and the Neogastropoda, which are rather specialized carnivores (Fig. 3).

Except for the highly adapted Neritacea, which we will leave for treatment later (p. 164), the Archaeogastropoda are all marine, and are herbivores or deposit scrapers, one or two species living upon sponges. Their shells are broadly divisible into two forms: a conical or top-shaped spire, or—derived from this—a flattened shell with a wide aperture pressed close to the ground and leading finally to the limpet type with complete loss of spiral coiling in the adult. Our most familiar British family with a full spiral is the Trochidae, represented by such intertidal genera as *Gibbula, Monodonta* and *Calliostoma*. A similar family in most parts of the world is the Turbinidae, with however only one British species, the small and prettily marked *Tricolia pullus* of western shores. Trochids have a circular horny operculum, in turbinids it is thick and calcareous. In two related European families the operculum is lacking, the aperture and foot very wide and the animal much more retiring, creeping into the shelter of rocks and ledges or remaining in quiet pools. These are the Haliotidae or ormers with a flattened shell, enormously enlarged body whorl and reduced spire, and the Fissurellidae or key-hole limpets which have no coiled spire. In both these families the shell is characteristically perforated or slit to allow a more direct exit of the exhalant current from the mantle cavity: by a row of small holes in the Haliotidae, or by a notch or apical foramen in most of the Fissurellidae (*see* p. 68). The ancient Pleurotomariidae are spirally coiled like a trochid, but distinguished by a spiral slit incising the body whorl and closing posteriorly as growth proceeds.

The true limpets (Patellacea) are the most specialized Archaeogastropoda, and at least in the Patellidae live a much less sheltered life. The flat cone of *Patella* serves to resist wave attack on exposed rocky shores, and the foot forms a highly efficient sucking disc. These limpets are however not at all immobile, crawling about and making prolonged grazing trips when the tide is in. In the tiny blue peacock limpet *Patina pellucida*, attached to the fronds or smooth stipe of *Laminaria*, the shell gives perfect protection from the surge of waves at the seaward face of the reef. Some of the smaller limpets of the family Acmaeidae live by contrast in quieter waters such as tide-pools; others are fully exposed to wave attack.

The order Mesogastropoda are much less conservative in their evolution: wherever molluscs can exist at all they have some representatives, and every adaptation we shall later find in the

opisthobranchs and pulmonates, the mesogastropods seem some-
where to have attempted for themselves. They mostly possess shells,
and an early and unspecialized form is the top-shaped spire of the
periwinkles (Littorinidae). Another type especially well represented
is the slender elongated spire, with many whorls, as in the Cerithi-
idae, Turritellidae and Scalidae. Most of these snails draw their

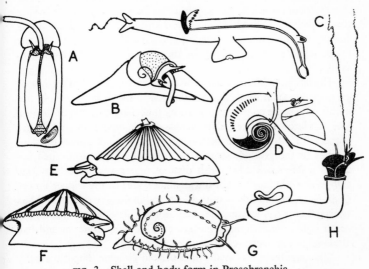

FIG. 3.   Shell and body form in Prosobranchia
A *Oliva*, B *Natica*, C *Pterotrachea*, D *Atlanta*, E *Diodora* (Fissurellidae),
F *Patella*, G *Haliotis*, H *Vermetus* (with secreted mucus strings used
in feeding). (E, F, G, after Yonge.)

long shell over sandy or muddy bottoms; but there is one family of
slender-spired snails, the Eulimidae, that are ectoparasites on
echinoderms (starfish, sea urchins and crinoids), crawling over or
hanging freely from the host's body (p. 176). The fusiform or spindle-
shaped spire is also common in Mesogastropoda. Such gastropods
may crawl about quite rapidly and are usually carnivores. The shell
aperture is prolonged into a spout-like anterior canal, projecting in
the line of advance. This is traversed by a pallial siphon bringing

water into the pallial cavity, and thus—by means of the osphradium
—sampling the environment ahead.

The highest and largest mesogastropods belong to the super-
family Doliacea, and are carnivores foreshadowing the evolution of
the Neogastropoda. The Cymatiidae have fusiform shells with strong
axial ribs and often rich ornamentation. They include the large
trumpet shells, *Charonia* (= *Triton*), and *Cymatium* and the elaborate
Argobuccinum which in many ways resemble Muricidae. Here belong
too the helmet shells (*Phalium*, *Cassis* and *Cassidaria*) of the family
Cassididae, the thin cask-shaped shells of the Doliidae, and the
flask-shaped Pirulidae, many of them smooth and burrowing in
sand.

The limpet habit has been evolved in several groups of the Mesogastropoda. Such limpets are usually slow-moving or entirely immobile and some collect their food by the ciliary currents of the gill.
The best known are the Calyptraeidae or chinaman's hat and slipper
limpets. In all these the periphery of the shell is drawn out and
reaches to the ground, so that an originally top-shaped shell becomes a depressed cone, with distinct upper and lower surfaces.
Calyptraea still has a small but distinct spire; in the slipper limpet
Crepidula fornicata this is almost lost, and in many Crepidulae it has
vanished entirely, leaving the shell an oval plate with a pocket beneath it for the viscera. Some are even dorsally concave and live
attached in the apertures of empty whelk shells.

The Capulidae are small, high-peaked circular limpets, usually
attached to bivalve shells (e.g. the British *Capulus ungaricus*). The
family Hipponicidae have a similar habit, but have become quite
welded to their substrate by a flat calcareous plate secreted beneath
the sole of the foot. They have in fact an outward resemblance to
certain bivalves.

One limpet-like genus, *Thyca*, classed near the Capulidae, has
taken up an ectoparasitic life on starfish; and from types such as this
follows a whole chapter of mesogastropod history with the production of more and more specialized and degenerate parasitic forms
(p. 178, Fig. 19).

The most aberrant of sedentary ciliary feeding gastropods are
those vermiform types whose shell has become loosened like a corkscrew or irregularly uncoiled as in a serpulid worm tube. They in-

clude two separate families.[131] The first, the Siliquariidae, are derived from the Turritellidae and in *Vermicularia* the ontogeny betrays phylogeny—the first part of the shell being a normal-looking turritellid. In the family Vermetidae (Fig. 3H) some species have almost abandoned ciliary feeding, and collect plankton by the secretion of long mucus strings. Many of these have lost the operculum and for protection retreat far up the long coils of the tube. A third uncoiled family, the Magilidae, are neogastropods. Their closest ancestors are small purpurid whelks of the family Coralliophilidae which have widened the body whorl until they can nestle like a limpet in a depression on coral. *Magilus* has evolved further, being deeply overgrown by coral. The early spiral shell is closed off and lengthens by a long straight tube, where the animal—a ciliary feeder?—lives with its aperture at the surface.

At another extreme are highly active gastropods that have developed a faster locomotion than creeping with the sole. Thus the pelican's foot shell, *Aporrhais*, though it can still crawl normally, possesses also a lunging movement. The body is reared above the ground on the extended 'waist' so that the heavy shell falls forward at each 'step'. A small operculum projects beyond the edge of the foot and is strengthened to form a digging tool. When *Aporrhais* is turned on its back, the foot seeks about for purchase and the operculum is thrust into the ground. The leverage of the foot then heaves the animal over.[204] *Aporrhais* still has a broad sole, but not so its tropical relatives, the family Strombidae. Here the operculum is drawn out into a dagger with a sharp or serrated edge. The foot is twisted to one side and forms a muscular hook. As the operculum is dug into the sand the foot is sharply flexed and the shell pulled along in a series of vigorous leaps. The strombids have large eyes mounted on optic tentacles and are the quickest and most alert of all bottom gastropods. The same type of leaping by the operculum and foot is practised by the carrier shells, *Xenophora*, which have flattened top shells looking somewhat like large Calyptraeidae. They camouflage their upper surface with the dead shells of bivalves and gastropods or garnish themselves with living tufts of coelenterates, sponges, polyzoa and tunicates.

Two groups of prosobranchs have become pelagic. The first, the fragile Ianthinidae or 'violet snails', make no attempt at swimming,

B

being truly planktonic and floating with the aperture of the globular shell held upwards.[195] *Ianthina ianthina* may either ride attached to the siphonophore *Velella*—on which it feeds—or may construct a buoyant raft of a tough transparent bubble-like secretion from the foot. Other species, such as *I. prolongata* and *I. exigua*, tow an apron-like raft from which the egg capsules are suspended.

The second pelagic group, the Heteropoda, includes some of the liveliest of all gastropods. Here the body is light and transparent, and—as we shall find later in the pteropods as well—there is a fine series of stages in reduction of the shell and modification for swimming The earliest family are the Atlantidae (Fig. 3D), small transparent snails up to 10 mm. long, with a compressed planorboid shell, kept upright in swimming by a sharp keel. They retain a thin operculum and a spiral visceral mass, and scull themselves along by undulating the middle of the sole, which is drawn out into a membranous fin. In the later families, the Carinariidae and Ptero-tracheidae, the body is much elongated and jelly-like, the viscera being concentrated in a small appendix on the dorsal side. *Carinaria* has a small shell like an elf's cap surrounding the viscera and mantle cavity. *Pterotrachea* (Fig. 3C) and *Firoloida* both lose the shell and mantle, and a naked ctenidium is attached to the dorsal side. The foot is a thin muscular flap, springing from the middle of the lower side, gracefully employed in sculling. In fast swimming the fin side is held uppermost and the viscera hang below. *Carinaria* has a rigid dorsal crest, but in the Pterotracheidae the body is quite smooth, and swimming is aided by lashing from side to side like a small transparent serpent. The buccal mass and its active radula are carried on a pendent proboscis like a trunk. A striking feature of all heteropods is their large eyes, which are tubular and slightly project-ing, being freely movable by small muscles. They have a blue metallic sheen, the rest of the body being colourless but for some high spots of purple or magenta.

Many prosobranchs plough along or burrow in sand and mud. Here the shell has less protective importance, and the operculum is often reduced or lost. The soft parts tend to spread round the shell which becomes smooth and polished. In the mesogastropod burrow-ing family, the Naticidae (Fig. 3B), it takes on a rounded shape and is partly submerged in the thick integument of the foot, which is broad and flat. Its front part, the propodium, is built up into a fleshy head-shield like a sand-plough which reaches back over the front of the shell, leaving a transverse slit behind it for the snout and tentacles. Side flaps of the foot, known as parapodia, spring up to cover the shell laterally and the spiral part of the animal so becomes absorbed in the new contour of the soft body.[129] This becomes almost bilaterally symmetrical, and the whole animal is converted into a flat, mucus-coated wedge for sliding over or into the sand. The inhalant siphon lies at the mid-line in front, and may be held erect or put up through the substrate when the animal is buried. In one species of *Natica* Thorson has shown how the animal slips a fold of skin over the exposed part of its shell to prevent a predatory starfish from securing a foothold.

The cowries (Cypraeacea) are not burrowers, but they have a rounded and sometimes smoothly polished shell, covered in life by integument. Still a mystery is the significance, if any, of the rich colour patterns laid down in their shells, invisible as they are in life. In many cowries the integument is beset with long papillae and is itself beautifully pigmented. The shell pigments contain porphyrin and may represent a waste product excreted in the shell. In the British *Trivia* the bright scarlet of the skin may give a warning of possible unpalatable properties of the animal. In the related Lamellariidae the shell is transparent and internal; the skin is never conspicuous but camouflaged to resemble the sponge or ascidian background.

The order Neogastropoda includes both surface-dwellers on rocky shores and burrowing forms. Of their four super-families, three are represented in Great Britain, one—the Toxoglossa (*see* p. 96)—only by small and unfamiliar offshore forms, such as *Mangelia*. The Muricacea include the large family Muricidae, with *Murex*, *Nucella*, *Trophon* and *Ocenebra* as British representatives, and specialized dwellers in coral reefs, the Magilidae (*see* p. 95). The Buccinacea has also two British families, the Buccinidae or true whelks and the Nassariidae. Abroad they include the large snails of the family Fasciolariidae, such as *Fusus* with its long-spiked anterior canal, and the Galeodidae, with the giant *Megalatractus*, two feet in length, and the American whelk *Busycon*.

The Volutacea—which have no British members—are sand-

dwelling neogastropods, usually with fusiform shells and built on
burrowing lines, as we have seen with the naticids (Fig. 3A). The
Volutidae have a long rectangular foot and a smooth shell; as well
as the large genus *Voluta* they include the giant oval baler shells,
Melo, which may reach eighteen inches in length. The Olividae are
the furthest evolved family, with polished fusiform shells entirely
covered by upgrowth of the foot. Like the Naticidae they are blind,
and the body is externally fleshy and bilaterally symmetrical, like a
bulloid opisthobranch. When burrowing they communicate with the
surface by a median inhalant siphon. The tropical Harpidae or harp-
shells are also burrowers, with a broad foot; they can practise
autotomy when hard-pressed, cutting off the hinder lobe of the
foot with the sharp edge of the shell. The Terebridae, tropical
Toxoglossa with long tapered spires, mostly trail over sand and
mud; a few species can burrow, using their long inhalant siphon
to communicate with the surface.

OPISTHOBRANCHIA

There are three broadly different types of opisthobranchs: those that
burrow in the substrate and possess thin external shells, those that
are flattened, naked and slug-like, often beautifully coloured and
externally symmetrical, and those that swim (Fig. 4). Shelled opisthobranchs are the earliest and belong mostly to the order Cephalaspidea, alternatively called Bullomorpha from the thin, bubble-like
shell. These must first have evolved along similar lines to burrowing
prosobranchs. They have a wide rectangular foot and a broad head
shield, formed here not by the building up of the front of the foot,
but by expansion of the head itself. Parapodia grow up at the
sides of the body and convert it into a dorso-ventrally flattened
wedge for sliding through or into the sand. Streamlining is carried
much further than in prosobranchs: the shell and visceral hump are
even more reduced and quite incorporated within the new lines of
the body. In early bulloids, such as *Haminea*, *Scaphander* and
Philine (Fig. 4B), the head shield is very large, and such excrescences
as tentacles, snout and siphon are drawn close to the outline of the
body, with the penis smoothly invaginated into the head. The head

shield tends to push the mantle cavity further back, and it may even
be this that initiated the reversal of torsion. At all events the mantle
cavity moves back along the right side during the history of the
opisthobranchs; and before it reaches its original posterior site it
has been quite lost, followed soon by the shell and the ctenidium.
Actaeon and *Ringicula* are the only bulloids with strong or sculptured external shells into which the body can withdraw. *Actaeon*
alone has an operculum. A progressive series in slug evolution runs
on through *Scaphander*, *Haminea*, *Philine* and *Runcina*. In *Haminea*

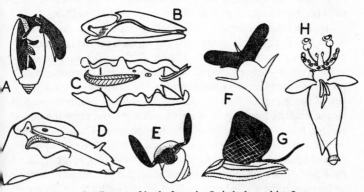

FIG. 4.   Range of body form in Opisthobranchia: I

A *Actaeon*, B *Philine*, C *Oscanius* (*Pleurobranchus*), D *Aplysia*,
E *Limacina*, F *Clio*, G *Cymbulia*, H *Pneumodermopsis*. (Not all to the
same scale.)

the shell is thin and bubble-like, in *Philine* it is transparent and quite
internal, and in *Runcina* it is lost altogether.[11, 145]

The burrowing apprenticeship and the streamlining of the body
have set the way for more ambitious developments. The gastropod
is now relieved of its cumbersome visceral coil and heavy shell, and
can develop either the flat slug-like body of a nudibranch, or can
become water-borne and swim. The Anaspidea or Aplysiomorpha
are rather primitive opisthobranchs. They are not burrowers but
have a plump high-built body, narrowing at the anterior end (Fig.
4D). The vestigial shell is a small chitinous plate, with only a hint of
spiral coiling. It is hidden in the roof of integument that reaches

across the small mantle cavity and ctenidium on the right side. All these structures are covered by parapodia, thin side-flaps of the foot, that can close above the body like a flask in the dorsal mid-line.[67]

In the Notaspidea, or pleurobranchoid slugs—such as *Pleurobranchus* and *Oscanius* (Fig. 4C)—the body is much flatter, the mantle cavity has quite disappeared, and there are no parapodia. The ctenidium is left naked, sheltered only by the margin of the mantle skirt on the right side. The shell—as in *Aplysia*—is usually embedded in the dorsal integument. It is, however, sometimes external and unexpectedly large, for example in the saucer-shaped shell perched on the top of the fleshy body of *Umbraculum*.

In the true nudibranchs the shell, mantle cavity and gill are finally lost in the adult. Henceforward we shall see the lavish evolution of the naked upper surface, with all those functions that devolve upon it—sensory, respiratory, defensive and camouflaging. A good example of an early nudibranch is the British *Tritonia*, a member of the group of Dendronotacea. These slugs are distinguished by the branched or foliose processes often put out from the dorsal surface, and concerned primarily with respiration. The anus still lies on the right side. The eyes are vestigial, having become so in the earliest opisthobranchs. The osphradium is also lost, being replaced by a pair of new olfactory head tentacles, the rhinophores, already to be seen in the shelled opisthobranchs. As well, the whole dorsal surface is highly sensitive to tactile stimuli. In the Doridacea (Fig. 5D), typified by *Archidoris*, *Goniodoris* and *Jorunna*, the anus has moved to the dorsal mid-line, and there is every appearance of bilateral symmetry save for the genital opening still on the right side. Around the anus appear a ring of five to nine pinnate secondary gills, which are sometimes retractile.

A different mode of respiration is used by the third group of nudibranchs, the Aeolidiacea. The integument is produced into slender club-shaped appendages called cerata (Fig. 5C). These either lie spearately in several rows, or may be clustered together in tufts and palmate bunches. They contain blood from the haemocoele and are invaded also by tubular branches of the digestive gland which—as evolution proceeds—becomes deployed upon the dorsal surface.

The small slugs of the Order Sacoglossa, which feed suctorially on green algae, are unrelated to other nudibranchs. Their whole dorsal surface may be respiratory, as in *Elysia* (Fig. 5G) and *Limapontia*, while in *Hermaea* and *Stiliger* cerata may be developed, as in aeoliids. In *Elysia* and *Tridachia*, the flattened margin of the body is coloured by special zooxanthellae which multiply there.

The colours of nudibranchs are nearly always beautiful; and it is sometimes difficult with the animal away from its background to tell whether they are really warning or camouflaging.[2] Many of the aeoliids are famed for their conspicuous reds, yellows and pinks upon a white skin. Aeoliids owe their immunity from enemies to the

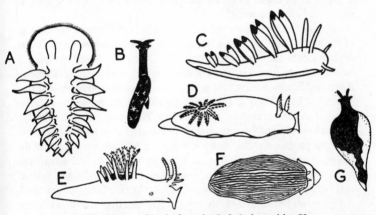

FIG. 5.   Range of body form in Opisthobranchia: II

A *Tethys*, B *Acochlidium*, C *Eubranchus* (an aeoliid), D *Archidoris*, E *Ancula*, F *Armina* (*Pleurophyllidia*), G *Elysia*. (Not all to same scale.)

habit of feeding on coelenterates and storing the stinging cells of these in 'cnidosacs' in the cerata (p. 98). In some species, however, bright colours may offer a cryptic resemblance to a coelenterate background; in this way *Doto coronata*, with whitish cerata, is able to hide among the tentacles and sporosacs of the hydroid *Clava multicornis*. *Aeolidia papillosa*—with greyish-brown cerata—rests unnoticed beside the tentacles of its anemone prey, *Anemonia sulcata*. *Calma glaucoides* with silvery grey cerata likewise conceals itself against the masses of blenny eggs on which it feeds. In the pinkish *Tritonia plebeia* the branched marginal papillae resemble the half-expanded tentacle crowns of the polyps of *Alcyonium* colonies. The brilliant reds and oranges of many dorids must be primarily warning colours, as are the black and orange longitudinal stripes of *Pleurophyllidia*. In *Rostanga rufescens*, however, brick red has a camouflage value seen against the red sponge *Microciona*. The herbivorous aplysioids rely mainly on camouflage colours, such as mottled greens, browns and yellows, together with the secretion of an offensive purple dye. The carnivorous pleurobranchids on the other hand develop bright reds and yellows, or reds against milk-white, which may be taken to be warning colours, the animal producing a distasteful acid secretion.

Nearly every group of opisthobranchs has produced a swimming offshoot: flattening and streamlining are preadaptations as useful to a water-borne mollusc as to a bottom dweller. The simplest types of swimming are found in the Dendronotacea, where—as in *Dendronotus* and *Scyllaea*—the foot is reduced to a narrow groove, and the animal flexes its body from side to side to an angle of 45°. In *Dendronotus* a screw-like spiral flexure may run along the body. Appendages from the dorsal surface are useful in swimming, and *Scyllaea* progresses with its back downwards, from the weight of its tentacles and dorsal papillae. It must be an ungraceful swimmer, being said to bear a grotesque resemblance to a four-legged animal with ears, such as a Skye Terrier![27] The large plump *Melibe* and *Tethys* swim back upwards by rows of leaf-like dorsal paddles. They have a cowl-like cephalic hood which they toss from side to side to snare swimming crustacea (Fig. 5A). *Phyllirhoe* and *Cephalopyge* are built to quite a different plan, being small, transparent and laterally compressed, with the foot entirely lost. They are permanently planktonic, swimming with graceful undulations (the name Phyllirhoe means 'flowing leaf') and their bodies are studded with tiny light organs.

The pleurobranchid *Oscanius* can swim by rippling the widely projecting edges of the foot and the mantle. Among the Sacoglossa the primitive shell-bearing *Lobiger* looks like a bulloid, but floats or swims with three pairs of specially developed fragile side flaps. The related *Oxynoe* is narrow and streamlined, moving with small rounded parapodia. The Glaucidae are a family of pelagic aeoliids, bluish-green in colour, and spreading out three bushy tufts of cerata at either side. These contain gas-filled diverticula of the gut, which are said to help in passive floating. Like *Ianthina*, *Glaucus* may attach itself both for food and transport to the undersurfaces of coelenterates such as *Velella* and *Porpita*.

It is the lower opisthobranchs with large parapodia that turn their bodies to best account in swimming. The sea-hare, *Aplysia punctata*, is a simple example; it can take short spurts off the ground by rapidly opening and closing the parapodia. *Dolabella* is a better swimmer, with still larger parapodial flaps. *Aplysia saltator* makes an essay in jet propulsion, keeping the parapodia closed and contracting them upon the water beneath which is spurted from a funnel-like opening. Still more expert is the slug *Akera bullata*, which has a bulloid appearance, but is a primitive shelled aplysioid. Here the parapodia are prolonged into a graceful cloak, spring from the sides of the foot and overlapping above and behind the back. The visceral mass with its shell hangs like a clapper inside. The parapodia open and close with a fine medusoid movement, and—borne up on its skirt—*Akera* rises in short spurts and swims gregariously, especially during the spawning season.[140] *Gasteropteron* is a true bulloid, not related to *Akera*, yet it has by parallel evolution acquired an exactly similar mode of 'medusoid' swimming.

The most active opisthobranchs are however the pteropods or sea-butterfles, light diaphanous forms that spend their whole life in the plankton. They are divided into two groups—the shelled and the naked—that resemble each other only in the way they swim. The two parapodia are drawn out into membranous wings, with narrow muscular bases. The shelled pteropods, or Thecosomata, are, generally, held to be derived from bulloids. The earliest family, the Limacinidae, are small molluscs never more than a few millimetres in diameter, with transparent spiral shells, sinistrally coiled as in bulloid larvae. The foot has a broad sole and bears an operculum, and from its sides are produced long parapodia, or 'wings', muscular at the bases and thin towards the tips. *Limacina* rows itself upwards in a broadly spiral course, using these as oars (Fig. 4E), and drops as a dead weight by holding them together motionless above the body.[133] The families Cavoliniidae and Cymbuliidae have both lost their spiral form and are bilaterally symmetrical. The cavoliniid shell may be a slender, elongated cone as in the genus *Creseis*, or as in *Clio* and *Diacria* a dorso-ventrally flattened case, drawn out into equilibrating spines at the sides and above (Fig. 4F); in *Cavolinia* it is inflated and flask-like. In all forms the mantle cavity opens and the wings emerge through a narrow slit at the anterior end.

The Cymbuliidae are larger pteropods, up to two inches across. They have no true shell but a chitinous *pseudoconcha* which forms a boat in which the whole animal lies. In *Cymbulia* a pair of broad-based wings are attached along the sides. They are flapped like a butterfly's wings with an up and down rowing movement; and they show also an undulation from the front backwards, which provides a forward thrust. In *Gleba* and *Corolla* the pseudoconcha is a wide saucer and the wings have grown together into a heart-shaped fringe which is moved gracefully in swimming like a skirt or the bell of a medusa.[199]

The second series of pteropods, the Gymnosomata (Fig. 4H), swim much faster than the thecosomes, and are so much modified that we cannot be sure from which groups of opisthobranchs they have sprung. The body is torpedo-shaped, either blunt-tipped or pointed behind. There is never a shell, mantle cavity or true gill. Secondary gills may develop as flaps or fringes, on the right side or behind; or—as in the British *Clione*—respiration may be through the general body surface. The paired wings are narrowly attached beneath, behind the head, and rest horizontally, being moved dorso-ventrally. The animal moves upwards or forwards by sculling with them, twisting them at the 'wrist' to allow a power stroke at both the upward and downward beat.[139A]

PULMONATA

As compared with the prosobranchs and opisthobranchs, the pulmonates—though a successful and numerous group—are rather conservative in structure. The shell, however, shows many of the adaptations met with in prosobranchs, a land snail like *Helix pomatia*, the edible snail, being rather representative in shape, rounded or turbinate, with a wide aperture. A long anterior canal is never developed in pulmonate shells and there is only one genus, the marine *Amphibola*, with an operculum. A frequent development, instead, is the presence of complex teeth and ridges, which to some extent guard the aperture against predators, as in ellobiids, vertiginids and many helicids. In the slender Clausiliidae there is in addition a loose sliding door known as a *clausilium* which fits into the grooves of the columella. During hibernation the higher pulmonates such as the Helicidae secrete an *epiphragm*, a temporary seal of dried mucus which may become very thick and even calcified.

There are several other widespread shell types. The first—found especially in small-sized primitive snails like the Endodontidae, and also in the Zonitidae—is flat and discoidal. These snails generally hide in crevices and under bark and ledges. Then there are the long spires of the Pupillidae and Cochlicopidae, or those of the Clausiliidae, tapered at either end, which may hang from dry walls or tree branches. Another type of long spire is the conical or fusiform shell developed in the Bulimulidae and their relatives.

The Pulmonata have also produced both limpets and slugs. The first are a speciality of the earlier and aquatic order Basommatophora, pulmonates bearing the eyes at the tentacle bases as in prosobranchs. The limpets of the marine Siphonariidae are the largest, and are entirely intertidal. They parallel the true limpets in their ecology, and on some tropical shores may replace them completely. Except for a shell sinus at the right side over the pallial opening, they are often difficult to distinguish externally from Patellidae. The minute *Otina otis*—living in high tidal crevices on western British shores, is a pulmonate limpet with a shell like an unperforated *Haliotis*.[136] In fresh water there are two entire families of limpet-like pulmonates, quite unrelated: the Latiidae, a primitive group living in Australasia, and the Old World Ancylidae, found both in lakes and in fast streams. In addition, the Planorbidae have a limpet form in *Patelloplanorbis*, almost indistinguishable externally from a *Calyptraea*; and the Lymnaeidae have a peculiar limpet in the genus *Lanx*, from North America.

Pulmonate slugs belong to the terrestrial order Stylommatophora, with the eyes carried at the tips of one pair of tentacles. Almost every super-family has at some stage contributed a specialized shell-less line.[190] As well as economy in calcium, the slug habit has many structural advantages: these molluscs can glide through narrow spaces, or—like *Testacella*—burrow actively for animal prey which can then be swallowed into a distensible body. Pulmonate slugs are generally higher built and more slender than opistho-branchs, sometimes dorsally keeled. Here the body has been re-organized without loss of torsion; the mantle cavity, which serves as a lung, generally opens anteriorly on the right side. The mantle forms a fleshy saddle in which a vestigial shell plate, or granules of calcium carbonate, are usually buried. Some slugs—such as *Testacella*, *Daudebarbia* and *Schizoglossa*—still carry a small limpet-like shell over the mantle. In the Testacellidae both shell and mantle are pushed back to the broader posterior end, and the front of the body is smoothly tapered for insertion in the soil.

An odd family of slugs, classed by some with the opisthobranchs, is the Onchidiidae, with one species, *Onchidella celtica*, in Britain. These are marine and intertidal and have a posterior lung opening in the ventral mid-line behind the anus. The body is flattened with a thick warty integument, and the onchidiids are in some ways like naked limpets, resisting desiccation fairly well and making long journeys exposed to warm air. In some species the back is studded with small tentacles bearing eyes, and most forms have developed special repugnatorial skin glands with a defensive secretion. The colour is dull and inconspicuous, usually black, or mottled grey or brown.[79]

SHELL ORNAMENT AND COLOUR

Apart from its basic design—usually fairly obviously adaptive—nearly every gastropod shell has other features whose function may not be in the least evident. These include the nature and arrangement of the sculpture, the ornament of the aperture, as well as many features of the operculum and the sculpture of the embryo shell. They are in fact the raw material of the conchologist, the very points that demarcate species from species, and they raise for us the re-curring problem of the non-adaptiveness of micro-evolutionary detail. Being brought up as selectionists, we often take it on trust that these characters—if not useful in themselves—may be geneti-cally involved with deeper features that are of advantage to the animal. This is a salve to orthodoxy, but in the nature of things difficult either to prove or refute.

Shell ornament seems to increase as we move towards later and higher groups. Mesogastropods and neogastropods have more varied shells than archaeogastropods; and the stylommatophoran pulmonates are more extravagant than the Basommatophora. As with the lip of the aperture, the final ornament may be withheld until growth is completed, for example in the Strombacea and many pulmonates. In the Cymatiidae and Cassididae, however, a thickened lip is laid down before each rest period, which later remains as an axial rib or 'varix'. In still other forms, such as the Muricidae, the provisional lip is resorbed before new growth begins. The Strombacea are one group where the aperture provides many puzzles. With more exact knowledge of the living animal some of its features may be shown to be adaptive, but a residue of detail remains which resists such explanation. In the earliest family, the Aporrhaidae, there may be a broadly winged lip, as in *Aporrhais pes-pelicani*.[204] In others, such as *A. occidentalis*, the lip has a thick, heavily callused pad. Derived from aporrhaids are the burrowing Struthiolariidae,[130] with a curved, restrained lip, and the tropical Strombidae, which have a profusion of shell types.

The lip is winged and heavily callused in *Strombus gigas* and its near relatives, wide and spiny in *Pterocera*. *Rostellaria* has a fusiform shell with a greatly extended anterior process or 'rostrum'. *Conomurex* is smooth, like a cone shell, with a diminished spire; some species bear nodules and spines like muricids, which in *Terebellum* the shell is thin, polished and fusiform, for burrowing. As Yonge has demonstrated, the canopied lip of *Aporrhais* and many strombids provides stability on the surface; and in those that work the shell into the soft substrate it may roof a space where the proboscis can forage without sand falling in. In many strombids there is a small sinus at the edge of the lip; observation of the living animal shows this to be a 'squint' for one of the optic tentacles, the other one peeping out by the inhalant canal. The lip may also bear special channels for carrying the exhalant current, always powerful in the Strombacea. In the primitive strombid *Rimella* the exhalant side of the aperture is drawn out into a narrow gutter that leads far up the spire and winds round to end on the normally up-facing side of the shell. With a burrowing habit, such a canal would admirably serve to carry the exhalant current to the surface of the substrate.

On the other hand, the inhalant current of *Rostellaria* does not traverse the anterior rostrum, and the long-channelled spines in *Pterocera* seem to have no function but that of stabilizing the shell.

Land operculate shells of the family Cyclophoridae show some extraordinary modifications.[2] In species of *Opisthoporus*, and *Rhiostoma* a narrow tube leads up the side of the body whorl from the aperture. This probably serves as a breathing siphon when the operculum is in place, though in the adult snail it is often imperforate. But what is one to make in adaptive terms of the genus *Opisthostoma*, where a normal trochoid land shell abandons its coiling towards the end of the growth, and reverses so that the aperture is carried to the tip of the spire? Or of *Cyathopoma*, in the same family, with its whorls loosely and openly coiled like a corkscrew?

Large gaps remain in our understanding of shell pigmentation in molluscs, though Comfort[52] has given an excellent review and added much to our knowledge. The shell is laid down by the mantle edge throughout life, but its pigments may be deposited intermittently with the resulting colour patterns. They provide 'a biochemical diary of the individual mollusc from the cradle to the grave'. Pigments may either play a useful role, or may form excretory deposits without obvious adaptive meaning. In the more primitive molluscs, the shell pigments seem nearly all of the latter kind. There is an interesting break between the porphyrin pigments of many members of primitive groups, on the one hand, and the higher prosobranchs, pulmonates and lamellibranchs on the other. Porphyrins are found widely in Archaeogastropoda (*Trochidae*, where they may form essentially the whole shell colouring, Fissurellidae, Acmaeidae, *Tricolia*, and Neritacea, including land forms), in some early mesogastropods such as the Cypraeidae, in some primitive opisthobranchs (*Actaeon*, *Haminea*, *Bulla* and *Umbraculum*) and in several chitons and scaphopods. They also occur in the early lamellibranch groups, the Pteriacea and Anomiacea. Aplysioids such as *Akera* and *Aplysia* possess integumentary porphyrins, as does the black slug *Arion ater*. Free porphyrins are absent in the ancient archaeogastropod *Pleurotomaria* and also in Patellidae. They are replaced by linear pyrols in several haliotids and in the green colour (glaucobilin) of the shells of Turbinidae. The purple in the ink of *Aplysia* is due to a chromoprotein, aplysiopurpurin, containing the pyrol mesobiliviolin. The purple of the Muricacea is unrelated, being a dibromo-indigotin, while of the characteristic pigment of the Ianthinidae or violet snails nothing is known with certainty.

Shell melanins are probably widely distributed in pulmonates, though the colour patterns become elaborate only in the Helicacea (especially the tropical ones) and the Bulimulacea. In Helicidae the 1–5 black-banded pattern is frequent, typified by the melanotic banding of shells of *Helicella* and *Cepaea* and the broken-up banding in *Helix*. The colouring of *Cepaea* shows a balanced polymorphism, and Cain and Sheppard[45] have shown experimentally the selective value of plain and banded forms in different environments, with reference to the main predator, the thrush: plain yellow shells are more abundant than brown shells in green habitats, while more brown shells are brought to thrush anvils, suggesting a 'predation polymorphism' (*see* also Goodhart[89A]). Dark banding may be in itself a disruptive colouring, but the various banding patterns show no differential predation and obviously other features are involved in the maintenance of this complex polymorphism. Highly pigmented shells are much more frequent in tropical arboreal pulmonates, such as many bulimulids. And in the shell-less arboreal New Zealand slugs (*Athoracophorus*) there are intricate leaf vein patterns traced in brown and red on a lighter ground.

The lower Stylommatophora and the Basommatophora tend to be plain coloured, mostly from non-pigmentary proteins in the periostracum, sometimes quinone tanned to browns, red-browns and yellow.

Indigoid pigments occur as in the purple gland in Muricacea, often too in their egg cases. Purple markings are common in such shells, but their identity is uncertain. H. B. Moore suggests that brown or purple shells in *Nucella lapillus* are due to a diet of *Mytilus*, of whose characteristic blue-black pigment nothing is known.

III

EXTERNAL FORM AND HABITS—
LAMELLIBRANCHIA AND CEPHALOPODA

THE gastropods have shown us a prolific variety in organization. The lamellibranchs and cephalopods—different though they are from each other—have concentrated on fewer structural patterns. Both attain great success by high specialization; and each class is very resourceful in the different ways its standard theme is given expression.

Lamellibranchs are much more sedentary than gastropods, though in most of them the foot is still well developed. Very few however crawl over the substrate in the primitive molluscan way. Many species burrow into soft sand and mud, or even bore into rock and wood. A large number are permanently anchored to the ground, and among these the foot is usually reduced and sometimes quite lost. Even here evolution is not exhausted: some of the least mobile of lamellibranchs have produced descendants that have broken free again to become swimmers, moving by expelling water on closing the valves of the shell.

In this chapter we shall give most attention to those bivalves where the shape of the body is less modified. Here the two symmetrical shell valves are drawn together by two equal adductor muscles, the one anterior and the other posterior. When these are relaxed the shell is opened by the elasticity of the *ligament*, which is a new structure peculiar to lamellibranchs. We may think of the mantle as originally a tent covering the whole body of the early mollusc. It soon became slit in front and behind so as to leave only a short connecting bridge in the dorsal line. Shell secretion was interrupted here and the ligament laid down instead, an elastic connecting strip continuous with the shell, but formed of uncalcified conchiolin, the organic substance of the shell. The ligament may lie slightly in front of, or more usually behind, the earliest point of the shell, the *umbo*; and it may be *external* (dorsal to the hinge) or *internal* (ventral to the hinge). The valves open by its elastic thrust when the adductors are relaxed, an external ligament being normally under tension, an internal under compression.[157, 218] Along the hinge line, the shell halves may develop teeth which interlock in various ways so as to prevent fore and aft displacement of the valves.

The adductor muscles probably arose from the enlargement and cross fusion of pallial muscles attaching the mantle to the shell. They now pass horizontally between the valves. Anterior and posterior pedal retractor muscles are also inserted on the shell near the adductors, and strike deeply into the body of the foot. The foot can protrude from between the valves and alter its shape by inflow of blood and contraction of its intrinsic muscles. Behind or at the base of the foot lies a gland from which many lamellibranchs—for part of their life at least—produce a *byssus*, a bundle of tough threads of tanned protein. In attached forms the byssus threads serve as mooring lines. In other species they are put out from time to time for temporary anchorage, or they may appear in the post-larval spat alone, the byssal gland becoming unimportant in later life.

The mantle edge consists of three lobes (Fig. 21A). The outer lobe (I) secretes the outer calcareous (*prismatic*) layer of the shell; the middle lobe (II) is sensory and the inner lobe (III) or velum controls the flow of water. The thin *periostracum* is secreted by a groove between I and II, and the inner calcareous (*nacreous*) layer by the internal surface of the mantle. In earlier bivalves the mantle cavity is generally widely open; in *Nucula* for example the water current enters in front and passes out behind. In higher forms, especially those which burrow, the mantle margins are in some degree fused by the coalescence of one or more sets of lobes. The apertures for the water current move to the posterior end where the mantle edge is drawn out into tubular siphons, the inhalant one ventral and the exhalant dorsal. These elongate with increasing depth of burrowing and develop their own complex radial and longitudinal muscles. According to the number of mantle lobes involved, siphons may be naked and muscular (lobe III only) (Tellinacea and Cardiacea); covered with periostracum by addition of lobe II (Mactracea and

Myacea); or even encased in shell by the fusion of lobe I (*Cuspidaria*).[218]

The siphons make the only effective contact with the world outside, and they may acquire sense organs such as tactile papillae, light sensitive spots and even clusters of eyes. As the mantle edges fuse, a pedal gape is left at the front half for the foot to emerge.

The siphons are inserted by special retractor muscles upon the interior of the shell, and here the line of attachment of the mantle is embayed to form a *pallial sinus*. Even in fossils the depth of this sinus gives very reliable information about the length of the siphons, and thus the habits. It is deep for example in Tellinacea and Myacea, rather shallow in Veneracea and Cardiacea.

The bivalve foot acts rhythmically, not as in gastropods by a wave of contraction, but by alternate lengthening and shortening. In protobranchs such as *Nucula* (Fig 2F), the sole is still a flat disc. This is used not for creeping but for thrusting ahead into the substratum like a plug, after which, as its longitudinal muscles contract, the body of the animal is drawn forward.

Among the less specialized of higher bivalves are the freshwater mussels, Unionidae, which are shallow burrowers or plough along half buried in the sand. The foot is a pointed tongue which can be extended forward by the contraction of small transverse muscles running through its thickness, and the consequent stretching of its longitudinal muscles. The transverse muscles then relax, and blood is forced in from the haemocoele, making the tip of the foot turgid and fixing it in the substrate. The longitudinal muscles next contract and the animal is rapidly drawn up to the foot, after which the foot elongates again and the movement is repeated. The mantle in *Unio* and *Anodonta* is slightly fused behind to provide two short siphons, a wide inhalant and a narrow exhalant, scarcely projecting beyond the edge of the shell.

The marine Tellinacea, on the other hand, are good examples of fast burrowers. Their two siphons are long tubes, especially the inhalant, and extend to several times the shell length (Fig. 6G). The shell is smooth and light and the whole animal very compressed in cross section. The outstretched foot forms a wide sheet of muscle, as thin as a knife as it plunges into the sand.[212] Another type of bivalve, of different shape and less committed to burrowing, is represented by the cockles (Cardiacea) (Fig. 6F) and the venus-shells (Veneracea). Here the shell is ovoid or globular, the valves thick and heavy and usually with prominent sculpture, radial or concentric. Strong ridges or sharp lamellae may keep the shell immobile when it is partly buried, and the rounded shape allows the waves to roll it on the surface without damage. The valves close very tightly, and never gape as in deeper burrowers. Cockles live near the surface,

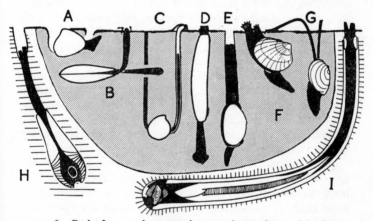

FIG. 6. Body form and posture in some burrowing and boring lamellibranchs

A–G Burrowing in sand, with foot extended in A (*Nucula*) and with siphons also shown in B *Cochlodesma*, C *Loripes*, D *Ensis*, E *Mya*, F *Cardium*, G *Tellina*, H *Pholas*, boring in rock or hard clay, I *Teredo*, boring in wood (part of siphonal wall removed to reveal gill). (Not all to the same scale.)

with the posterior third often exposed. Their siphons are short and often bear light receptors. The foot is long and narrow, rounded in cross section and of firm muscle. In some cockles, as likewise in Cyprinacea and in Trigoniidae, it can be flexed almost double, and the tip inserted beneath the shell, lifting the animal off the ground in a surprisingly strong leap.

With deeper burrowing, new specializations appear. In the more advanced lamellibranchs, particularly those of the order Adape-donta, the mantle edges are almost entirely fused, leaving only a small gape for the foot. The siphons are very long, generally lying parallel and surrounded with a common leathery sheath. These deep burrowers fall ecologically into two groups, the first typified by the fast-moving razor shells (Solenacea) and the second much less mobile, containing the clams (Myacea) and the borers into hard substrata, like piddocks and shipworms (Adesmacea).

The shell of *Solen* or *Ensis* (Fig. 6D) is long and thin, straight or slightly curved like a razor. It is beautifully adapted for slipping vertically or obliquely into the ground, and these bivalves will burrow as fast as one can dig. The shell is open at the front and hind ends, and its shape has been achieved by great elongation of the posterior half—the umbones are at the extreme anterior end. Fully half the mantle cavity is occupied by the piston-like foot, that can be protruded from the front of the shell, pointed and plunged into the sand. Once embedded it is made turgid with blood, and swollen to a thick bulb, while the shell and the animal are pulled after it.[26] The ventral edges of the mantle are entirely fused, except for a minute 'fourth aperture' lying posteriorly towards the base of the siphons.

With extension of the foot during burrowing, the shell valves are often adducted. This results both in the forcing of blood from the body into the foot, and in the expulsion of pallial water through the pedal gape. At times it seems that the substrate is made momentarily more permeable in this way, as in the operation of water-jetting in sinking a pile. In some cases the quicksand or thixotropic effect may apply, which Chapman and Newell have shown to be important in the burrowing of lugworms. The wet sand may be converted by agitation to its more permeable sol phase as the foot goes down, reverting then to a gel state and holding the foot immobile.

In the gapers and clams (Myacea) the shell is rectangular or ovoid (Fig. 6E), in no way suited for fast burrowing. Bivalves such as *Mya* and *Panopea* live at a depth of twelve inches or more in compact sand or mud. The long siphons with their common leathery sheath can no longer be accommodated in the shell. The foot is small and the pedal opening narrow and easily closed. Rapid digging is in fact impossible, and if once dislodged from their deep stations the adult clams have little chance of re-imbedding. The shell hinge is very simple and loses most of its teeth, since the valves need no longer be rigidly locked against desiccation or enemies. By the contraction of one or other adductor muscle, the valves can indeed be rocked in a horizontal plane on a fulcrum at the hinge. The front halves can thus be drawn apart, and in some clams like the American *Platyodon* hard substrata can be mechanically excavated by ridges on the shell. The burrow comes to form a mould of the animal, oval in section with dorsal and ventral ridges.[214] Pallial hydrostatic pressure may be very important in the movements of these bivalves with closed mantle cavities. When the siphon tips and pedal gape have been closed, the siphons may themselves be extended by the contraction of the adductors against the pallial water.[47] Or by building up water pressure, then closing and shortening the siphons, the valves may be opened against the wall of the burrow, with a consequent abrading action.

The boring habit is perfected in those bivalves that enter rock. There are already some Myacea such as *Saxicava* that nestle in crevices or existing holes, taking hold of the end of the burrow with the plug-like foot or the byssus, and abrading it with ridges on the shell. In the true rock-borers or piddocks (Pholadidae)[166] (Fig. 6H) the mantle is closed save for a small pedal aperture in front. Here the valves gape widely and the foot can be extended and made turgid, to grip the end of the burrow like a sucker. The ligament in the piddocks is much reduced (Adesmacea). The valves are joined mainly by the adductors, which can rock them transversely on the hinge fulcrum. Part of the anterior adductor has now spread outside the shell, and unites the valves dorsally to the hinge and in front of the umbones. In some species this exposed muscle is protected by one or more accessory plates of shell. The anterior and posterior adductors now serve respectively to open the valves and to draw them apart in front. On the anterior half of each valve the sculpture is sharp and abrasive, with teeth like a file. As the foot takes its grip the shell is hauled forward to the extreme end of the burrow. As the valves open, the shell is rotated alternately in either direction by special contractions of the pedal muscles. The burrow is thus made circular in section. The pholad shell is broadest in front, and the burrow is enlarged at its deep end so as to imprison the animal. In *Pholadidea* and *Martesia*, when boring ceases, the edges of the valves are approximated by further growth, the front of the shell becoming spherical, and the pedal gape closed so that the foot can no longer protrude.

Even in pholads the fused siphons are very long, and they may be protected by a horny or calcareous covering round their base. In the Teredinidae or shipworms (Fig. 61), which bore into wood, the siphons enlarge enormously at the expense of the rest of the body, and secrete the structureless calcareous layer which lines the burrow. The *Teredo* animal is limp and worm-like, consisting almost wholly of the conjoined siphons, the inhalant one containing an extension of the mantle cavity with most of the gill. The siphon tip is protected by shelly plates known as pallets, while at the anterior end the small visceral mass is covered by the true shell.[166] As in pholads, this forms the abrading tool. The hinge provides a rounded boss on which the valves rock sideways, and there is also a second ball joint at the ventral margin of the shell. The posterior adductor provides the power stroke, contracting to draw the valves apart in front, till their razor-sharp edges chisel the wood. The anterior adductor then contracts to draw them together. Between movements, the foot loosens its grip, and moves a little way round the burrow; the animal turns eventually through 180° and then reverses. In both pholads and shipworms, spoil from the burrow is carried through the mantle cavity by the pedal gape, and ejected from the siphons behind.[214]

So far we have passed over those numerous bivalves that live permanently attached at the surface. The reason is that most of these are far more modified than those that burrow. The majority of them form a fairly natural group, those—in the main—that used to be classed as Filibranchia and Pseudolamellibranchia (*see* p. 183). They are an older stock than most of the burrowers, but in shell form and habits they are some of the most specialized bivalves of all (Fig. 20). They include the true mussels (Mytilacea), the pearl oysters, wing shells and fan-mussels (Pteriacea), the scallops (Pectinacea), the saddle oysters (Anomiacea) and the true oysters (Ostreacea). The shell may be cemented to the substrate or occasionally lie free; but the majority—at some time in their life—anchor by the byssus. In the noah's ark shells and file shells, and rather less in *Mytilus*, the foot is still active. In most of the others it is vestigial or quite small. The mantle edges are little fused; there are usually no siphons and water generally enters round a wide circumference especially in the scallops, pearl oysters and true oysters.[215]

The mussels, Mytilidae (Fig. 20B), are less modified than most of this group. The byssus emerges in front from the ventral side and the foot lies at the anterior end. It can be protruded to prise the mussel free from the byssus and even to creep about. By encroachment from the foot and byssus, the anterior adductor muscle is reduced, and the posterior adductor enlarges at its expense. These changes are pushed ahead in later forms, until a single large adductor (the posterior) alone remains, at the centre of the shell.[218]

The evolution of bivalves with a single adductor (the Monomyaria) deeply involves the mantle cavity, and we shall postpone discussion of their adaptations until we can return to them with a fuller acquaintance with internal anatomy (see p. 184).

One further habit must however be mentioned here, the ingenious method of swimming by clapping the valves, evolved by the scallops and their relatives. The Pectinacea are well pre-adapted for swimming: the valves are circular with a pair of squared lugs at either side of the hinge. The hinge is short, the mantle cavity being open all round save at the extreme hinge point. The valves open to 30° by a powerful internal ligament, and can be quickly closed to expel water by the single central adductor muscle. In addition the mantle bears efficient light-sensitive organs, and a curtain-like fold, the *velum*, controlling the direction of water expulsion. Swimming may be in two directions (see Fig. 21F): 'forward', with the velum lowered around the mantle edge, so that water is expelled mainly at the two lugs on the hinge side. A slight downward escape of water past the velum gives an upward thrust to the shell. Alternatively an 'escape movement' can be performed by swimming hinge-first, with the velum raised and water expelled around the curved mantle margin, which now lies at the trailing edge of the shell. The swimming of *Pecten* cannot be called elegant: even compared with opisthobranch standards, it is laboured and short-sustained. Its great interest is in illustrating once again the evolutionary versatility of sessile lamellibranchs.[172, 202]

The prime result of all cephalopod design has been to produce a swimming mollusc. The great majority of species move about by jet propulsion from the mantle cavity. We may regard all cephalopods, past and present, as having been able to swim, including in this class, by definition, all those early forms in which the body was first lightened by the incorporation of closed chambers in the apex of the shell. From one orthoconid nautiloid we have in fact fossilized impressions left in a soft substrate by the trailing of the conical shell as the animal alighted after jet swimming. There is good reason to think that the living *Nautilus* is, in its swimming, typical of shelled cephalopods in the past, and we may first consider the external structure of this form.

The shell of *Nautilus* is smooth, thin and light, forming a plane spiral, exogastrically coiled, that is, with the coil held aloft dorsally, and the mantle and body space lying below and opening in front (Fig. 2H). The shell is divided into some thirty compartments, increasing in size towards the most recent, which is the occupied body chamber. All the previous chambers are cut off by transverse septa. In *Nautilus pompileus*, the best-known living species, each new chamber overlaps and encloses the sides of the previous ones. They are filled with gas, resembling air but containing more nitrogen relative to oxygen. A shelly tube, the *siphuncle*, runs through the chambers to the apex but does not open into them. It carries a vascular siphon which is a narrow prolongation of the tip of the mantle. The gas enclosed in the chambers increases the animal's buoyancy, though its pressure is evidently unable to be varied. The shape and effective specific gravity of the body can however be adjusted within a considerable range by extension or retraction of the soft parts in relation to the mantle cavity. Living *Nautilus* is confined to the Indo-Pacific area. The three species live near the bottom in depths of up to 500 metres, but may have a considerable vertical range, coming into higher levels at night.

The *Nautilus* animal, while obviously related to squids and cuttlefish, is nevertheless very different from all other recent cephalopods. The soft body is surrounded by the mantle and can be completely accommodated inside the mantle cavity in the final shell chamber. The tentacular crown of the foot, which surrounds the mouth, consists of two sets of lappets forming an inner and an outer circle. Their edges are fringed with small tentacles, some ninety in all. slender and annulated, and retractible into basal sheaths. They have no suckers, but are strongly adhesive. Above the head, against the rounded bulge of the shell, lies a fleshy hood which closes over the withdrawn animal. On the lower side lies the funnel, a modified part of the foot, formed of two separate halves that overlap in the middle line. Water passes into the mantle cavity round its whole edge, but the outward jet comes from the funnel alone. Sideways movements of the funnel are employed for steering and changing direction. Water is forced out by the rapid retraction of the animal by its adductor muscles, and by the contraction of the funnel muscles themselves. At the same time all other exits are closed by contact of the body with the rim of the mantle. The mantle—being closely applied to the shell—is unable to contract in itself, as it does in all naked cephalopods.

Many of the early nautiloids were quite straight and conical. The external shell formed a long *orthocone*, divided up by septa and traversed by the siphuncle, which was sometimes very wide. Others were tightly or openly coiled, usually in plane spirals, but sometimes helical. We shall, in a later chapter, say much more about these and the evolution of the vast extinct cephalopod faunas;[10] but to understand properly the modern squids and cuttlefish we must refer first to the fossil belemnoids (Fig. 23c). These had straight cigar-shaped shells, generally up to five or six inches in length. From them arose all living cephalopods save *Nautilus*, and the belemnoids and modern cephalopods constitute together the sub-class Coleoidea.

The belemnoid shell was already internal, and differed from that of nautiloids in several ways. The chambered part—now called the *phragmocone*—was rather short, inserted behind into a much larger calcified *rostrum*, which forms the familiar cigar-shaped fossil. In front the phragmocone was produced into a chitinous shield, the *pro-ostracum*, to which the mantle muscles were attached. Such a shell gave at once support for the tissues, and the same combination of buoyancy and rigidity as we find in living squids.

Squids and cuttlefish, forming with the belemnoids the order

Decapoda, have two long tentacular arms, able to be retracted into sheaths, and a circlet of eight short arms. The tentacles bear clusters of suckers at the tip, the short arms generally have them in several rows along the under surface. Each sucker is strengthened with a horny ring. In the octopuses and their near allies (order Octopoda) there are eight arms only, all long and tentacular; the suckers run right along and have no horny rings.

The modern cephalopod shell has lost many of its original parts (Fig. 23). In the pen of the squids the chambered phragmocone and the rostrum have disappeared altogether. The horny *gladius* and its *rachis*, or shaft, correspond to the pro-ostracum. The sepioid shell is more complete. In the well-known cuttle-bone of *Sepia* we have the persistent outer or uppermost side of the belemnoid phragmocone, now broad and flat, with the septa crowded together in the form of innumerable chalky laminae (Fig. 23E). There is a vestige of the rostrum in the pointed hinder end, but the pro-ostracum is missing. The smooth inner surface of the cuttle-bone represents the siphuncle so widely opened out that the lower wall of the shell has vanished. The small bathypelagic cuttlefish *Spirula*, three or four inches long, is unique among living forms in having a plane-coiled phragmocone, with an open spiral (i.e. a *gyrocone*), formed of about twenty-four chambers with simple concave septa and a siphuncle (Fig. 23G). The shell is almost surrounded by the tissues of the aboral fourth of the body, which bears rounded fins. The animal, buoyed up by the shell, hangs head downward, semi-vertically, and moves by short spurts of the funnel, catching small crustaceans and fish.[10]

Most squids are long, and rounded in cross section (Fig. 7B), whilst cuttlefish are shield-shaped and flat. The mantle is always thick and muscular, investing the lower aspect of the body, part of the sides, and opening in front. Its circular muscles can now contract freely, and this emancipation from the shell has allowed great improvements in locomotion. The funnel is now a complete conical tube, opening in the lower mid-line, and the power of the water jet is greatly increased. In modern decapods every principle making for quick propulsion and diminished water resistance has been beautifully exploited. Fishes alone can swim so fast or adeptly, and only in higher teleosts do we find such a clean and single-purpose design for speed. The commonly observed squid *Loligo*—a foot or more in length—gives a good picture of a squid in action. The broad-based triangular fins serve as horizontal stabilizers; they are much used in hovering but are closed down in fast swimming. As well as the fast backward spurt, headward swimming is very efficient, with the reversal of the funnel direction, the retracted tentacles forming a wedge-shaped transverse prow. As in all fast cephalopods the side entrances of the mantle have developed fleshy valves and a *resisting*

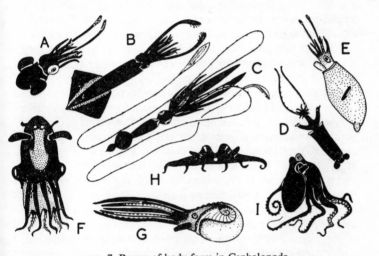

FIG. 7. Range of body form in Cephalopoda

A *Sepiola* (6 cm.), B *Onychoteuthis* (30 cm.), C *Chiroteuthis* (c. 100 cm.), D *Bathothauma* (20 cm.), E *Cranchia* (10 cm.), F *Vampyroteuthis* (20 cm.), G *Argonauta* (50 cm.), H *Opisthoteuthis* (10 cm.), I *Octopus* (80 cm.). (Approximate overall lengths in centimetres.)

apparatus of cartilage studs and sockets. These serve as 'dome-fasteners' by which the mantle can be buttoned to the head on either side to prevent any passage of water except by the funnel.

Squids are the fastest of the Cephalopoda. An alternative design is that of the cuttlefish, which is a much more leisured swimmer. *Sepia* hovers close to the bottom in inshore waters, feeding on shrimps and small fish which it stirs from the sand by short funnel jets. The mantle is rather pointed at its tip, and along either side runs a narrow marginal fin. This produces a slow backward movement when the funnel is out of use, or by shutting down on one side can be used for steering. A related family of benthic cephalopods is the Sepiolidae (Fig. 7A), small cuttlefish with a rounded body and a total length of little more than an inch. The fins form large rounded flaps attached at the middle length of the body. By their action *Sepiola* and *Rossia* can scoop up the sand and nestle into it, where it lurks in watch for small crustaceans. It can sometimes be taken in a hand-net in shallow water near the surf. The smallest of all cuttlefish are the several species of *Idiosepius*. These are only 15 mm. long and live in tide pools. On the dorsal surface of the mantle they develop a small sucker by which they can temporarily attach to the fronds of green algae such as *Ulva*.

Cephalopods, particularly the bottom-haunting sepioids, have brought the art of colour change and camouflage to a high pitch. Unlike the static patterns of opisthobranchs, the colours of cephalopods are under nervous control, unrivalled in delicacy in the animal kingdom. Total transformation of colour is possible in some species in less than two-thirds of a second. The skin has several types of chromatophore, small elastic bags filled with pigment, expanded by radial muscles and contracting by their own elastic power. The pigments are of the nature of *ommochromes*, derived from the amino-acid tryptophan. In sepioids the chromatophores form three layers, bright yellow near the surface, with a middle layer of orange red, and a deeper layer of brown chromatophores. In addition greens and blues may be produced as structural colours.

Sepia officinalis—as studied by Holmes[103]—has the finest colour repertoire. First, there are many colour changes that are concealing or *cryptic* in effect. The normal 'zebra' pattern of dark transverse stripes displayed when swimming can be changed to a pale mottled brown and grey when lurking over a sandy bottom. On a white or pale background all the chromatophores contract to cause total pallor. *Sepia* can also produce a creditable imitation of a chequered black and white surface; such ability is probably of advantage on a ground scattered with large stones or white pebbles. On disturbance or anger there follow vivid changes of colour giving a 'terrorizing' conspicuousness. Large black spots like eyes appear on the dorsal surface; or the body may momentarily become pale, except for a

pair of black stripes flickering along the back, or alternating in rapid
succession with the zebra pattern. When harder pressed, a flattened
posture may be assumed, by depressing and broadening the body.
The eyes become more conspicuous by bulging the irises, and the
body colour alternates between general pallor and deep black spots.
During hunting, brilliant colour waves may sweep over the back and
arms, and a heightened impression of movement is created. The
male *Sepia*—as shown by Tinbergen—also produces a sexual display, swimming alongside the female, spreading the broad lateral
arms and making vivid play with the dark stripes.[185]

Pelagic cephalopods employ a simpler colour change. *Loligo* and
Argonauta have two types of chromatophore, red and yellow,
Ommastrephes adds a third colour, blue. Colour change is generally
from a deep red or purple blush to a blanched colourless effect.
Octopus and *Eledone* have also brown chromatophores and can
match themselves very effectively to the bottom. Cephalopods of
very deep waters may be permanently deep red or purple, or even
black (*Vampyroteuthis*); or, as in the abyssal octopods, the chromatophores may be quite lost.

Almost all cephalopods except *Nautilus* possess the ink-sac, a
glandular diverticulum of the rectum opening just inside the anus.
It releases a dense cloud of melanoid pigment, serving as a protective
smoke-screen on fright or stimulation. Ink may provide not only a
smoke-screen, but combined with colour change enables a neat
deceptive trick to be performed. Thus a small sepiolid squid is
reported to react to danger by first quickly assuming its dark colour,
next emitting a compact cloud of ink to form a roughly shaped
decoy, and then rapidly blanching and darting away unnoticed.

There can never have existed a true example of a flying mollusc,
but some of the smaller fast-moving squids of the family Onycoteuthidae can in fact take to the air efficiently. The *Kon-Tiki* account
has made the habits of these 'flying squids' well known. They are
distinguished by the appearance of hooks as well as suckers in rows
upon the arms. The fins are prolonged behind the body into a wide
horizontal vane; and by strong funnel jets the animal can rise out
of the water and become airborne, using the outspread tail fins as
a gliding plane. *Onycoteuthis* (Fig. 7B) is most often collected afert
stranding on the decks of ships like flying fish. Its reason for 'flying'

is probably the same, to escape from fast-moving predators. The tunny fish relies largely on hooked squids for its food.

In the living Octopoda all trace of the shell is finally lost. Only in the paper nautilus, *Argonauta* (Fig. 7G), do we find a special case. Here the fragile 'shell' is a recent adaptive development, a neo-morph formed of calcified conchiolin secreted by expansions of two of the arms. It occurs only in the female, where it forms a boat for carrying the egg-mass. The Octopoda are most typically represented in coastal waters by *Octopus* and *Eledone*. These are much more adapted to the bottom than the majority of decapods, though we must be careful not to generalize from them to the Octopoda as a whole. This order is rich in abyssal and bathypelagic forms, some of them strangely specialized and aberrant.

The body of an *Octopus* is short and rounded. Fins are lacking, as in nearly all Octopoda, and there is little attempt at streamlining. Though *Octopus* moves fastest by swimming with the funnel, it also makes a much more versatile use of tentacles than do other cephalo-pods, and spends most of its life in intimate contact with the bottom. Short darting movements are made by gentle funnel spurts which increase in power until the animal leaves the ground, and swims horizontally with the tentacles trailing behind. On coming to rest the body may be pulled along nimbly, lightly supported on the tips of the suckered arms. The food, consisting of crabs and other slow crustaceans, is caught not by a lightning strike with a prehensile tentacle as in squids and cuttlefish, but with a swift pounce from above, with the arm circlet and its narrow web widely spread. As well as the visual powers common to nearly all cephalopods, *Octopus* has fine discriminatory powers in the sense organs of the tentacles: Wells and Wells (*see* p. 160) have demonstrated a well-developed 'chemo-tactile' sense, and the Octopodidae are pre-eminently the cephalopods of the sea-bottom.[192]

In a few genera of cephalopods the web developed between the arms may be used for swimming. This is particularly an adaptation of certain Octopoda, where the funnel may be finally abandoned in locomotion.[175] The arm membrane is only slightly shown in the Octopodidae, but many other octopods develop a larger web. A similar arm membrane is employed for swimming in the decapod genus *Histioteuthis* and in the small vampire squids *Vampyroteuthis*

(Fig. 7F). In the deep-water octopods of the super-family Cirro-teuthacea, the web is very wide and occupies nearly the whole length of the eight arms. The animal is bell-shaped, the web hanging like a skirt and the hump of the mantle carrying two broad fins. *Cirrothauma* and *Cirroteuthis* live at great depths and in total darkness. Uniquely among cephalopods, *Cirrothauma* has degenerate eyes and both genera probably rely chiefly on touch. The under-surfaces of the tentacles (inside the web) bear rows of tactile fila-ments on either side of the suckers, and these are said to gather fine particles of food which are then wiped off into the mouth in the manner of a holothurian.

In *Opisthoteuthis* (Fig. 7H) the body is still more modified, flat-tened and circular like a jellyfish, fringed by the tips of eight tenta-cles. The mouth is at the centre of the web, and on the upper surface are two fins, a small funnel opening, and a pair of eyes. The last are very prominent, for the animal lives at no great depths but in the more shallow waters of the continental slope.

IV

MANTLE CAVITY AND GILLS

ANIMALS with delicate gills seldom expose them directly to the world outside; and in the molluscs one of the first distinctive features to evolve was the mantle cavity. This provides protection for the gills against injury or clogging with silt; and it allows an oriented water current to enter and pass out in a definite direction. The incoming current brings not only oxygen, but many other substances both useful and harmful to the mollusc. Particles of sediment, for example, must be carefully collected and rejected; chemical substances are constantly being tested by the osphradium; and in many molluscs microscopic current-borne food is brought in. Sperms, too, may travel into the mantle cavity of the female. Various products of the body are likewise extruded from the mantle cavity in the exhalant current, such as faeces, excretory matter, gametes and secretions, such as protective mucus, purple and ink. Indeed, from a mere cloaca with gills, the mantle cavity has evolved into the main vestibule and centre of commerce of the body. In those molluscs protected by a shell, it provides a space where the head and foot can be withdrawn to safety. As Graham has said, the mantle cavity is at once the strength and weakness of the molluscs. It offers many new mechanical problems; and once these are solved it opens up a new range of evolutionary possibilities. In the bivalves and some gastropods, for example, it provides the intricate ciliary feeding apparatus; and in cephalopods—equipped with powerful pallial muscles—it has become the chief locomotor organ.

Taking our primitive mollusc with two gills as the starting point, we find the mantle cavity lying posteriorly. It may extend along the sides of the foot by narrow grooves, and at either side of the rectum lie the paired organs (gills, osphradia and hypobranchial glands), known as the *pallial complex*. Or since—in typical molluscs—each gill is associated with an auricle and a coelomoduct, all these structures together may be referred to as the *pallio-pericardial complex*.

In the Amphineura[208] the mantle cavity is still primarily posterior. The more primitive chitons such as *Lepidopleurus* have the gills confined to this part of the body. The original pair has, however, increased to six or seven on either side, and the gill rows extend forward in deep channels between the side of the foot and the girdle. In this way the mantle cavity and gills reach as far forward as the head; higher chitons may have as many as seventy pairs of gills, the largest alongside the renal opening behind, and the size diminishing gradually in front and more abruptly behind. Each of these gills is a true ctenidium, with separate filaments, and the ciliation of each filament corresponds closely with that of gastropods. The curtain of gills divides the mantle cavity into two narrow chambers on either side: an inhalant chamber between the gill row and the skirt, and an exhalant chamber inside the gill row and against the side of the foot. Water may pass into the inhalant chamber at any point where the girdle is lifted from the ground, and the median exhalant current passes out behind the anus. The osphradium lies not at the entrance to the mantle cavity, but at the posterior end, though *Lepidopleurus* and some other chitons have additional sense organs at the base of each gill.

In both groups of worm-like Amphineura (Aplacophora) the mantle cavity is a small bell-like space at the posterior end. In *Chaetoderma* it can be rhythmically opened and closed. Simple though it is, this small mantle cavity—together with the radula—stamps the Aplacophora beyond doubt as early molluscs. *Chaetoderma* has two large plume-like gills, one at either side of the anus. In *Neomenia* these are even simpler, merely a circlet of small skin folds with blood from the haemocoele flowing directly into them.

In the newly discovered monoplacophoran, *Neopilina*, Yonge has questioned whether the five pairs of lateral gills described by Lemche are really true ctenidia, in spite of their correspondence with the auricles and coelomoducts. It is more convenient to regard ctenidia as originally paired organs, with a definite morphology and arrangement of cilia, situated in a posterior mantle cavity. In the chitons, though some authors have looked for a metameric pattern, there is

C

no correspondence in number between the shell plates and the gills and—as in the vast majority of molluscs—there are no more than two auricles and kidneys. Nevertheless, both the Monoplacophora and the living *Nautilus*, with two pairs of pallio-pericardial organs (p. 84), are unquestionably ancient; and a fuller knowledge of *Neopilina* may modify many of our present views on the history of the mantle cavity.

GASTROPODA

We have already seen in the Gastropoda (p. 20) how torsion has brought the mantle cavity to the front of the body and has reversed the topography of all the pallio-pericardial organs. We have suggested too that the forward-facing position of the mantle cavity must be of advantage to the adult as well as to the larva. Clean water is now drawn in from ahead of the animal and the pallial entrance is brought into a working relation with the anteroceptors, or sense organs of the head. With the chemosensitive osphradium at its base, the inhalant point of the mantle may be drawn out into a long siphon, and this may be employed as a movable nostril and a forward-seeking exploratory organ.

Torsion is brought about in the modern gastropod by the asymmetrical development of the shell muscles in the early larva. The single retractor muscle in existence when torsion begins has a right-sided insertion on the shell and sweeps over the gut to a leftward attachment to the foot. By its contraction the visceral mass is rotated dorsally and to the left (Fig. 1B). The post-torsional right shell muscle is delayed in development until metamorphosis and then hypertrophies to form the principal (and in later gastropods the single) columellar muscle withdrawing the animal into the shell.[58]

The earliest shells generally classed with the Archaeogastropoda belong to the fossil Bellerophontacea. Here—as in *Bellerophon* and *Sinuites*—the shell is bilaterally symmetrical and coiled into a backward-directed plane spiral; it differs from that of any living archaeogastropod in showing the scars of two symmetrical retractor muscles. The palaeontologist Knight—who has recently published careful studies of these molluscs—holds that there is strong evidence that torsion had occurred in the Bellerophontacea, and that the mantle cavity faced forward. In the absence of asymmetry of the muscles, as suggested by the fossil scars, Knight suggests torsion could have taken place by the development of one muscle of the pair a little in advance of the other, by a mutation in the early veliger larva.[116]

Going back further than the Bellerophontacea, we find in the Cambrian shells that disclose no suggestion of torsion. These we must exclude by definition from the class Gastropoda and place in the class Monoplacophora. Such shells may be very variable in shape, and usually display several symmetrical pairs of muscle scars. A genus such as *Archaeophiala* in the Lower Cambrian has a cup-shaped shell with six to eight pairs of scars. This could have been succeeded by the taller horn-shaped shells of the Mid-Cambrian *Helicionella*, with the apex tilted forward. Here the muscle scars were reduced to one symmetrical pair, by the heightening and narrowing of the forwardly coiled shell.[58]

Between these Monoplacophora and the Bellerophontacea torsion must have intervened and the true Gastropoda have been ushered in. In the earliest forms with torsion the mantle cavity thus retained its complete bilateral symmetry. This was soon to be lost, even in the family Pleurotomariidae, which is represented in rocks of Ordovician age. Bilateral symmetry is found primitively in no living archaeogastropod, though there are four modern families still with paired gills, equal or sub-equal. These are known together as the Zeugobranchia and include the Pleurotomariidae, with its one surviving genus, the Haliotidae, the Scissurellidae and the Fissurellidae.

Spiral coiling is in itself a peculiarly deep-seated feature of the Mollusca, and is shown in some form by gastropods, cephalopods and bivalves, as well as—we now know—in the larval shell of *Neopilina*. Almost every gastropod has at some stage a coiled shell and visceral mass: the limpet-like Fissurellidae and the true limpets (Patellacea) show a brief coiled stage before regaining external symmetry. At any early stage in gastropod history the coiling had become bilaterally asymmetrical, to allow a more compact disposal of the viscera. This involved the pushing of the coil out of the median longitudinal plane, usually to the right, with the production of the familiar dextral twist of most gastropods. And this in turn brought about early rearrangements in the mantle cavity. After right-handed spiral coiling the mantle cavity is longer and more spacious at the peripheral side (on the left), and—as well—the lowest whorl of the visceral mass may bulge deeply into the cavity on the right (axial) side. This restriction of space leads to the reduction of the pallial organs of the right side, though the full effects of coiling have not yet appeared in the Zeugobranchia.[211] In *Pleurotomaria*, though spirally coiled, there are still two gills and hypobranchial glands, about equally large. In *Haliotis* and *Scissurella*, where the large shell muscle obtrudes against the mantle cavity on the right, the gill of this side is a little smaller. In the Fissurellidae, where coiling is lost, the gills are equal, with resumption of bilateral symmetry.

In all these zeugobranchs the exhalant currents cross the gill to the mid-line of the mantle, where in various ways the shell and mantle cavity have been secondarily opened so that the exhalant current and the faeces may pass out more directly. In the Bellerophontacea the shell is notched by a median dorsal slit. In the living *Pleurotomaria* and *Scissurella* the body whorl of the shell and mantle are slit open by a long fissure as far back as the anus. In *Haliotis* there is a row of separate holes, the earlier ones sealing up as the shell grows. Some fissurellids, such as *Emarginula*, retain a slit in the front of the shell. In *Diodora* and the keyhole limpets, *Fissurella*, this closes to leave a small hole at the top of a volcano-shaped shell. In the slug-like *Scutus* the shell is reduced to a small shield and buried in the integument.

In the Zeugobranchia (Fig. 8B) each gill is attached to the floor of the mantle cavity by a suspensory membrane, and along the attached edge passes the efferent blood vessel to the auricle of the heart. At the free edge of the axis runs the afferent vessel from the wall of the mantle. Along either side of the axis, alternating at the two sides, runs a row of triangular gill filaments (Fig. 8A). Each is supported at one free margin by a chitinous skeletal rod, and consists of a double fold of thin integument. This encloses a narrow blood space communicating with the two blood vessels, and gaseous exchange takes place here.

The water current enters the mantle cavity ventro-laterally to either gill. Before reaching the gill, it is tested by the osphradium, then passes between the ctenidial filaments, and leaves the mantle cavity in the dorsal mid-line.[211]

Cilia are confined to the edges of the filaments and to a well-marked tract just behind the free edge overlying the skeletal rod. These last are the lateral cilia: they are responsible for passing water between the filaments and thus for creating the whole pallial current.

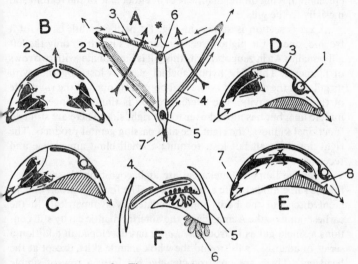

FIG. 8. The gastropod mantle cavity

A Gill filaments of the zeugobranch archaeogastropod *Diadora*, showing on the left lateral cilia 1), frontal cilia, 2) and abfrontal cilia, 3) and on the right the position of the internal skeletal rod 4). 5) Efferent blood vessel, 6) afferent blood vessel, 7) supporting membrane.

* Point at which waste particles collect for rejection.

B–E Schematic sections of the gill and mantle cavity.

B Zeugobranch archaeogastropod, *Diadora*; C A higher archaeogastropod, *Trochus*, with a single bipectinate gill; D A monotocardian prosobranch *Buccinum*, with a single monopectinate gill; E A ciliary feeding monotocardian, *Struthiolaria*, with elongate filaments; F The opisthobranch *Aplysia*, with a reduced mantle cavity and plicate gill. 1) rectum, 2) shell slit, 3) hypobranchial gland, 4) vestigial shell, covered by pallial integument, 5) purple gland, 6) opaline gland, 7) 'endostyle', 8) food groove.

(A–D, after Yonge.)

Along the same edge of the filament runs a tract of frontal cilia; on the other edge lie the abfrontal cilia. These two tracts carry particles either to the tips of the filament or to the axis of the gill (* in Fig. 8A). Material may be rejected from the tips or carried anteriorly, and is compacted with mucus provided both by filamentar glands and by the large *hypobranchial glands*. These are thick folds of epithelium, lying on the mantle roof at either side of the rectum and mesially to the gills.

A cross section is shown in Fig. 8c of the mantle cavity of a trochid, one of the higher archaeogastropods in which only the left gill remains. As in zeugobranchs this gill is bipectinate, with two rows of filaments. The right hypobranchial gland is lost, together with its gill, and the anus and both renal pores now open at the right side of the mantle cavity. The efferent region is thus no longer in the middle line, but has moved over to the right side. There are still two functional kidneys, the right one also passing genital products. The right auricle is all but lost, forming a small blind appendage and receiving no vessels.

The true limpets, Patellacea, are archaeogastropods specialized for the same mode of life as the chitons. The foot is a broad attachment disc, and the body appears bilaterally symmetrical. In the earliest family—the Acmaeidae—the anterior mantle cavity still contains a single gill as in trochids. *Lottia* has developed in addition a series of adaptive 'gills' round the whole mantle skirt, except at the head end. These are not true ctenidia but form a row of simple flaps, hanging side by side from the mantle. The pallial cavity now reaches effectively right round the animal between the foot and the mantle skirt; respiratory water passes inwards between the pallial gills. In *Patina* (family Patellidae) the true gill is lost and the pallial gills function alone; finally in true *Patella* they form a complete circle extending over the head as well. Water can now enter and leave around the whole mantle edge. The limpets, being sedentary, have thus made an attempt at radial symmetry in the mantle cavity, though not in the rest of the body. What the chiton has achieved by multiplying the true ctenidia, the limpet has gained by substituting a ring of pallial gills.[211]

An archaeogastropod like *Trochus* is posed for the evolution of all the later prosobranchs, with a single gill and auricle. These fall into the two orders Mesogastropoda and Neogastropoda, and are sometimes known together as Monotocardia. Fig. 8D shows a section of the mantle cavity of *Buccinum*. The gill is now monopectinate, that is, reduced to a single row of filaments. The frontal, abfrontal and lateral cilia are developed as before. The last-mentioned maintain the water current; the frontals and abfrontals collect particles which are rejected from the tips of the filaments towards the exhalant side of the mantle cavity. The hypobranchial gland is especially large and secretes abundant and very viscous protective mucus. In the Muricidae and in some Volutacea a portion of this gland is responsible for the well-known purple secretion, chemically a dibromindigotin. This is not known to have any protective function, and its role—if any—is obscure. It is more probably an excretory substance.

The Monotocardia show various devices for regulating the direction of the ingoing and outgoing water currents. In higher mesogastropods and in almost all neogastropods the foremost part of the shell aperture is produced into a long or short spout known as the *anterior canal*. Through this runs a fold of the mantle forming an incomplete tube which is the *inhalant siphon*. This may project well in front of the advancing animal, or may be held erect like a median hollow tentacle. It carries the effective opening of the mantle cavity well in advance of the animal; and in carnivorous prosobranchs the great development of this inhalant siphon, or 'movable nostril', is related to the high development of the osphradium, which lies beside the front of the gill just behind the base of the siphon, where it opens into the mantle cavity.

The osphradium is the molluscan chemoreceptor which tests the quality of the water entering the mantle cavity. It is extremely large in carnivores, especially in the whelks and the cones, where it can detect living and dead animal food at some distance away. The simplest osphradia, as in Archaeogastropoda and lower Mesogastropoda, form merely a patch or a line of sensory cells. In later forms the osphradium becomes bipectinate, like a small accessory gill, as may be well seen in *Buccinum*. For *Neptunea antiqua* (12 cm. long) Yonge showed that the 240 osphradial filaments have a sensory area of as much as 5 sq. cm.[211] Particles are carried in between the filaments by cilia, and at the free edge of each filament lies a narrow zone of mucous cells and rejectory cilia. The passage of particles over the filaments has led Hulbert and Yonge to suggest a further and perhaps more general function of the osphradium, that of a mechanoreceptor, to estimate the amount of sediment entering the mantle cavity. In general, however, the largest osphradia are associated with carnivorous life rather than with especially sedimented surroundings. An exceptional carnivorous group are the pelagic heteropods, which live in clean water; they have vestigial osphradia and detect their prey with their powerful eyes.

In the South American and Indian amphibious snails of the Ampullariidae (*Ampullarius* and *Pila*) there is no anterior canal, but the inhalant siphon is greatly developed. It can be extended to much more than the length of the body and reaches up to the surface of the stagnant oxygen-poor water where these prosobranchs live. The mantle cavity is partly partitioned by a fleshy fold, and develops a pulmonary chamber or vascularized lung at the left of the gill. By pulsation of the mantle, and inward and outward movements of the head and foot, the lung may be filled through the siphon with atmospheric air.

Life in turbid waters brings an increased sanitation problem.[207] In many mesogastropods the gill filaments become long and finger-shaped with their rejectory cilia powerfully developed (Fig. 8E). Examples are the British *Aporrhais* and the tropical Strombidae and the carrier shells, Xenophoridae. As Yonge first pointed out, such gills are pre-adapted for ciliary feeding. It is but a small step to convert the pallial organs into collectors not only of waste, but also of useful particles that can be ingested as food. This is essentially what has happened in the lamellibranchs, and in a limited number of mesogastropods as well. One such family of ciliary feeders is in fact the New Zealand Struthiolariidae, the direct descendants of the Aporrhaidae, though unknown to Yonge when he foresaw this trend.[130] The gill receives an extra mucus supply from a glandular and ciliated tract, running along its axis in the path of the incoming current. Mucous strings are carried from here on to the frontal surface of the gill and thence to the tips of the filaments. Such a mucous tract was first described by Orton in *Crepidula*[149] by the rather unsuitable name of 'endostyle', by analogy with the ventral tract in the pharynx of early chordates. The glands on the gill filaments also contribute mucus for food-collecting, as possibly the hypobranchial gland as well. The main source of mucus apart from the endostyle is however a ciliated gutter running forward along the right side of the mantle cavity floor. Particles are thrown into this food groove from the tips of the gill filaments which dip down into it. They are then carried forward to the head, where the food groove debouches by a small spout behind the right tentacle. The proboscis and the radula are from time to time turned back to pluck off strings of mucus-bound food from the opening of the groove.

As well as the Struthiolariidae, two other families of ciliary feeders live on muddy or sandy bottoms, the marine Turritellidae[93] and the freshwater Viviparidae.[54] Ciliary feeders on hard substrates include the Calyptraeidae (*Calyptraea* and *Crepidula*), the Capulidae and the vermiform Siliquariidae and Vermetidae. The last-named family have not persevered with ciliary feeding, and in later genera the gill becomes very small. Instead, long mucous strings are secreted from the pedal gland below the mouth (as in *Vermetus gigas*) (Fig. 3H), forming efficient plankton traps which are later hauled in by the radula and ingested.

OPISTHOBRANCHIA

From the beginning of opisthobranch evolution the mantle cavity tends to move back along the right side to its posterior position as torsion is reduced. This involves the decreased importance of the ctenidium, until—as we have seen—new methods of respiration by the adaptation of the dorsal body wall are provided in the nudibranchs. In primitive shelled opisthobranchs the ciliated filaments of the prosobranch gill are generally replaced by thicker fleshy folds, to give a *plicate gill*. Such a condition is shown by the Cephalaspidea (bulloids), the Anaspidea (aplysioids) and the primitive shelled sacoglossans (*Oxynoe*, *Cylindrobulla* and *Lobiger*). In the Notaspidea, such as *Pleurobranchus* and *Umbraculum*, the mantle cavity is at last quite lost, but a conspicuous naked ctenidium still survives, under the right side of the mantle skirt.

In early opisthobranchs, however, such as the bulloids, that live on a sandy or muddy bottom, the hypobranchial gland and ciliary cleansing arrangements of the mantle cavity are still very important. The mantle cavity is frequently—as in *Scaphander*—drawn out posteriorly to the right of the animal into a spirally coiled caecum. This lies outside and quite separate from the rest of the body. In the burrowing *Actaeon* it is extraordinarily developed, coiling independently around the visceral spire, and reaching to the apex of the shell. The exact function of this caecum is not known—it possibly provides an accessory respiratory surface. The hypobranchial mucous gland extends right to the tip of it, and there are strong inward and outward ciliary currents that carry water through it, and serve as a flushing system for removing sediment.[87]

The thecosomatous pteropods, though they have lost the gill, have a broad shield-shaped hypobranchial gland and a very spacious mantle cavity. In the Limacinidae, at least, the pallial ciliary currents and the mucus from this gland serve to collect food particles: a food string is passed out from the exhalant side of the mantle cavity, as previously seen for example in *Crepidula*, and is periodically pulled into the mouth by the radula. In the Cavoliniidae, ciliated fields on the posterior sides of the wings collect food, which is carried to the mouth by ciliary tracts at the sides of the foot. In the Cymbuliidae these pedal tracts are elevated upon a spatulate 'proboscis', at the tip of which lies the mouth; ciliated fields on the wings are lost, and in *Gleba* the radula is lacking.[199]

In the aplysioids (Fig. 8F) the mantle cavity has dwindled to a small triangular recess, at the middle of the right side. The fleshy gill partly projects from it, and there are two important sets of glands, both evidently protective in function. On the roof is a brownish-yellow gland—the homologue of the hypobranchial gland—secreting a deep purple substance (aplysiopurpurin—p. 46). On the floor discharge the grape-like clusters of the *opaline gland*, producing a colourless noxious secretion.[67]

PULMONATA

The pulmonates have followed a very different course. There is never a true gill, and though the shell may be lost, the mantle cavity nearly always keeps its anterior (post-torsional) position. Its roof is lined with an anastomosis of thin-walled blood vessels, and the cavity becomes air-filled, to act as a lung. The external opening is very small, a circular pneumostome on the right side, rhythmically expanding and contracting in land pulmonates. Nearby—outside the mantle cavity—open the anus and renal organ. The hypobranchial gland is lost, and the osphradium where present is usually extra-pallial; the pallial cavity is henceforward a closed lung and nothing more.

Such a lung does not confine the pulmonates to land: it is in fact an ideal organ both for aerial and aquatic respiration, and the majority of lower pulmonates, constituting the order Basommatophora, are truly amphibious.[135] Terrestrial evolution has occurred several times, and is seldom one-way. The Basommatophora fall into two series. Marine members—such as the siphonariid limpets, and the Amphibolidae—have become thoroughly re-adapted to submerged life. The mantle cavity is again filled with water and the osphradium is internal. A secondary intra-pallial gill, built up of narrow folds of epithelium, is developed, though never a ctenidium. The higher Basommatophora are dwellers in lakes, ponds and rivers; they have arrived there not from the sea or estuaries, but by varying degrees of re-adaptation from terrestrial life. The Succineidae—living amphibiously in marshes—are classed as primitive Stylommatophora; yet they are extremely similar in many ways to the Lymnaeidae, and some members of this family, such as *Lymnaea truncatula*, and *L. palustris*, are marsh dwellers with an air-filled lung, and live essentially out of water. Other lymnaeids, such as *Lymnaea stagnalis*, come to the surface regularly to fill the lung with air, and are said to drown if this is prevented. At the other extreme are deep-water species, such as *L. abyssicola*, which never surface. Intermediate species include perhaps the majority of Lymnaeidae, and also the Physidae, such as the British *Physa fontinalis*. In *Physa* and in *Lymnaea peregra*—a ubiquitous species tolerating many habitats—Hunter[111] has found several distinct physiological states in different populations. Individuals living near lake margins can occasionally come to the surface and take in air, as they do frequently under laboratory conditions. In others, further from land, the mantle cavity may contain a gas bubble that is possibly used as a physical gill; while in those in deepest water the cavity is permanently filled with water and respiration is entirely aquatic.

The Planorbidae and the Ancylidae are the most purely aquatic of pulmonate families. Here the pallial cavity is disused, and in Ancylidae it is almost lacking. Instead, a secondary external gill is developed by the enlargement of a pallial lobe, lying just outside the pneumostome. In the ancylids this lobe is served by the ordinary vascular circuits of the mantle, but, at least in *Planorbis corneus*, a complete afferent and efferent circulation is developed. The external gill becomes elaborately pleated and folded, though it is never ciliated like a ctenidium. Several species of planorbids, such as the tiny *P. crista*, can tolerate very foul water; and *P. corneus* possesses haemoglobin serving as a respiratory aid and oxygen store in conditions of low oxygen pressure.[46]

The terrestrial slugs of the family Athoracophoridae deserve mention. Here the lung has lost its blood vessels and serves as a small vestibule with its wall produced into fine tubules that ramify in the underlying blood spaces. Though some suspect these canals to be glandular, critical experiments may yet confirm that these slugs are unique among molluscs in having developed respiratory tracheae.

There are finally two families of specialized slug-like Pulmonata, with a long ventral foot, a narrow pallial skirt and the anus and renal pore opening at the extreme posterior end. The first is the intertidal Onchidiidae (p. 44), with a small pulmonary chamber forming a vestibule for the anus. It is only doubtfully a pallial cavity. The second family, Vaginulidae, are terrestrial forms in tropical America, Asia and Africa. They have no pallial cavity at all and respire by the moist integument.

LAMELLIBRANCHIA

The most complex molluscan gills are found in the lamellibranchs. With some exceptions the bivalves are sedentary ciliary feeders, and the cilia and mucous tracts of the mantle cavity play the central role in their life. In the evolution of their filtering organs the lamellibranchs are paralleled by other ciliary feeders, such as polyzoans, brachiopods, tubicolous worms, Amphioxus and tunicates. The resemblances extend to the details of the lateral cilia which create the current, the frontal cilia which collect the food, and the tracts of mucous glands and cilia which transport and sort it. But the lamellibranchs stand out alone in the beautiful elaboration of these mechanisms, especially the sorting and straining cilia. Filtering is very efficient: particles down to 1_μ in size can often be retained, and many species rely chiefly on the 'ultra-plankton' as food. The papers of Orton[150] and Kellogg,[115] and more recently of Yonge,[210], [215] Atkins[32] and McGinitie,[124] have built up a lively picture of the working of the bivalve mantle cavity.

The gills are bipectinate (i.e. with two rows of filaments) and equal on either side. To understand their derivation from earlier gills, we must first describe one of the primitive Protobranchia, such as *Nucula*,[209] where the gills are relatively smallest (Fig. 9A). They lie behind the foot at the back of the mantle cavity, with the inner filaments from either gill touching in the mid-line. Such ctenidia, though larger, clearly recall those of early gastropods and their forerunners; though uniquely specialized in some characters, the protobranchs are in other ways a fine transitional group. In *Nucula* the filaments of each gill are triangular leaflets. In section the gills extend across the mantle cavity to form together an inverted W with short wide limbs. The inhalant chamber lies ventrally and the exhalant chamber above. Currents are carried between the filaments by the lateral cilia. Along the lower edge run the frontal cilia, on the upper edge the abfrontals. Their beat is so arranged as to carry particles towards the middle line, where the two inner filaments loosely interlock by cilia. Here the particles are rejected into the inhalant chamber. Above the gills, in the exhalant chamber, are found paired hypobranchial glands, absent in most later lamellibranchs. The anus and renal organs open into this chamber, and there is also—near the posterior adductor muscle—a pair of small osphradia.

The pallial water current enters in front and after passing through the gills goes out behind. The current serves for respiration, and the gill cilia, while rejecting particles, do not in *Nucula* collect food. On either side of the foot, lying in front of the gills, are the very broad labial palps, which are the largest of the pallial organs. On their inner faces they are lined by ciliated sorting ridges, and their posterior ends are produced into long grooved tentacles, known as the *palp proboscides*. These emerge from the shell and collect food particles from the soft substrate, which are carried in by cilia and sorted on the palps. Thus *Nucula* is not a ctenidial feeder; but the development of labial palps was—as Yonge has shown—perhaps a necessary stage in the evolution of filter feeding, first enabling the mouth to be raised above the ground.

Like some other primitive groups, the Protobranchia are very diversified.[209] In the Malletiidae (including *Yoldia* and *Malletia*) the gills are strongly fused by cilia in the mid-line. The interfilamentar spaces are reduced to rows of pores, and the gills acquire muscle fibres, functioning as a rhythmical pumping membrane drawing water from inhalant to exhalant chambers. Both inhalant and exhalant currents are posterior, passing through short siphons. In the Solenomyidae the shell is tubular and flexible, being only partly calcified. The mantle edges partly fuse and the foot passes through the anterior end like a muscular piston, extruding mucus-bound sediment from the mantle cavity. By forcible expulsion of water, darting and swimming movements are performed. The ctenidia are large and their currents collect food, the palps being small, without proboscides and are never protruded from the shell.

In the remaining bivalves the gills are more specialized.[173] A history of this class could be written from their ctenidia, and their degree of specialization corresponds fairly well with the general evolutionary level. Above the prosobranchs the gill filaments elongate, then double back upon themselves. The first stage—the *filibranch* condition—is seen, for example, in *Arca*, *Mytilus* and *Anomia*. Each gill separately now forms a W in section, with long narrow limbs. Fig. 9B shows some points of anatomy. The gill axis lies at the middle angle of the W. The central limbs are the *descending lamellae*, the outer limbs the *ascending lamellae*, made up of the reflected distal parts of the filaments. Each V of the W forms a demibranch; there are thus an inner and an outer demibranch, each two lamellae thick, in either gill. In each demibranch the component filaments become attached to each other side to side. With filibranchs this is achieved simply by scattered discs of stiff cilia that interlock like hairbrushes; for this reason the filaments are easily pulled apart and the gill may take on a frayed appearance in dissection. In addition, connective tissue junctions run between the descending and ascending limbs and thus hold together the two lamellae of each demibranch.

In the gills of Ostreidae, Pectinidae and Pteriacea, which are described as *pseudolamellibranch*, the reflected distal tips of the filaments have coalesced laterally with the mantle, and mesially with the

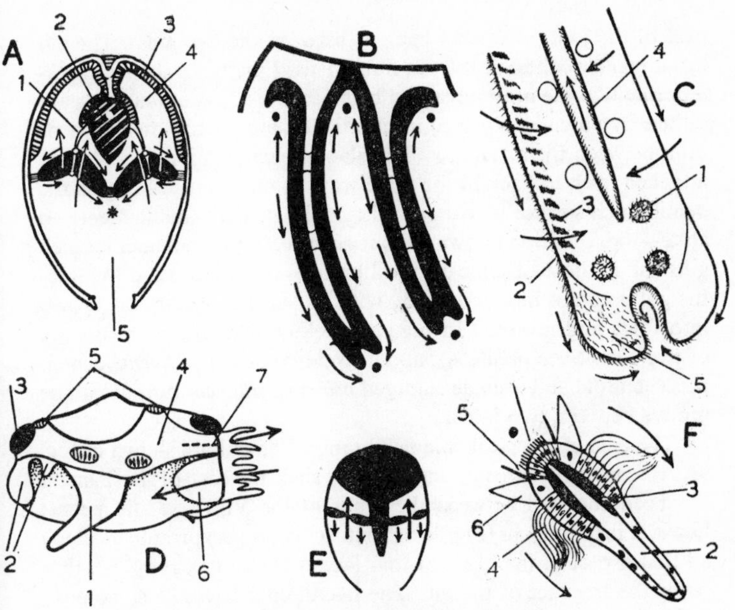

FIG. 9. The lamellibranch mantle cavity

A Transverse section of *Nucula*, showing the arrangement and ciliary currents of the gills. 1) suspensory membrane, 2) visceral mass, 3) hypobranchial gland, 4) exhalant chamber, 5) inhalant chamber.

* Point where particles are rejected from gills.

B Transverse section of the left gill of *Mytilus* (filibranchiate type), showing ciliary currents.

• Indicates an orally directed longitudinal current.

C Surface view of the tip of a gill filament of *Mytilus*. 1) ciliated attachment discs, 2) frontal edge with frontal and laterofrontal cilia, 3) lateral cilia, 4) abfrontal cilia (lost in eulamellibranch gills), 5) terminal cilia.

D Left side view of *Poromya*, a septibranch. 1) foot, 2) labial palps, 3) adductor muscle, 4) septum with perforations, 5) septal muscles inserted on shell, 6) valve fold of inhalant siphon, 7) exhalant siphon.

E Section of a septibranch mantle cavity.

F Section of a eulamellibranch gill filament. 1) frontal cilia, 2) blood space, 3) skeletal rod, 4) lateral cilia, 5) microlaterofrontal cilia, 6) eulaterofrontal cilia.

(A, after Yonge; B, after Atkins.)

base of the foot (or further back as between the two gills). The gill has a greater cohesion than in filibranchs. Finally, in the *eulamellibranch* gill of the most advanced bivalves, the adjacent filaments are united by vascular cross connections, leaving narrow openings or *ostia* between them. The two lamellae of each demibranch become attached back to back in the same way. In most lamellibranchs the demibranch surface is without folds and flat, with the filaments all alike—the condition known as *homorhabdic*. In pseudolamellibranch gills and in those of some eulamellibranchs (Cardiacea and Myacea) the gill becomes more complex, with its surface plicate, or thrown into folds and grooves. In pseudolamellibranchs the filaments are of two sorts (*heterorhabdic*): about twenty *ordinary filaments* constitute each fold and a single enlarged *principal filament* runs along the groove between two folds.

The cilia of a typical eulamellibranch filament are shown in Fig. 9F. Abfrontal cilia are no longer found, since the edge of the filament has been enclosed between the limbs of the V. These still persist however in filibranchs (Fig. 9c). Frontal cilia are very prominent along all that aspect of the filament that faces the mantle cavity, i.e. they cover the free face of the gill. The lateral cilia have the same position, just behind the frontal edge, as in gastropods. They pass the water current between the filaments, through the ostia, into the interlamellar space which leads above into the *suprabranchial chamber*, carrying water backwards towards the exhalant siphon. Lying between the lateral cilia and the frontals is another set of cilia peculiar to the bivalves, the *laterofrontal* cilia (5, 6). In pseudolamellibranch and most filibranch gills these form one row of small *microlaterofrontal* cilia; in nearly all others, that is, in protobranchs and eulamellibranchs, there are two rows, small *prolaterofrontals* and much larger *eulaterofrontals*. The latter form triangular platelets, probably from the fusion of several separate cilia. They beat relatively slowly towards the middle of the frontal edge, at right angles, that is, to the frontal cilia. Each row of eulaterofrontal cilia forms a flexible comb, and the two rows bordering each ostium provide a sieve stretching right across the water space, and straining off particles for retention on the frontal surface of the gill.[32]

Various tracts of cilia beat anteriorly and posteriorly along the margin of the gill, transporting either collected food to the labial palps (in oral grooves) or rejected particles backwards. Such currents run in grooves along the demibranch margin or dorsally at the inner or outer base of the gills. Particles are brought to them by the frontal cilia beating up or down the filaments.

The filtering power of the gill may be varied by altering the width of the ostia or the speed of the current; filtration is probably chiefly the function of the laterofrontal cilia. Some workers, especially McGinitie,[124] have held that particles are filtered and transported over the gill in a thin sheet or network of mucus, secreted partly by the filaments, partly by glands at the base of the gill. The mucous sheet has an extremely small mesh size and bacterial particles can be filtered and large molecular aggregates perhaps adsorbed upon it. Thus clams can be fed for long periods on filtered meat extract, and in some experiments haemocyanin and haemoglobin were removed from the water in molecular form.

All authors would allow the importance of mucus in rejecting waste. Some, however, have questioned whether the sorting mechanisms of the gill could function, if particles were wholly embedded in a mucous sheet. Ciliary sorting is highly important in the bivalve gill, and Atkins has described the varied and ingenious methods, all contriving to exclude over-large or coarse particles from the oral grooves running to the palps and mouth.[32]

I. *In plicate gills.* (*a*) *Pecten* and others. The plicae may be approximated so as to close the channels between them and present a wholly rejecting surface to the mantle cavity.

(*b*) *Pinna* and Anomalodesmata. There are two marginal grooves, a safe oral groove led to by the principal filament at the bottom of each channel, and a superficial rejectory groove led to by the filaments of the plicae.

II. *Protection of the marginal oral groove.* (*a*) By approximating its edges (in *Solecurtus, Lutraria* and *Cardium*), or (*b*) by long fans of guarding cilia excluding coarse particles (many genera on muddy bottoms).

III. *Rejecting by specialized frontal cilia.* (*a*) Strong cirri in *Mactra, Spisula* and *Donax*, and (*b*) by cilia beating in the opposite direction to the food-collecting cilia (Arcidae and Anomiidae).

In Arcidae and Anomiidae the frontal cilia and marginal grooves are chiefly rejectory, and food is carried to the mouth along the dorsal grooves at the inner or outer gill bases.

The mucous sheet may be normally so fluid that the sorting cilia can project through it, or manipulate particles within it.

Particles excluded from the oral groove are thrown off the gill on to the sides of the foot or the mantle wall. The finer material carried in the grooves eventually arrives at the point where the demibranchs terminate between the bases of the labial palps.[198] Though smaller than in protobranchs the palps are very prominent, hanging as a pair of triangular flaps on either side of the mouth. Their outer sides are smooth; inside—where particles impinge—they are traversed by ciliated ridges and grooves. The palps form a sorting mechanism of a kind used repeatedly by molluscs, both in the mantle cavity and in the stomach. Heavier or coarser particles are carried into the grooves, where they are passed to the margin of the palp and rejected from its tip. Lighter material moves up the palp across the crests of the ridges to arrive at the mouth. Sorting is by size and weight, with little reference to quality, and coarse and unsuitable particles are at times found to enter the stomach.

In turbid waters the overspill from the gills and palps must be continuous. It is bound together with mucus and rejected from the mantle cavity as *pseudofaeces*; exit is by the pedal gape, or—in those bivalves with an extensively fused mantle and long siphons—pseudofaeces may travel posteriorly in a ciliated rejection groove running along the pallial suture to the base of the inhalant siphon, which expels them. The exhalant siphon passes only water, with renal products and true excreta; pseudofaeces are unable to reach it.

In some lamellibranchs part of the normal gill is lacking. The small, free and commensal bivalves of the Erycinacea have reduced or lost the outer demibranch, perhaps owing to the decreased gill surface ratio required with reduced body size. In the Teredinidae, where the gill is prolonged into the base of the inhalant siphon, only a modified inner demibranch survives. In the Anomalodesmata the outer demibranch is turned up dorsally and often loses its reflected lamella.

The same is true of many Tellinacea, and in this super-family the gill surface is much reduced in comparison with the labial palps, which enlarge to approach the gill in size. All the Tellinacea are deposit feeders on the rich organic layer of the surface of the substratum, which they reach with the long inhalant siphon. Yonge has pointed to fundamental differences between Tellinacea and the majority of bivalves that feed by filtering suspended particles. The food deposit is coarser and heavier than plankton; it is sucked in with the inhalant current and by muscular action of the tip of the inhalant siphon which wanders freely over its available territory. Much of the entering deposit is probably drawn forward and thrown directly on to the surface of the palps; both here and in the stomach, sorting must be very rigorous. As compared with suspension feeders, the gills play a much smaller role in the collecting and grading of particles.[212]

The most extraordinarily modified lamellibranch mantle cavities are found in the small group Septibranchia (Fig. 9D), sometimes considered a separate order, and containing only three genera—*Poromya*, *Cetoconcha* and *Cuspidaria*. The ctenidia no longer exist as such, being converted into a horizontal muscular septum, spreading from the base of the foot to the mantle, and extending right back to the siphons. The septum is inserted on the shell by its own muscles, and completely divides the mantle cavity into ventral and dorsal chambers, communicating with the inhalant and exhalant siphons respectively. It is perforated in *Cuspidaria* by four or five pairs of ostia, in *Poromya* by two pairs of larger branchial sieves. It can be raised and lowered to form a pump, driving water intermittently through the openings from ventral to dorsal chamber. In *Cuspidaria* the septum develops peculiar striated muscle fibres; in *Poromya* it is much more delicate, and this genus leads on from *Verticordia*, one of the order Anomalodesmata with more normal but already very muscular gills. Septibranchs live in very deep water, burrowing shallowly in mud and ooze. They are no longer ciliary feeders but scavengers, ingesting the whole bodies or fragments of dead or moribund crustaceans and other small animals. As well as the gills, the labial palps are much reduced and retain no sorting function.[200]

CEPHALOPODA

Here—as we have seen—a very powerful pallial current is created not by cilia but by muscular contractions of the funnel, in *Nautilus*, and the mantle in other living forms. This provides the motive power for jet propulsion, and the increased flow of water through the mantle current also meets the respiratory demands of higher metabolism and greater activity. In a squid, cuttlefish or octopus, the mantle cavity is a deep space enclosing the lower surface and sides of the body. It contains a pair of large bipectinate gills suspended one at either side of the rectum (Fig. 15c). Increased size and the strong pumping force mantle have necessitated great modifications in the structure of the gills. They are suspended by their *afferent* edges, not efferent as in gastropods, and the water current is driven from afferent to efferent side. The filaments are firm and fleshy, no longer ciliated, and thrown into primary and secondary folds to increase the respiratory surface. In modern cephalopods—not *Nautilus*—the flow of blood through the gills is increased by the development of fine capillaries within the filaments. In addition, the blood flow through each gill is assisted by a pulsatile *accessory branchial heart*, lying at the base of the gill on the course of the afferent ctenidial vessel, and placed in an annexe of the pericardium. Pallial contractions drive water between the gill filaments at great pressure. As well as the normal afferent to efferent flow (Fig. 15D) outwards towards the funnel, there may be considerable backflow between the filaments. This pressure is partly withstood by the chitinous skeletal rods along the afferent edges of the filaments. With the loss of the ciliary tracts of the gill, the hypobranchial glands disappear as well. The osphradia are found in *Nautilus* alone.[211]

Nautilus has neither gill capillaries nor branchial hearts; and the funnel contractions are less efficient than those of the mantle in other cephalopods. Lacking these improvements, *Nautilus* has developed increased respiratory efficiency by the duplication of the ctenidia to two pairs. These gills are attached only by their bases. With the gills, the auricles and the renal organs also increase to four. Whether this duplication was ever widespread in cephalopods, or in molluscs at large, or a special occurrence in a few genera, we cannot tell. The recent discovery of *Neopilina*—with five pairs of these structures—suggests that this may have been a deep-seated feature in many early Mollusca.

The haemocyanin of cephalopod blood is a highly efficient oxygen carrier compared with that of Gastropoda (Redfield, 1934).[170] There is a high utilization of oxygen from the pallial water—63% in

Octopus vulgaris, as compared with 5%–9% in sedentary lamelli-branchs which have increased their pallial current for feeding purposes. The Gastropoda, with a smaller gill, and with no muscular pumping, pass a much smaller volume of water, from which they make a high utilization of oxygen (estimated at 56% in a *Haliotis* species, 38% in a *Murex* and 79% in *Tritonium*).

V

FEEDING AND DIGESTION

THE first molluscs probably all fed on fine particles. Food was scraped up by the broad radula, which was covered with many rows of small, uniform teeth. A good deal of sand and other indigestible matter must have been swept into the mouth along with diatoms and fragments of decaying plants. Such a mixture of particles is a far more difficult food to deal with than flesh or fluid or plant tissues. And since the early molluscs had inherited the method of intra-cellular digestion, there was the problem not only of collecting and transporting food, but also of grading it into coarse and fine particles, since only the smallest could be phagocytosed by the digestive gland. Continuous transport and ciliary sorting were thus among the earliest functions of the molluscan gut.

The radula varies in length and number of tooth rows according to the rate of wear from the diet. Only the front rows are in use at one time, and the most recently formed part is enclosed in a posterior caecum in which the teeth are secreted by special *cuspidoblast* cells. In addition to the radula, the buccal cavity carries on its side walls a pair of chitinous-edged *jaws*.

The radula in microphagous molluscs is constantly at work (Fig. 10c). It brings particles to the roof of the buccal mass, where cilia take them to the oesophagus. Here they are bound in strings with mucus, partly from the 'salivary' glands and partly from the wall of the oesophagus. Behind the buccal mass the gut has few muscles, and works largely by cilia and mucus.

The early molluscan stomach (Fig. 10A) has a very characteristic structure. It tapers back into the wide tube of the first part of the intestine. This is lined by strong, transversely beating cilia, and its contents form a stiff mucous rod, plastered with faeces and continually rotated by the cilia. This rod may be called a *protostyle* (2), since it is the forerunner of the molluscan *crystalline style*, and the part of the intestine where it rotates is known as the *style sac*.

The head of the style projects into the stomach, and the food string (10) from the oesophagus is wound on to its free end, being twisted into a tight spiral and in this way gradually moved into the stomach, as well as by the action of cilia in the oesophagus. From the other end of the rod, small faecal pellets are periodically nipped off, to be moulded by the cilia of the intestine. The revolving style stirs the stomach contents, and close to its head the wall is covered by a

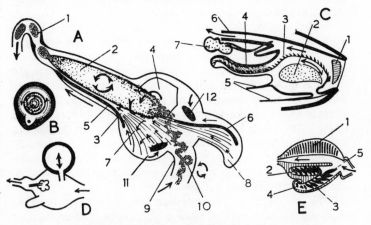

FIG. 10.   The gastropod digestive system

A Generalized form of the stomach in an early prosobranch. 1) intestine with faecal pellets, 2) protostyle in style sac, 3) intestinal groove, 4) gastric shield, 5) minor typhlosole, 6) major typhlosole, 7) ciliary sorting area, 8) posterior caecum, 9) oesophagus, 10) food string, 11), 12) openings of digestive diverticula.

B Section of style sac.

c Diagrammatic median section of generalized buccal mass. 1) jaw, 2) odontophore, 3) radula, 4) radular sac, 5) retractor muscles, 6) oesophagus, 7) salivary gland.

D Buccal mass of *Onchidoris* showing spherical buccal pump.

E Buccal mass of *Alderia* in median section. 1) transverse muscles of dorsal wall, 2) radular sac, 3) ascus sac, 4) worn detached teeth at tip of ascus sac, 5) tooth in use.

cuticular *gastric shield* (4), which prevents abrasion by coarse particles. The rest of the stomach is lined with fine ridges and furrows covered with cilia, and acts as a *sorting area* (7), such as we have previously seen on the labial palps of bivalves. As the food string is rotated near this area, particles are all the while detached. Coarser material is flung into the deeper grooves and taken by cilia to the intestine. Finer particles are kept in suspension by the cilia on the ridges and gradually reach the paired digestive diverticula. The mucus of the food string becomes less viscous with the lower pH of the stomach fluid—about 5-6—and this too assists the shedding of its load. The intestinal pH is higher, about 8, and the viscous mucus here binds the contents into firm pellets.[132, 156]

In this way the molluscan stomach became adapted for its two main tasks, ciliary rotation of the food string and ciliary sorting of detached particles. Most other animals, since they have extracellular digestion, lack sorting areas in the stomach. But we are beginning to find that many microphagous animals make use of some kind of windlass turned by the cilia of the gut. Tunicates form their food string by twisting in the oesophagus, Amphioxus has a rotating area in the colon, polyzoans, brachiopods and *Phoronis* in the pylorus, some enteropneusts at the back of the gill area. Only in molluscs, however, do the style and sorting area together take on such specialized functions, and only here does a crystalline style later develop, carrying in its substance a digestive enzyme.

The two digestive diverticula lead from the stomach to much-branched glandular follicles. These exhibit a cycle of absorption and secretion. Most of the digestion being intracellular, the absorbing cells produce a protease, amylase and lipase. Extracellular enzymes are available too, secreted by the oesophagus in glandular pouches opening singly or in series into its middle length. The salivary glands may produce enzymes as well, particularly protease in carnivores. In both gastropods and lamellibranchs that possess a crystalline style in the style sac, this rod liberates its own store of carbohydrate-splitting enzymes as its substance dissolves in the stomach. Recent work suggests that an amylolytic enzyme may sometimes exist along with a protostyle. Finally, the amoebocytes of the blood stream play an important part in digestion. They migrate freely into the gut from the blood system and phagocytose particles within the stomach.

They may then retreat back into the epithelium, or surrender their contents for final absorption by the digestive gland.[107]

PRIMITIVE GASTROPODA AND AMPHINEURA

Most Archaeogastropoda have a gut very similar to this early type and indeed form the basis of many of our ideas about it. The majority, such as the Trochidae, Haliotidae and Fissurellidae, show the typical *rhipidoglossan* radula (Fig. 11c), a wide ribbon with long and numerous marginal teeth for sweeping up deposits or rasping algae. In the Trochidae and Haliotidae the sorting area of the stomach migrates into a special gastric caecum, spirally coiled, from which issue two graded streams of particles, fine material to the digestive diverticula and coarse to the intestine. Such a sorting caecum—as represented in Fig. 10A—may well be an ancient feature, for we shall find it again in both lamellibranchs and cephalopods.

The digestive systems of the chitons (Polyplacophora)[76] and the archaeogastropod limpets (Patellacea)[91] may be considered together, for they are modified in similar ways. Both groups are mainly intertidal herbivores, often ceasing to feed when exposed. The continuous action of a mucous string and a style capstan would be less appropriate and the style sac is never fully represented. Large amounts of algae and comminuted deposits are swallowed intermittently. The radula has a reduced number of strong rasping teeth in each row (Fig. 11D), and—especially in limpets—its teeth are rapidly worn and need constant replacement. The radula is thus very long. The oesophagus bears lateral secretory pouches, referred to in chitons as *sugar glands*, which produce amylolytic enzymes. It is dilated further back into a storage crop.

The stomach in limpets is a small and featureless sac that has lost all trace of caecum or gastric shield; it forms merely a bend in the gut where the paired digestive diverticula open. In chitons the stomach is more complex. The oesophagus and diverticula open into a ventral sac lined with cuticle, and from here a chamber corresponding to the style sac leads to the intestine. In this part the mucous food string is rotated by cilia and its fluid contents are squeezed out, to be forced into the digestive diverticula. In both limpets and chitons the digestive gland produces enzymes for splitting cellulose-like substances. The intestine is long and much coiled, storing faeces between tides.

The worm-like Aplacophora have an extremely simplified gut. In *Chaetoderma*—feeding on detritus and foraminifera in deep-water ooze—the radula is represented by very few large pointed teeth, or even only one, directly eversible from the buccal floor. In the Neomeniomorpha the buccal bulb is suctorial: the animals live on the fluid protoplasm of hydroids and gorgonians, and the radula comprises one or several sharp-cusped teeth (Fig. 11A). The rest of the digestive tract is a straight tube, and the stomach itself is lined with digestive cells.[99]

LATER PROSOBRANCHIA

Only slight changes are needed to convert a microphagous gastropod into a macroherbivore, a ciliary feeder or even a carnivore; and each of these habits is soon developed. Many limpets and trochids feed on the thalli of large algae, while some fissurellids no longer eat algae but graze upon sponges. The early Mesogastropoda were destined to a wide radiation in feeding habits, and further prosobranch evolution is in great part a story of changing diets.

The Mesogastropoda begin with snails of the periwinkle type (Littorinidae), which may browse upon algae like trochids, or feed on the detritus layer of the substratum. The periwinkles have—like the limpets—a very elongated radula, with strong rasping teeth, and the radular caecum is coiled like a watchspring. The stomach is a spacious sac, serving as a store for bulky intermittent food, and there is no rotating protostyle.[96] Periwinkles of the sub-genus *Melaraphe*, such as the British *Littorina* (*M.*) *neritoides*, rasp lichens and blue-green algae from the barren rocks above high spring tide. Others, such as *L. obtusata* and the related *Lacuna*, live almost solely on fucoid algae. Like nearly all mesogastropods, they have a radula of the *taenioglossan* type (Fig. 11E), a narrow ribbon with only two pairs of marginal teeth, two laterals and once central in each row. Such teeth may be adapted for a variety of tasks: picking up particles, cutting and shredding, as well as sweeping and grazing.

We mentioned in the last chapter those Mesogastropoda that employ the gill in ciliary feeding. Some genera—such as *Viviparus, Turritella* and *Struthiolaria* are selective deposit feeders; others—for example the sedentary Calyptraeidae and the sessile Vermetidae and Siliquariidae—live on a hard substrate and capture suspended food, in many vermetids with the assistance of mucous traps. In these ciliary feeders the buccal mass and salivary glands are small, and the oesophagus is a narrow mucus-secreting tube with no enzymes. The radula forms a series of tiny grappling hooks for seizing and hauling into the mouth portions of the food string prepared in the mantle cavity.[207] The stomach has evolved along the same lines as in the lamellibranchs, and within the style sac lies a crystalline style, a flexible hyaline rod composed of muco-protein. The sac may form a closed caecum, by-passed by the intestine, and the style loses all connection with the faecal string. It retains however its attachment to the oesophageal food string which is wound in by it as by a capstan. As the style rotates it is slowly thrust into the stomach where its outer layers are dissolved, releasing amylolytic enzymes gradually and continuously, independent of any secretory rhythm of the gut.[95] The crystalline style is not confined to ciliary feeders: all Rissoacea and Cerithiacea possess it, while in the Strombidae and Xenophoridae—which feed upon coarse, poorly sorted deposits— the style capstan is firm and robust, reaching a length of more than half that of the animal.

Prosobranchs have become carnivores in several ways, and the gut usually shows a striking contrast with that of herbivores or ciliary feeders.[97] The diet is smaller in bulk and feeding is intermittent. The style sac and sorting area disappear and the stomach itself is reduced to a simple bag into which enzymes pass from the digestive gland. Digestion is wholly extracellular, the digestive gland merely secreting enzymes and absorbing. It is now the mouth parts and the buccal mass which become specialized for the harder task of procuring living animal food. The radula, while short, is equipped with sharp, cutting teeth. In the carnivorous Neogastropoda, each row is reduced to three strong teeth, or sometimes only one. The salivary and oesophageal glands enlarge for the secretion of pro-tease, and become stripped away from the gut wall, connected with it by long narrow ducts. In this way the whole anterior gut is free to slide forward through the nerve ring, as the proboscis—with the buccal mass at its tip—is everted like the finger of a glove. In some families the extruded proboscis may reach four or five times the length of the rest of the animal.

Many families have developed carnivorous ways by easy stages, grazing not on algae but on sponges and other encrusting animals. *Diodora*—among the Archaeogastropoda—already shows this trend. The Cypraeacea or cowries—primitive Mesogastropoda—are another good example. Tropical cowries are generally grazing herbivores with style sac, sorting area and gastric caecum, living on cropped algae or bottom deposits.* The small British *Simnia* has come to feed on the tissues of the coelenterates *Eunicella* and *Alcyonium*, crawling over them and grazing with a short snout. *Trivia* has next developed a proboscis, and feeds at leisure on the compound ascidian *Diplosoma*, eating the zooids as it ploughs them out of the test. Finally, *Erato* dips its long proboscis expertly into the mouths of zooids of *Botryllus* and *Botrylloides*, cleaning out the tissues from within.[83] The Lamellariidae are a related family feeding on ascidians; *Cerithiopsis* grazes on sponges and *Bittium* selects foraminifera from the bottom deposits.[97]

Such stationary prey needs no active pursuit and one family, the Ianthinidae, has carried the habit of feeding on coelenterates from benthic to pelagic life. These violet snails live by exploiting the drifting siphonophore, *Porpita*, and *Velella* clinging beneath the disc for transport when not using their own raft, and feeding on it as well, rasping away the tissues to the bare chitinous 'skeleton' of the siphonophore.

A sluggish carnivorous life points the way to parasitism. First, some sedentary gastropods have become permanent associates of other animals. *Hipponyx* has the harmless habit of settling on the shells of *Turbo* and eating its faecal pellets. That such a habit is an ancient one is shown by the Palaeozoic gastropod *Platyceras*,[10] which had already settled on the calyx or arms of crinoids often near the anus and evidently lived too on faeces. Modern capulids carry this habit further, attaching near the edge of a mussel or scallop shell. *Capulus ungaricus* is a ciliary feeder, intercepting particles from the ingoing feeding current of the host. It also has a suctorial tendency; and leads on to the limpet-like *Thyca* which

* Kay (personal communication).

plunges its proboscis into the tissues of starfish and echinoids. Such forms perhaps initiated the long series of endoparasitic mesogastropods living in echinoderms (*see* p. 178).

Ectoparasitic gastropods are of more or less normal appearance. There are two families to be considered, feeding on the blood and body fluids of sedentary invertebrates, such as worms, echinoderms, bivalves and crustaceans. In the Eulimidae, associated with echinoderms, the proboscis is short. Jaws and radula are both lost, and the pharynx forms a muscular pump with proboscis glands by which the tissues of the host are softened. The Pyramidellidae—which Fretter and Graham now suspect to be opisthobranchs—have elaborate mouth parts, exquisitely modified for piercing and sucking. The chitinous edges of the jaws are opposed to each other and prolonged into hollow stylets, running along a tube formed from the buccal lips. The stylets are divided so as to form an upper suctorial and a lower salivary canal. The radula is lost, all hard parts being formed from the jaws. The muscles of the pharynx form a sucking pump, and the ampullae of the salivary glands are muscular as well, providing a pump for the enzyme-carrying saliva. With a diet of fluid protein the rest of the gut is exceedingly simple.[86]

Not all mesogastropod carnivores have sluggish habits. The fast-swimming Heteropoda, with movable telescopic eyes, are active predators, catching medusae, small fish, copepods and pteropods and themselves falling prey to larger heteropods. The large *Pterotrachea* and *Carinaria* carry the buccal bulb at the end of their flexible 'trunk', periodically thrusting out the sharp-toothed radula to seize prey, or even to attack the human finger-tip.

The Neogastropoda have carried flesh-eating to a high level; and with them we must mention some remaining mesogastropods. There are three tribes of whelk-like Neogastropoda, the Buccinacea, Muricacea and Volutacea (together forming the Rachiglossa), and a fourth tribe, the Toxoglossa, composed of very specialized carnivores, represented by the Conidae and Tere bridae andinBritain by the Turridae.

A typical rachiglossan radula, with three sharp-cusped teeth, is shown in Fig. 11F. The Buccinacea are the least specialized of Rachiglossa; they feed on dead or decaying animal matter, as in the Nassariidae, or frequently as in the Buccinidae on living flesh. The anterior shell canal and the osphradium are always well developed,

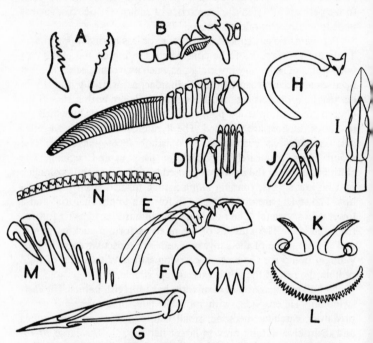

FIG. 11.   Representative examples of the radula in Amphineura and Gastropoda

A *Lepidomenia* (Aplacophora), B *Boreochiton* (Polyplacophora), C *Margarita* (Archaeogastropoda—rhipidoglossan type), D *Patella* (Archaeogastropoda—docoglossan type), E *Vermetus* (Mesogastropoda—taenioglossan type), F *Nassarius* (Neogastropoda—rachiglossan type), G *Conus* (Neogastropoda—toxoglossan type), H *Scaphander* (Cephalaspidea), I *Alderia* (Sacoglossa), J *Doris* (Nudibranchia), K *Goniodoris* (Nudibranchia), L *Aeolidia* (Nudibranchia), M *Rhytida* (Stylommatophora—carnivorous type), N *Helix* (Stylommatophora—herbivorous type). B–H and M are half rows of teeth, showing central teeth the right of the series and the complete left half of the row; in N some of the marginals are omitted. Whole rows with teeth reduced in number are shown in A (two teeth), I, L (one tooth), K (four teeth).

and are used in detecting food. With some species of *Alectrion*, if a piece of decaying meat is placed between glass sheets the snails converge from a good distance around this 'sandwich' and insert the narrow proboscis to a length of four or five inches between the sheets, till the radula at its tip is able to rasp the food.

Such a use of the proboscis foreshadows the habits of the Muricacea, many of which are shell-borers, feeding on live bivalves and gastropods.[98] They drill a neatly chiselled hole through which their long proboscis is inserted to reach the tissues within. In muricaceans such as *Urosalpinx*, *Ocenebra* and *Nucella* boring is chiefly mechanical. The shell is gripped with the foot, and the odontophore extruded. Short strokes of the radula abrade the shell, a few strokes in one direction and then—after twisting through an angle—a few in another, the hold being gradually deepened. These genera have an accessory pair of salivary glands absent in the whelks, and opening on the edge of the mouth. They may well play some part in boring, perhaps assisting by their secretion in softening the calcium carbonate during excavation. *Nucella lapillus* feeds on both mussels and acorn barnacles. The latter are not drilled but are smothered with the foot, till the valves can be dislodged. The same method is used by some species of *Thais* with gastropods such as trochids and turbinids, which are gripped with the foot until the columellar muscle relaxes and the operculum can be dislodged. Some species of thaids have a strong tooth at the rim of the shell, which they are credited with using as an oyster knife. *Murex fortispina* in New Caledonia takes *Arca* in the same way. The Coralliophilidae are stationary purpurids which have lost the radula and feed suctorially on coral tissues. From them has arisen the uncoiled *Magilus*, evidently a ciliary feeder.

One group of mesogastropods, the Naticidae, prey upon burrowing bivalves, which they bore by the acid secretion of a small gland on the underside of the tip of the proboscis which is pressed against the shell. The broad foot securely holds the prey, and the etched or softened shell may be finally excavated by the radula.[31] The larger sand-burrowing Mesogastropoda, Cassididae and Doliidae, generally live on echinoids and bivalves, either smothering them or plunging the proboscis into the soft parts, as does the tun-shell *Dolium perdix* with large holothurians. Most of the tropical Volutacea—among the Neogastropoda—burrow in sand and take prey by smothering with the foot in the same way. They include the volutes, the olive shells, the harp-shells and one of the largest of all gastropods, the broad-footed baler shell *Melo*, eighteen inches in length.

The most highly specialized carnivores are found among the Toxoglossa or 'arrow-tongues'. Central and lateral teeth are lacking, the radula (Fig. 11G) consisting of long slender marginals at either side. In the family Conidae these are reduced to a single pair in each row, of great size and prolonged into slender harpoons with a groove carrying a neurotoxic secretion from the large salivary glands. The tropical cones all capture moving prey.[117] Some take particular kinds of annelids (nereids and euniciids and terebellids), others feed on bulloid opisthobranchs. *Conus marmoreus* feeds on other cones, and four species—*C. cattus, C. striatus, C. tulipa* and *C. geographus*—catch live blennies and gobies. The prey is located by the testing of the pallial current by the large osphradium, after which the cone crawls towards it and 'covers' it with the poised proboscis. During a successful strike a single tooth is everted which harpoons the fish and injects saliva. Its struggles stilled, the whole fish is quickly engulfed by the distended proboscis. Digestion is rapid, beginning while most of the fish is still in the pharynx and crop. If the first strike fails, a second tooth is employed for another attempt. Most Toxoglossa appear to produce poisonous saliva; and that of the Australian *C. geographus* has proved fatal to man.

OPISTHOBRANCHIA

Many of the feeding habits shown by the Prosobranchia have been paralleled or improved upon by the opisthobranchs, and these gastropods are above all masters of the grazing carnivorous and suctorial life. As in prosobranchs, and in pulmonates too, the earliest opisthobranchs are microphagous browsers. Primitive bulloids such as *Actaeon* have a broad radula with small uniform teeth, and traces of the style sac and sorting area. At an early stage, however, both opisthobranchs and pulmonates cease to depend much on mucus and cilia, and the gut becomes more muscular.[132]

Most of the Bullomorpha have a large oesophageal gizzard, furnished with chitinous or calcified tooth plates, while the stomach is small and simplified, little more than a vestibule for the digestive diverticula.[77] Just as in prosobranchs, browsing on detritus has led to carnivorous ways, especially in those bulloids that can invest their prey with the broad foot. While *Actaeon* and many species of *Haminea* are deposit feeders, most forms have acquired strong sickle-shaped radular teeth (Fig. 11H) for seizing shelled prey, which is then crushed in the gizzard. Thus—in a series of descending size—*Scaphander* swallows whole bivalves and gastropods, *Philine* feeds on *Nucula* and young bivalves, *Retusa* on *Hydrobia ulvae* and *Cylichna* on foraminifera.

A special offshoot of the bulloids is seen in the thecosomatous pteropoda, which are small pelagic ciliary feeders. The gill is lost, but the pallial mucous gland and ciliary currents on the wings and mantle collect food. The bulloid gizzard is still present, an unusual organ—it was supposed—in a ciliary feeder, until it was found in *Limacina* to form a tiny mill for crushing the cases of diatoms.[133]

The Anaspidea (or Aplysiomorpha) are almost the only macroherbivores among the opisthobranchs.[67] The majority feed by cropping living seaweeds with their paired jaws and broad radula. The gut is more complicated than in bulloids, with a storage crop and the gizzard divided into two chambers—an anterior one for masticating and a posterior one with delicate teeth for straining. The stomach is reduced: its posterior caecum—when present in opisthobranchs—serves not for sorting but for fashioning faeces.

The gymnosomatous pteropods are a law unto themselves. They are sometimes held to have arisen from aplysioids, but in feeding bear no resemblance to them or to any other opisthobranchs. They are active predators like heteropods, living chiefly off the schools of thecosome pteropods with which they are always found. *Clione* and *Pneumodermopsis* are familiar Atlantic examples. All their weapons are concentrated in the buccal mass, which forms an elaborate armoury indeed. The radula has sharply pointed exsertile teeth. It is reinforced by a dorsal chitinous jaw, and by a sheaf of prehensile hooks, carried in an eversible pocket at either side of the buccal cavity. In addition, the Pneumodermatidae have a set of branched buccal tentacles, clustered with stalked or sessile suckers, while the Clionidae show a circlet of adhesive oral papillae, the *cephaloconi*.[139A]

Elsewhere the opisthobranchs can show few active predators. Of those that catch moving food the most interesting are the slow-

D

swimming nudibranchs of the Tethyidae (*Melibe* and *Tethys*). These
have a wide cowl over the head which is thrown from side to side as
they swim, to collect amphipods, isopods and large copepods.[27] The
gizzard of *Melibe* is often crammed with crustacea up to an inch
long, while the large species of *Tethys* feed on *Squilla*.

The dorids, tritoniids and aeoliids are sluggish carnivores, grazing on sessile animals. Least specialized are those Doridacea that
feed on sponges. Of the British Dorididae, *Archidoris pseudoargus*,
for example, prefers *Halichondria*, *A. stellifera* takes *Stylotella*, and
Rostanga rufescens lives on *Microciona*. The radula is broad, and
with numerous hook-shaped rasping teeth (Fig. 11J). There is no
gizzard, but a sac-like stomach where food is vigorously churned
and digested extracellularly. Fluid food is then absorbed by the
digestive gland and its breakdown completed intracellularly. Residual sponge spicules are compacted into faeces in the caecum.

In the Goniodoridae the gut is adapted for suctorial feeding, and
these nudibranchs graze on polyzoa and ascidians. Thus *Acanthodoris pilosa* and *Onchidoris fusca* feed on *Alcyonidium*, and *Goniodoris* species on *Botryllus* and *Dendrodoa*. Each radular row has only
four teeth, two of them curved and sharply serrated (Fig. 11K). Only
the juices of the food are ingested, sucked up by a powerful buccal
pump on the dorsal wall of the pharynx, whose movements are co-
ordinated with the opening and closing of the mouth in pumping
food down the oesophagus. The buccal pump shows every stage in
development from *Acanthodoris*, where it is a shallow open chamber,
to *Onchidoris fusca* (Fig. 10D), where it is like a small pea attached by
a narrow stalk. The rest of the gut is simplified; the faeces are of
small bulk, merely a yellow outflow from the digestive gland. The
Doriopsidae have progressed further in suctorial feeding: the radula
is quite lost and the whole pharynx forms a tubular pump.[74]

The tritoniids feed on sessile coelenterates and this habit has
been passed on to aeoliids, which have acquired a remarkable adaptation of the gut.[94] The digestive diverticula branch into a series of
tubules lying in the club-shaped cerata on the dorsal surface of the
body. Opening by a pore at the tip of each ceras is a small cnidus sac,
separated by a sphincter from the digestive gland. In the epithelium
lie numerous undischarged nematocysts, half or a dozen or more in
each cell, where they have been stored from the coelenterate prey.

Such an association of aeoliids and nematocysts poses many questions. How does the mollusc remain immune to them? Discharge is probably prevented by the low pH of the gut and the chitinous coat of the nematocyst, wrapped in mucus. They come into action only when the animal is injured and a ceras forcibly detached. Though they cannot be discharged spontaneously, the nematocysts must still be of great use in giving immunity from predators. With them—as we have seen—the aeoliids have developed pronounced warning colours of extreme beauty.

The small aeoliid *Calma glaucoides* varies its diet of hydroids by attaching its concave 'face' to the eggs of blennies, obtaining the yolk with its piercing radula and muscular pharynx. With such an economic fat and protein diet, the anus is closed, since the small amounts of faeces can be stored during life in the digestive cells.[70, 178]

The last group of opisthobranchs, the Sacoglossa, are also suctorial, but in a very different way from any other gastropods. They are herbivores living on the cell sap of algae.[89] *Hermaea bifida* feeds on red *Griffithsia*, while most others are very specific to particular green algae, thus:

Hermaea dendritica, Elysia viridis, Caliphylla mediterranea on *Codium* and *Bryopsis*.
Alderia modesta, Limapontia depressa on *Vaucheria* and *Rhizoclonium*.
Limapontia capitata on *Cladophora arcta* and *Enteromorpha*.
Acteonia cocksi on *Cladophora rupestris*.

The large cells of these algae are lanced one by one as the filament or thallus is passed between the lips. The radula (Fig. 11I) has a single tooth in each row, a small blade fashioned precisely for the type of cell in question. The radula lies in a peculiar ⊃ -shaped tube, with limbs directed forward and opening at its bend into the floor of the pharynx. Only one tooth is in use at a time, and these originate in a continuous series in the upper limb of the tube, the worn teeth being stored when detached in the lower limb, which is called the 'ascus sac'. The pharynx (Fig. 10E) is a powerful force pump. Its roof is highly contractile and the lumen may extend behind into a pair of muscular pockets. These work in concert with an oesophageal valve near the entrance to the stomach. The food is entirely fluid and the stomach forms a mere vestibule for the spacious digestive gland.[71, 78, 89]

The Pulmonata are chiefly herbivores, and most of their aquatic members (Basommatophora) browse on fine deposits with a broad many-toothed radula. It is only the primitive Ellobiidae and *Otina* that show any trace of the style sac, and in nearly all genera there is a gizzard rather like that of bulloids, though formed not from the oesophagus but by emphasis of the muscular stomach wall. The mudsnails (Amphibolidae) are virtually unselective deposit feeders. The mud they swallow is comminuted by the gizzard, which serves also as a pump for moving the stomach contents. The intestine forms a long double spiral, storing the bulky faeces. The Siphonariidae or pulmonate limpets parallel the true limpets by browsing on algae: the buccal mass and radula are very powerful and the intestine very long.

The freshwater Planorbidae and Physidae crop green plants as may also many Lymneidae, while the Ancylidae scrape the surface for finer particles. A few species of *Lymnea* float upside down on the surface film, where they collect microscopic food by a mucous sheet drawn over the sole by cilia and intercepted by the radula. The tropical prosobranchs *Ampullarius* and *Pila* can feed similarly: Cheeseman[48] has shown how they form with their foot what the physical chemist calls a 'Langmuir trough', collecting the surface monolayer of protein and condensing it into fibrous masses for ingesting.

Land pulmonates are faced with a prolific supply of plant food: leaves, shoots, berries, fruits and fungi, but above all decaying vegetable matter. The radula (Fig. 11N) forms a broad file, with many thousands of small unspecialized teeth. The gizzard and sorting area are now unnecessary, and the stomach is replaced by a long, thin-walled crop. Through this the brown digestive fluid ebbs and flows. Extracellular digestion is very thorough, and includes cellulose. The splitting of cellulose was for long credited to the snail's own enzymes. Florkin and his co-workers in France have now claimed it to be the work of bacterial populations which flourish in the sheltered environment of the crop and intestine.[72]

A few families of land pulmonates have become carnivores, living chiefly on earthworms and on other snails and slugs. The most spectacular are probably the southern Rhytididae, including the large discoidal *Paryphanta* species up to four inches across. These have an enormous buccal mass, and numerous blade-like or pointed radular teeth. A six-inch-long earthworm may be seized with this radula and smoothly drawn in like a strip of macaroni as the radula is rolled back over the odontophore. The British slug *Testacella* burrows for worms which it ingests in the same way. Species of the large *Glandina* in southern Europe and Central America feed on land operculates, and are said to file through their shells with the radula in the mode of a *Natica*. The British Zonitacea are an omnivorous or scavenging group, with carnivorous leanings. Species of *Oxychilus*, for example, follow small helicids along their slime trails. The Australian *Strangesta capillaris* follows the slime tracks of *Helix aspersa*, attacking it first at the root of the tail, and continuing till the prey is destroyed. With half-grown prey, *Strangesta* enters the mouth of the shell and expands like a balloon to burst the victim's shell.

SCAPHOPODA

The tusk-shells are microcarnivores. The captacula form dense clusters of adhesive tentacles at the sides of the head, streaming out widely through the sand to search for and secure living foraminifera and sometimes bivalve spat. These are hauled towards the mouth, up to a hundred at one time being crammed into the broad flat proboscis. The radula is of relatively immense size, with five teeth in each row. Strong erectile laterals seize each foram in turn and remove it to the buccal mass. The oesophageal pouches are small and apparently do not secrete; there are no salivary glands. The stomach is a muscular bag where food is triturated and undergoes extracellular digestion. There is no style sac and only vestiges of caecum, sorting area and shield.

LAMELLIBRANCHIA

Lamellibranchs are almost all ciliary feeders on suspensions or deposits. Food is collected by the gill and labial palps, and no bivalve has a radula, buccal mass or salivary glands. The oesophagus is short and the intestine a mere transport tube for faeces. The stomach and style sac are, however, much more complex in lamellibranchs than in any other molluscs (Fig. 12A). The evolution of the sorting areas and sorting caecum, and the crystalline style with its enzymes, shows a striking parallel with what we have seen in ciliary-feeding gastropods. In both groups the functions of the stomach are to sort a mixture of particles, to carry what is worthless to the intestine, to convey fine fragments after preliminary extracellular digestion to the digestive diverticula, and to ensure that waste matter returning from the diverticula reaches the intestine without re-mixing with the food. It is a little difficult to explain the intense specialization of the stomach wholly in terms of the needs of a ciliary feeder. By comparison with deposit-feeding gastropods the food is small in bulk and already partly sorted on the gills and palps. One might have thought the bivalve stomach had a simpler task to perform. Its evolution may, however, be only one part of a general trend of advance repeatedly found in this highly specialized group. Its pattern is beautifully adapted to functional needs, perhaps not wholly conditioned by them.

The researches of Yonge[198] and Graham,[96] and later of Owen[156] and Purchon,[167] have taught us much about the working of the stomach in lamellibranchs. The whole action is dominated by the rotation of the crystalline style, which—except in the protobranchs and septibranchs—is a long, flexible rod, hyaline and usually colourless. As in style-bearing gastropods (p. 91) it is built up of concentric layers of muco-protein, secreted by the edge of the typhlosoles that cut off the style sac from the intestine. In many higher families ('eulamellibranchs') the style sac is cut off completely from the intestine by the fusion of its bounding typhlosoles: in Anisomyaria such as Pectinidae, Ostreidae and Mytilidae, the sac communicates by a slit with the intestine, and the style may become permeated with minute food particles. These have been 'retrieved' by catching up in the viscid style substance as they travelled along the intestine, and are thus returned to the stomach for further digestion. The crystalline style always contains amylase and glycogenase, which are set free in the stomach as part of its head dissolves; in some species a cellulose-splitting enzyme has recently been identified as well. The head of the rotating style bears upon or is partly surrounded by a flange of protective cuticle of the stomach wall, known as the gastric shield. After removal from water or cessation of feeding,

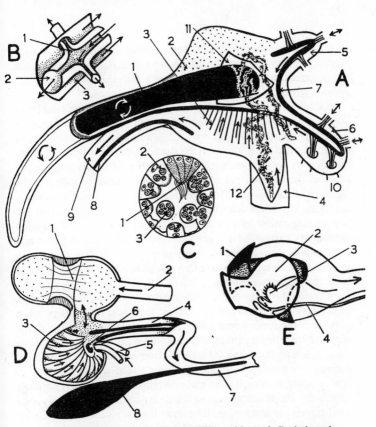

FIG. 12. Digestive system of Lamellibranchia and Cephalopoda

A Schematic view of a eulamellibranch stomach. 1) crystalline style, 2) cuticulate wall, 3) ciliary sorting area, 4) oesophagus, 5), 6) two divisions of sorting caecum, 7) major typhlosole, 8) minor typhlosole, 9) intestine, 10) opening of digestive diverticulum, 11) gastric shield, 12) food string.

B Arrangement of typhlosole within the caecum, in relation to openings of digestive diverticula (after Owen). 1) inhalant passage to diverticulum, 2) groove in typhlosole, 3) exhalant passage.

C Section of a terminal lobule of a bivalve digestive gland. 1) young cells bearing cilia, 2) absorbing-digesting cell, 3) sphere formed by fragmenting of digestive cell.

D Dissection of the stomach and intestine of *Sepia*. 1) gizzard, 2) oesophagus, 3) caecum with ciliated leaflets (coiled in *Loligo* and with a caecal sac), 4) first part of intestine, 5) ducts of digestive gland, 6) their opening into the caecum, 7) rectum, 8) ink-sac.

E Buccal mass of *Sepia*, viewed as if transparent, showing the upper and lower jaws 1) and 2) forming the beak, the odontophore with the radula, 3) and the opening of the duct of the posterior salivary gland 4).

especially where the style sac is open to the intestine, the whole style gradually dissolves, and some high tidal bivalves—such as *Lasaea rubra*—pass through a regular cycle, in which the style almost disappears when the tide is out and is later re-secreted.[138]

As well as being an enzyme store, the style keeps its original function of a stirring rod and a windlass. One or more food strings from the oesophagus are wound on to it, or thrown by it into a tight spiral. As these are drawn into the stomach, particles from them are shed, partly by contact with the stomach wall but mainly by the effect of the lowered pH of the stomach contents in reducing the viscosity of the mucus. Moreover the free particles in the stomach are repeatedly swept across the ciliary sorting area. The lightest are kept in suspension by cilia at the crests of the ridges and undergo preliminary extracellular digestion, both by the style enzymes and the amoebocytes. These are finally conveyed, minutely divided, to the digestive diverticula where they are phagocytosed and digestion is completed intracellularly.

As in early gastropods, most bivalves show a gastric caecum, which may be a feature of the earliest molluscs. Into this pouch a portion of the sorting area and the often numerous openings of the digestive diverticula retreat, together with a prolongation of one of the typhlosoles bounding the style sac from the intestine. Within the caecum this typhlosole frequently forms a tube within a tube (Fig. 12B) sending a branch into each diverticular aperture. The inner tube is the incurrent passage to the diverticulum, into which sorted food travels for absorption. The outer tube is an excurrent passage carrying waste material returned from the digestive cells to the intestinal groove. Along the ducts of the digestive gland, the outgoing passage alone is ciliated, the ingoing current proceeding by counterflow to the passage of particles outward (*see* Owen[154]).

The terminal tubules of the digestive gland (Fig. 12c) contain young, non-absorbing cells, often bearing long cilia, and mature cells which phagocytose particles from the lumen and become filled with greenish or yellow food vacuoles. Residual waste is extruded by the fragmentation of the tips of the mature cells to form spheres packed with coloured vacuoles which are returned to the stomach. Traces of enzymes may by the same means be made available for extracellular digestion. The intestinal groove is usually, however, closed from the stomach by a valve formed by the typhlosole, so that rejecta from the sorting areas is joined by waste from the digestive gland, without contact with food in the stomach.

Graham, Purchon and Owen have shown in detail how the stomach may become modified in higher eulamellibranchs. Here the sorting caecum is frequently divided into two, both opening separately into the stomach. They receive the multiple apertures of the digestive diverticula and a prolongation of the typhlosole now winds its path through both caeca. In certain deposit-feeding groups of lamellibranchs the stomach may serve as a triturating region, particularly in the Tellinacea which combine a very massive crystalline style with a heavy gastric shield.

The deposit-feeding Protobranchia are a special case. In many ways their stomach is primitive and simple. As in early gastropods the style sac is short and thimble-shaped, containing not a crystalline style but a protostyle composed of faeces. The caecum is rudimentary and the sorting area is simple. The wall of the stomach is strongly muscular and its cuticle and gastric shield serve as a triturating surface for roughly sorted food. Amoebocytes are absent, and, contrary to what was recently believed, Owen has found that the style sac secretes amylase and that digestion is completely extracellular, the digestive gland being a secretory organ.[156]

Special feeding habits in bivalves are few but of much interest. We shall mention elsewhere the symbiotic relation of the giant clams (Tridacnidae) with photosynthetic algae; in this family the normal feeding organs—gill, palps and crystalline style—are still, however, functional. In the wood-boring bivalves of the Adesmacea (*Teredo* and *Xylophaga*) these organs are extremely small and plankton collecting by the gill is no longer relied on. Instead the stomach develops a special storage diverticulum which is crammed with woodshavings that constitute the principal food. Analysis of faeces shows that a high percentage of cellulose and hemi-cellulose is removed from this wood; and these genera are some of the few molluscs that avail themselves of a more or less pure cellulose diet. Part of the digestive diverticula in *Teredo* forms a region filled with amoebocytes freely ingesting fine wood fragments, while the digestive epithelium also phagocytoses particles of wood directly.[163]

The small order Septibranchia have lost the ctenidia and greatly reduced the labial palps and the style sac. They are no longer ciliary feeders but suctorial scavengers on deep-water mud and ooze. They suck into the mantle cavity and ingest large particles of decaying animal remains and other detritus. The stomach acts as a triturating gizzard.[200]

Of the feeding of *Entovalva*, an endoparasite of *Holothuria*, little is known. The gut and pallial organs are however very simple, and it may well be that pre-digested food is absorbed through the body wall.

CEPHALOPODA

Almost all cephalopods are active predators. The feeding habits are less diverse than in gastropods, and the gut shows elaborate modifications for carnivorous life. Unlike the lamellibranchs, which have emphasized the stomach alone, the cephalopods show every part of the digestive system well developed. As in the whole of cephalopod biology, the keynote is speed and the attainment of a new level of efficiency. The familiar squids are pelagic, feeding on fish, larger crustacea and other cephalopods; cuttlefish take fish and crustaceans such as prawns, and *Octopus* feed on crabs and other slower-moving Crustacea. It would be fascinating to know something of feeding and digestion in deep-water squids, but our knowledge is at present almost wholly of more familiar inshore forms, much of it due to the studies of Dr. Anna Bidder on *Loligo* and other genera.[37] There must be many variations in detail, and probably wider differences, too, in other cephalopods. None the less, *Loligo* may be a little more representative of cephalopods than would be any single snail of the wide variety of gastropods.

Most cephalopods are of large size, and the digestive system has achieved speed of action by reducing its reliance on the ciliary and mucous mechanisms of other molluscs. Smooth muscles are now all-important (the gut is for the most part highly muscular), and there is a delicate nervous co-ordination of peristaltic movements, the opening and closing of sphincters and the activity of glands. The splanchnic ganglion, lying alongside the stomach, is a part of the sympathetic nervous system that has not called for special notice in other molluscs. In cephalopods it is responsible for the well-integrated rhythms of the complicated stomach and digestive gland. The action of the buccal mass and the salivary glands is also under nervous control. Slow intracellular digestion is no longer found. Food travels rapidly through the gut and extracellular digestion of a heavy meal may in *Loligo* take as little as four hours. Cilia are of importance only in one region of the stomach.

In *Loligo*, captured food is held at the mouth by the circlet of eight short arms, and is bitten up by the two overlapping jaws. These have the appearance of a strong parrot beak. The radula is relatively weak, far too small for rasping and breaking up food. There are two sets of salivary glands, a small anterior pair which secrete mucus, and larger posterior ones whose duct opens at the tip of the odontophore. In addition to mucus these produce a poison of the tyramine group (parahydroxyphenylethylamine) which quickly disables the prey. They secrete a powerful protease as well. The food is bitten into small pieces before ingestion. In squids and cuttlefish there is no crop, and this broken-down food is carried through a narrow oesophagus straight to the stomach. The octopods and the nautiloids have a deep crop, where fragments of crab meat or other food are packed after a meal.

The molluscan stomach is represented in cephalopods by two separate chambers communicating by a sphincter (Fig. 12D). That part of the early stomach which was lined with cuticle now forms a strong muscular gizzard. The ciliated part, especially the sorting area, gives rise to a thin-walled caecum. In many families this is coiled in a helical spiral, and its interior is closely lined with tall ciliated leaflets which converge on the intestine. In many squids, such as *Loligo*, it is prolonged into a thin-walled tapered *caecal sac* which extends to the end of the visceral mass. At the junction of the gizzard and the caecum the ducts of the digestive glands open and the intestine begins.

The cephalopod digestive gland also exists as two separate organs. The first and largest is a long yellowish-brown gland of two fused lobes with paired, narrow ducts. Clustered round these ducts as they enter the stomach are the follicles of a second and smaller gland, wedge-shaped, cream in colour and about one-tenth the size of the larger. We know little as yet of the difference in secretion of the two glands or their separate role in digestion. The outflow of the one is brown, of the other colourless. Until we can use more precise names, we may retain the old terms 'liver' and 'pancreas' respectively.

The different functions of the stomach are carefully regulated. In *Loligo* food goes first from the oesophagus to the gizzard, where its mechanical breakdown is completed. It is mixed here with 'pancreatic' fluid which has flowed in by the opening of the sphincter leading to the caecum. Partly digested food is from time to time released into the caecum as the sphincter relaxes, and there it receives the 'liver' secretion.

For a while the two secretions are confined to separate chambers, and a separate stage of digestion may go on in each. As food is gradually yielded from the gizzard to the caecum the ciliated leaflets efficiently remove indigestible solid fragments, which are carried to the intestine. This recalls the sorting activity of other molluscan stomachs, though there is in *Loligo* no protostyle rotating in the intestine, and all other movements of food are performed by muscle. The smooth part of the caecum, including the long caecal sac, is an absorbing area, and absorption later spreads to the intestine. Last of all, the valve between the gizzard and intestine opens and a compact bolus of faeces enters, made up of the last remains left in the gizzard.

Nautilus and octopods differ from decapods in having a very distensible crop attached to the oesophagus, which is packed with bitten-up food after a meal. In contrast with *Loligo*, digestion of a meal in *Octopus vulgaris* may take twelve to fourteen hours. Here the liver is the absorptive organ, and since its phases of secretion alternate with those of absorption, assimilation of the crop contents takes place in several instalments. In *Sepia officinalis*, too, Bidder finds the liver to absorb with digestion prolonged up to eighteen to twenty-four hours.[37A]

The cephalopod gut has achieved many of the advances found in the higher chordates. This is especially true of the perfection of nervous control, the speed of digestion attained in *Loligo*, the reduced importance of cilia and the loss of intracellular digestion. The radula is now insignificant compared with the jaws; and the chief ciliated area that remains has a new use—rapid clearance of waste after digestion. The essential pattern of the molluscan gut, however, remains; some of its features are very stable, but—as Bidder has shown—'the cephalopods have been able to use the molluscan inheritance to form a digestive system of startling efficiency'.

VI

BLOOD, BODY CAVITY AND EXCRETION

IN ALL molluscs but cephalopods the general body cavity is filled with blood brought back from outlying venous sinuses. The true coelom comprises only the pericardium and the cavity of the gonad. In chitons, gastropods and lamellibranchs the head, foot and viscera are supplied directly with blood by closed arteries from the ventricle. There are in molluscs no true capillaries except in the advanced and well-endowed cephalopods; in other classes blood seeps from the arteries into pseudovascular spaces in the connective tissue. In gastropods, peripheral blood from the head, foot and much of the mantle is returned into a central space known as the *cephalopedal sinus*. From the visceral mass it is brought back to a *visceral sinus*. Both these spaces discharge into a *subrenal sinus* lying near the columellar muscle at the base of the visceral mass. From the subrenal sinus blood is distributed in varying proportions through the respiratory organs and the kidney before returning to the heart. There is an extensive *renal portal system* into which all or part of the venous blood may go, passing thence either to the gill or directly to the auricle. By an alternative route, the *rectal sinus*, blood may be sent along the mantle roof straight to the gill without deploying through the kidney. Re-oxygenated blood always returns by the efferent branchial vein directly to the auricle.

Several memoirs ([12, 56, 67]) describe in fine detail the arrangement of the molluscan vascular system. In this book we can only—by the diagram in Fig. 13—show the general course of the circulation in the monotocardian prosobranch *Struthiolaria*, an example not too untypical in its broad features of the Gastropoda at large.

Some molluscs lack a heart. In the Scaphopoda there are no well-defined blood vessels of any sort, and the pericardium is also lost, though paired kidneys remain. Blood circulates between the organs largely by contractions of the body wall, and is re-oxygenated in simple transverse folds of the mantle roof. In some Sacoglossa, among gastropods, the blood is pumped not by a heart but by the muscles of the body wall, especially—in *Alderia* and *Stiliger*—by contractions of the club-shaped cerata.[71] Even when present, the heart may play but a minor part in the shifting of blood: changes in

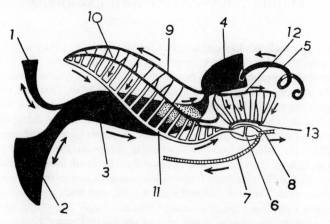

FIG. 13. Scheme of circulation in a mesogastropod prosobranch, based on *Struthiolaria*

1) proboscideal sinus, 2) pedal sinus, 3) cephalopedal sinus, 4) subrenal sinus, 5) visceral sinus, 6) heart, 7) anterior aorta, 8) posterior aorta, 9) rectal sinus, 10) afferent branchial vessel, 11) efferent branchial vessel, 12) afferent renal (or renal portal) veins, 13) efferent renal veins.

the shape of the body redistribute blood on a scale impossible for the ventricle, and in many gastropods and lamellibranchs the aorta as it leaves the heart is valved against forcible backflow through the arteries.

The presence of blood in the connective tissue spaces gives it another function besides its respiratory and trophic ones: it can now serve as a fluid skeleton giving temporary rigidity to special parts of the body, while repeatedly altered in shape by the action of the muscles of the body wall. The simplest example of a fluid skeleton is that of the body of an annelid worm, a cylinder of fixed volume whose length and diameter are constantly varied by the action of antagonistic circular and longitudinal muscles upon the contained coelomic fluid. Comparable examples in molluscs are changes of shape in such blood-filled organs as proboscis, pallial siphon and penis of prosobranchs and the optic tentacles in pulmonates.

In the trochid *Monodonta* Nisbet has recently shown how the buccal mass and odontophore are protracted by the shifting of blood into the head, through the depression of the muscular floor of the mantle cavity. The cephalopedal sinus is equipped with special diaphragms and septa that can hold blood in the required positions.

The bivalve foot—as we have seen—works by means of a haemoskeleton. During extension it receives a certain influx of blood and it elongates by the contractions of its transverse muscles against the relaxing longitudinal muscles. In large-footed bivalves such as the Tellinacea (e.g. *Tellina* and *Gari*) the lengthened foot then expands suddenly in volume by the relaxation of the transverse muscles through massive inflow of blood. It is withdrawn by the simultaneous contraction of both the longitudinal and the transverse muscles. Inflow of blood obviously involves a change in the size of an organ as well as a change in shape. It is not certain that this happens in all lamellibranchs: in a shallow burrower like *Cardium* or *Venus*, with a thick compressed foot, the volume change is less obvious from mere inspection. Critical comparison is still needed between the volume relations at various stages of the foot and of the central blood depots.

Most gastropods crawl (p. 28) by passing a wave of contraction forward along the sole of the foot. The exact muscular mechanism has never been well described. The gastropod foot is built up of longitudinal muscles running the length of the sole, and radial muscles striking into the sole from above. When the foot is expanded an appreciable proportion of the animal's blood can be locked up in its sinuses, and it is evidently upon small local pockets of blood in the muscular meshwork that the two main sets of muscles antagonize. Lifting of successive parts of the foot from the ground during passage of the contractile wave is probably achieved by contraction of the radial muscles, and the flat posture may be restored when the wave has passed by contraction of the longitudinal muscles, and smoothing out of the area previously folded.[158]

Much adjustment of shape can result merely from antagonism of different intrinsic components of a muscular organ. In a very complicated form this is responsible for the protrusion of the human tongue, and may have its counterpart in the rapid uncoiling from their sheaths of the tentacles in squids and cuttlefish. Here we are concerned with a solid muscular organ, the blood having quite lost its skeletal function in cephalopods.

In some situations, too, including the molluscan foot, two sets of muscles may antagonize, not upon pockets of blood but against fluid connective tissue, allowing local changes in form in an organ of constant volume. Picken has suggested that many of the gross mechanical properties of molluscs are due to the excessive wateriness of their tissue proteins. This would explain their labile body form, and account for the ease with which the tissues squeeze out or disintegrate, 'a quality which stamps the mollusc almost as certainly as any morphological criterion'.[160]

Many molluscan muscles are attached to the shell, for instance adductor and columellar, and pedal retractor, muscles, others to cartilaginous endoskeletal elements, as in the buccal mass and in the cephalopod head. Others have no hard skeletal base and contract solely against blood or fluid connective tissue. The water in the bivalve mantle cavity may also—as Chapman and Newell have shown—form an efficient hydroskeleton. Thus—in the Myacea—where the mantle edges are firmly fused, the siphons and pedal gape can be closed after water has been taken in. The contraction of the adductors against the built-up water pressure brings about the extension of the siphons in *Mya*.[47] And in the rock and wood-boring bivalves (Adesmacea) the withdrawal of the siphons, and the contraction of the posterior adductor against pallial water pressure, may help to open widely the anterior halves of the valves, causing abrasion of the substrate by the ridges on the shell.

In the clam *Scrobicularia* the paired siphons have been shown to elongate by contraction of radial muscles running between the lumen and the external wall. The lumen may thus enlarge in diameter at the same time as the siphon lengthens, the volume of the blood-filled space, however, remaining constant.[47]

In one gastropod, *Natica*, where the foot is noted for its massive dilation, it has been suspected that the deformable medium is not blood but sea water taken in from outside. The original experiments of Schiemenz, though widely quoted since, are not fully satisfactory. He maintained that turgescence was due to entry of water through one or more very small slits at either edge of the foot, and that this water occupied a series of spaces quite distinct from the blood system. No one has yet demonstrated these slits or the morphology of the presumed 'aquiferous system'. Morris recently demonstrated that the Australian naticid *Uber* probably takes in water, but to a very much smaller extent than first supposed. Inflation is at first by blood in the normal way, and this could be procured in animals out of water. Swelling was then augmented by sea water; forcible contraction of the animal still extruded a certain volume of fluid otherwise unaccounted for, after taking into account pallial cavity water and blood from ruptured vessels.[129] Other gastropods such as Olividae and bulloids are capable of great turgescence, but no one has suggested they take in sea water.

Cephalopods are much larger than other molluscs and have a much faster tempo of life. As well as the arteries of other molluscs their high metabolic rate demands a closed circulatory system with veins and capillaries. Locomotion is by pallial jet propulsion; and arms and funnel are moved by interplay of complicated intrinsic muscles. It is no longer necessary nor possible to lock up large volumes of blood as a haemoskeleton, and the body space is not blood-filled but forms a true coelom, evidently developed independently for cephalopod needs. This new cavity has an endothelial lining and communicates widely with the gonadial coelom. The heart lies within it, and it is in fact an extension of the pericardium around the rest of the viscera. From the coelom renopericardial ducts open to the kidney near the external renal orifices, and in *Nautilus* these have lost their connection with the kidney to open directly to the exterior. In the Octopoda, for reasons still uncertain, the pericardial coelom is again reduced and the heart excluded from it. It forms only a pair of capsules round the branchial hearts, and these communicate with the gonocoele by a pair of long narrow ducts which also open externally. These have been incorrectly called 'aquiferous ducts' and the coelom a 'water vascular system'. It is possible that such external coelomic openings may serve to equalize the coelomic and pallial pressures during the forcible contraction of the mantle cavity in locomotion.

Recent embryological work has shown that the old belief in the existence of a perivisceral coelom in chitons is not justified. Further findings on the extent of the true coelom in *Neopilina* will be of the highest interest.

EXCRETION

Like many coelomic surfaces, the molluscan pericardium takes on excretory functions. Two types of excretory organ are developed. First, the pericardial epithelium may itself be thickened to form deep brown-coloured pericardial glands. In lower gastropods and in many lamellibranchs these usually lie over the auricle wall. In higher gastropods the glands are on the pericardial side-wall, and in some lamellibranchs (e.g. Unionidae) they may form extensions leading from the pericardium into the tissues of the mantle, known as Keber's organs. In cephalopods they constitute the glandular appendages of the accessory branchial hearts.

The coelomoducts which open by renopericardial apertures from the pericardium are usually glandular, forming a renal organ or kidney, extracting nitrogenous waste from the blood which is supplied by the renal portal system. Molluscan kidneys have various forms. In chitons they are paired symmetrical tubes, each prolonged forward from its pericardial opening near the renal pore, and provided with numerous small dendritic outgrowths ramifying along its whole length. In Gastropoda the kidney is usually a thick-walled sac, much expanded and massively folded within. In higher Gastropoda only the left post-torsional kidney remains. In Heteropoda and some Gymnosomata the kidney is thin-walled and transparent, while in the dorid nudibranchs it is greatly subdivided into slender branches ramifying among the viscera. In the Prosobranchia the kidney opens into the hinder part of the mantle cavity, in higher Opisthobranchia directly to the exterior on the right side; in the Pulmonata its duct is narrowly drawn out alongside the rectum to open with the anus outside the mantle cavity. The kidneys of bivalves are paired tubes, each bent on itself as a ⊃ ; the lower (or proximal) limb is glandular, and opens from the pericardium, while the upper (or distal) limb is a thin-walled bladder opening into the mantle cavity. In the primitive Protobranchia the whole tube is excretory. In the Cephalopoda the kidneys are inflated sacs with smooth outside walls. Their glandular tissue had shifted to form the spongy mass of renal appendages surrounding the afferent branchial veins which pursue their course through the middle of either kidney.

The blood in the heart has a high hydrostatic pressure. From it, through the walls of the auricles and ventricle, is continuously transfused a clear filtrate into the pericardium. This fluid is isotonic with the blood but with much less non-mineral matter. With the secretions of the pericardial glands, it passes through the renopericardial openings to the kidneys. Here the products of nitrogenous excretion are added to it by the action of the lining cells. Inorganic substances may be taken back into the blood, and the composition of the resulting urine is determined by the extent of renal secretion and of reabsorption of ions.[160] In freshwater lamellibranchs such as *Anodonta* and in gastropods like *Lymnea*—where retention of inorganic ions is important—most of the salts are resorbed in the kidney so that the urine becomes hypotonic to the blood and pericardial filtrate. And in other molluscs, too, even when the blood is isotonic with sea water, some amount of ionic regulation exists, resulting in the conservation of physiologically valuable substances. Thus, in the blood of the marine gastropods *Buccinum*, *Neptunea* and *Pleurobranchus* calcium and potassium exceed the equilibrium values with sea water. There is a slight elimination of magnesium, while sodium and chlorine are in almost identical concentration with that of sea water. In the active bivalves *Pecten* and *Ensis* there is a similar picture; but there is less accumulation of potassium in the more sedentary *Mya*. In the very active cephalopods regulation extends to all the ions, potassium and calcium being much in excess of their sea-water value, magnesium and chlorine only slightly above, and sodium and sulphate rather below. Molluscs appear to take up inorganic ions from sea water by absorption through the gill and exposed body surface rather than by the gut. At least with potassium, magnesium and chloride, and usually with calcium, this can take place against a concentration gradient by performance of osmotic work.[160, 174]

Most marine bivalves have little power of osmoregulation when placed in lowered salinities. Marine *Ostrea* and *Mytilus* are able to prevent loss of salts in fresh water only by tightly closing the shell.

The marine *Scrobicularia* can live in the lowered salinities of brackish estuaries, but is also unable to osmoregulate. The osmotic pressure of its internal medium varies with that of the outside water over a wide range.[75]

In the freshwater molluscs *Anodonta* and *Lymnea* Picken[160] has demonstrated a high daily water flux through the kidneys. These molluscs must in fact constantly bale themselves out to maintain their blood concentration. Even so, in *Anodonta* Picken finds the extraordinarily low blood osmotic pressure of 5% of that of sea water. *Anodonta cygnea* with the pericardium experimentally opened filtered five times its own weight of water daily, though in intact animals Potts has recorded a much lower rate.[164] In *Lymnea* the fluid flushed out by the kidney is mainly water, serving to carry away excretory products after the salts have been resorbed.

In land pulmonates water must be no longer baled out but conserved. Here the renopericardial aperture is very small and little if any fluid is sacrificed from the pericardium to the kidney. A form of nitrogenous excretion is evolved which requires little water. Like birds and reptiles, land gastropods excrete almost insoluble uric acid. They are said to be *uricotelic* and white crystalline deposits accumulate in the gland cells of the kidney, being discharged as spherules at rather long intervals—four to six weeks in the Roman Snail, or remaining during hibernation in a 'kidney of accumulation'.

In the large African snail *Achatina*, which was studied by the insertion of fine catheters,[23A] there was no significant passage of fluid from the pericardium to the kidney. Filtration takes place directly into the lumen of the kidney, probably by blood pressure in the renal wall. Great resorption of water occurs in the kidney, partly by increasing the hydrostatic back pressure when the sphincter of the ureter is closed. As in other land forms, there is no free flow of urine from the kidney.

In cephalopods the pericardial glands have become attached to the accessory branchial hearts. The chief sites of filtration are the glandular renal appendages lying on the afferent branchial vein. This vessel is peristaltic, and its contractions appear to force small amounts of fluid through the walls of the small blood vessels which open in a labyrinth from this vein.[23A]

Uricotely occurs whenever snails migrate to land, irrespective of whether or not they are true pulmonates. In land operculates such as *Cyclostoma*, derived near littorinids, the uric acid content is very high (more than 1000 mg. per g. dry weight of kidney). Among shore littorinids there is an ascending series in uric acid content, the comparable figures being 1·5 g. in *Littorina littorea*, 2·5 g. in *L. obtusata*, 5 g. in *L. rudis* and 25 g. in the supra-tidal *L. neritoides*. The figures for Helicidae are extremely high—as much as 600, 720 and 800 g. in different individuals of *Helix pomatia*. In pulmonates that have returned to aquatic life uricotely is progressively lost. The series *Lymnaea stagnalis* (115 g.), *Planorbis corneus* (41 g.), *Ancylastrum fluviatile* (4 g.), and *Lymnaea peregra* (0·2 g.) shows this, though apparently not in strict order of aquatic readaptation.

Some freshwater operculates such as *Viviparus fasciatus* (35 g.), and *Bithynia tentaculata* (150 g.), were found by Needham to have relatively large amounts of uric acid; and this agrees with other evidence pointing to a common evolutionary origin of some groups of terrestrial and freshwater prosobranchs. *Hydrobia jenkinsi*, which has only recently—since about 1900—migrated to rivers from brackish water, has no uric acid.[143]

Most aquatic molluscs excrete ammonia, either directly or in part converted to amines and urea. Ammonia is a poisonous substance requiring solution in a large volume of water, and the freshwater bivalve *Anodonta* appears partly ammonotelic. Bivalves, in fact, being thoroughly aquatic, seem rarely to form uric acid at all. Needham found the nitrogenous excreta of *Mya arenaria* distributed as 21·5 parts ammonia, 4·5 parts urea and 18·0 parts amino-acids and creatine. The renal sac fluid of cephalopods yields a very high proportion of ammonia, sometimes one-third to two-thirds of the non-protein nitrogen, with smaller amounts of purines, amines, urea and sometimes uric acid. There is never the high rate of conversion of ammonia to urea seen, for example, in mammals. In the water of a cephalopod aquarium there may be even an higher proportion of ammonia to other nitrogenous matter than in the urine; additional ammonia is thus probably excreted by the gills. As well as the pericardial glands and kidneys, the cephalopod digestive gland is an important excretory organ. In 100 g. of fresh 'liver' of *Octopus* were detected 30–50 mg. of ammonia, 6–25 mg. of urea as well as 3–17 g.

of uric acid. As in the vertebrate liver, excretory products may be primarily formed in the digestive gland. They are extracted from the blood by the pericardial glands, renal organs and gills.[61]

In other molluscs, especially in gastropods where the kidney is, as in some opisthobranchs, reduced, the digestive gland may discharge excretory products straight into the gut. Special excretory cells are developed, particularly in those herbivores where the digestive gland returns to the lumen chlorophyllous pigments taken up by the blood. The gastric fluid of *Aplysia* is known to contain both urea and uric acid, and the digestive gland was found to yield 13 mg. urea to 100 g. fresh weight.

BLOOD

The respiratory pigment of Gastropoda and Cephalopoda is haemocyanin, a copper-containing compound carried in the plasma, which it colours faintly blue. This has similar oxygen-carrying properties to haemoglobin, though different molluscs vary widely in the oxygen pressures at which their haemocyanin becomes saturated. Thus the bloods of most gastropods are saturated at low oxygen pressures, a factor fitting many Gastropoda to occupy habitats of poor aeration. On the other hand, cephalopod haemocyanin becomes saturated only at relatively high oxygen pressures, and these active molluscs are extremely sensitive to oxygen lack. Dissolved oxygen never forms more than about 3% of the total blood volume in molluscs, except in cephalopods, where the percentage is 8 to 11, as compared with 20% in mammals.[170]

A few gastropods that live in especially poor oxygen conditions have developed haemoglobin, which is here capable of working at very low oxygen pressures. In *Planorbis corneus* living in foul muds, for example, the haemoglobin is saturated in all parts of the body and thus useless, in a medium containing more than 7% dissolved oxygen. With pressures from 7% down to 1% (where the animal dies), haemoglobin is useful; it is never so in molluscs for aerial respiration. The fast-working muscles of the gastropod buccal mass frequently contain muscle haemoglobin, which may possibly work as an oxygen store during muscle contraction.

It is not certain that any lamellibranch has haemocyanin, and in most species studied there is no oxygen carrier in the internal medium, the blood oxygen concentration being that of the outside water. Such a mechanism is able to supply sufficient oxygen to a sedentary animal by reason of the ample surfaces for oxygen uptake in the enlarged ctenidia and mantle. Some bivalves, particularly those living in poorly aerated substrata, possess haemoglobin, contained in non-amoeboid corpuscles. Examples include many of the Arcidae, and *Solen legumen* living in muddy sand in the Mediterranean.[119, 179]

The commonest blood corpuscles of molluscs are stellate amoebocytes which cluster together in immense numbers in clotted blood. These cells pervade the whole molluscan body; they migrate out of the blood spaces and pass freely through the connective tissue, entering the mantle cavity and the lumen of the gut. They may aggregate in large depots near the wall of the gut, and appear to have a wide variety of functions, based upon their powers of phagocytosing fine particles.[76, 183] Haeckel first observed the uptake of carmine by molluscan amoebocytes, many years before the pioneer experiments of Metschnikoff on phagocytosis. Amoebocytes may serve as important vehicles of excretion, conveying particles into the lumen of the gut, into the pericardium and renal organ, through the outer body wall, or through special strips of permeable epithelium into the mantle cavity. In bivalves they may emerge from the ctenidial blood spaces on to the surface of the gill, where they take up food particles, then either retreating into the epithelium or being ingested at the mouth.[198]

In the stomach of chitons, gastropods and bivalves, the amoebocytes may be important agents of non-localized intracellular digestion. They freely engulf food particles such as diatoms, or artificially fed starch or fat or blood corpuscles, which they digest, afterwards re-entering the epithelium or cytolyzing to yield their contents for absorption by the digestive diverticula. Takatsuki has shown in the oyster that the amoebocytes have a wide complement of digestive enzymes.[183]

Wagge has demonstrated the importance of the amoebocytes of *Helix* in lime transport and shell repair. Calcium carbonate from the diet is stored in protein spheres in special lime cells of the digestive gland, whence it may be released to the lumen from time to time for the regulation of the pH of the gut contents. Amoebocytes and alkaline phosphatase are both active in the digestive gland cells and at the site of shell secretion. The amoebocytes have access both to the lime stored in the digestive gland and that laid down in previously secreted parts of the shell. Especially in land pulmonates where lime may be in short supply, repair materials—if not provided with the food—may be withdrawn from elsewhere in the shell. No lime is stored in the secreting edge of the mantle. At a broken part of a shell, amoebocytes densely collect, arranging themselves in a sheet to form a continuous organic membrane, which is then calcified. The mantle epithelium plays little part either in forming the membrane or in laying down the deposit of calcium carbonate.[189]

VII

SEX AND REPRODUCTION

AT THE beginning the molluscs had no separate genital ducts. Paired or single gonads opened into the pericardium and the coelomoducts (renal organs) carried eggs and sperm directly to the sea, where fertilization normally took place. Such an archaic state persists today in some Aplacophora and—as we now know—in *Neopilina*; and the gametes still pass through both kidneys in early bivalves, and through one in Archaeogastropoda and Scaphopoda. With few exceptions fertilization is external.

The chitons—which are otherwise primitive—have acquired separate ducts leading from the gonocoele and opening by distinct genital pores. The gonad is single and median, and the sexes are separate. Most species produce a large number of eggs which they may shed freely or—sometimes in the same species—enclosed in short mucous strings secreted by the gonoduct. In *Lepidochitona cinereus* the eggs have a protein membrane, like a ruff or pie-frill, produced by the follicle cells of the ovary. The larva is a modified trochophore spending only about six hours in the plankton and having sufficient yolk for its needs without planktonic food.

The Chaetodermomorpha have separate sexes and a single gonad. In the Neomeniomorpha, which are hermaphrodite, the gonad is paired, and some early reproductive specializations appear: the renal organs, through which the gametes pass, are equipped with simple egg-shell glands and sperm receptacles and there are protrusible cloacal spicules which seem to be copulatory organs.

In primitive gastropods—as in the earliest molluscs—the eggs have very little yolk, and—being fertilized externally—can have no thick protective capsule. The first larva is a freely swimming trochophore, followed after a few hours by a veliger. Such molluscs are

121

mostly restricted to shallow inshore seas. The life history is a critical barrier to new habitats: external fertilization in fresh water is impracticable, for free sperms are usually unable to resist lowered salinity. Thus the Archaeogastropoda, and the chitons too, are for the most part marine and coastal. A few groups only, like the surviving Pleurotomariidae, and some lepidopleurids, have gone into deeper waters.

Gastropods of whatever kind have but a single gonad, and all the Archaeogastropoda, except the specialized Neritacea, use one of the renal organs, i.e. the post-torsional right kidney, for the passage of gametes. The gonad may open directly into the kidney (*Patella* and *Haliotis*) (Fig. 14A), into its duct, or as in trochids into the renopericardial duct. In the higher prosobranchs the renal function of this kidney is quite lost and it then survives incorporated as a short section of the genital duct; it may still retain a narrow pericardial connection, the *genitopericardial duct*.[80]

The genital products in most Archaeogastropoda are thus discharged far back in the mantle cavity. Except in Neritacea there is no penis, and hardly ever a secretory oviduct. The sexes can be distinguished only by the colour of the gonad and the sort of gametes it produces.

Limpets like *Acmaea* and *Patella* shed their eggs singly into the plankton. They have no protective covering—only a thin membrane and an albumen layer which is soon lost. In *Haliotis*, as in most trochids, and in *Tricolia pullus*, the eggs are also shed singly but are further surrounded by a thin gelatinous coating. In the Fissurellidae —such as *Diodora*—these gelatinous sheaths are joined to each other so that the spawn is deposited in a coherent layer. A few higher trochids, such as *Cantharidus* and *Calliostoma*, have progressed further. They form a gelatinous egg ribbon attached to the substrate and secreted by the lips of the renal oviduct or—in *Calliostoma zizyphinum*—by part of the female's mantle wall.

Even in archaeogastropods a free-swimming larva is not always found. Only nine out of the seventeen British species have trochophores; in the rest—including *Diodora* and *Calliostoma*—the veliger hatches from the egg membrane at the creeping stage. Larval life is frequently short. While *Patella* spends ten days in the plankton, *Haliotis* is limited to about forty hours, and torsion is not finished until after settlement.[57]

In those molluscs that shed their eggs and sperm into the plankton—this includes some archaeogastropods and nearly all marine lamellibranchs—great wastage might be expected from failure of fertilization. Many species, however, have adjusted their spawning behaviour to permit economy of gametes. Thus some species of *Patella*, as well as at least one *Helcion* and *Gibbula*, will not shed their sex products unless close to one of the other sex. In many molluscs, too, the males spawn first and shedding of eggs is only induced in the presence of sperms (some chitons, *Haliotis* and *Ostrea*). In still other forms, particularly lamellibranchs, there is 'epidemic spawning', perhaps controlled by temperature and food abundance, or showing lunar periodicity as in *Pecten opercularis*.[184]

Further evolution in gastropods demanded special genital ducts (Fig. 14), first to convey and to receive sperm at internal fertilization, and then to provide better nutritive and protective layers for the eggs. These were prerequisites for shortening the larval life, or for retaining and brooding the embryos. With this achieved many new habitats were opened up, especially on land and in fresh water. Both these habitats were occupied by the first mesogastropods: it is probably not a coincidence that the Neritacea, the only archaeogastropods to develop an oviduct and a penis, have at once run through the whole programme of later pulmonate evolution. They have spread to rivers and freshwater lakes, and to tropical rain forests.

Both sexes obtained a glandular genital duct by pressing into service part of the right side of the mantle. The genital opening was first brought forward by an open furrow as far as the front of the mantle cavity. In the female this soon became closed to give a glandular tube by which the eggs were carried from the original genital opening to the mantle edge. Glands were differentiated in the order in which secretions were placed round the egg (Fig. 14B)—first a coat of albumen, then a tough capsule, and finally—as in some littorinids—a mass of jelly. Thus appeared in sequence an albumen gland, capsule gland and sometimes a jelly gland. In addition, now that the new opening could be reached by the male's penis, a ciliated channel ran up the female duct to a receptaculum seminis, a pouch inserted between the albumen and capsule glands (Fig. 14B). From the new female aperture, near where the mantle joined the body wall, a ciliated groove ran forward along the head and foot to the ground level. By this means the fertilized eggs could travel forward and be fixed against the substrate.[80]

In most mesogastropods an elaborate spawn is formed, the young hatching either as veligers or at the crawling stage. There is a wealth of information on egg masses and larvae to be found in the papers of Lebour and Thorson. In some of the littorinids and other early families the separate capsules are laid in an egg mass of jelly (*Littorina littoralis* and *Lacuna*). *Littorina littorea* and *L. neritoides* on the other hand have planktonic egg capsules and veligers, while *L. rudis* is viviparous. In other mesogastropods groups of several eggs are usually enclosed in thick capsules. In the Rissoidae these are lens-shaped or spherical and attached to the substrate. In the Turritellidae they are fastened in grape-like clusters. *Cerithiopsis* places them in nests in sponges. The Lamellariidae and Triviidae plant vase-shaped capsules in the tests of the compound ascidians on which they feed. The Calyptraeidae protect the thin capsules under the parent shell. In the Naticidae the egg capsules are glued together with sand, to form the characteristic smooth ropes or egg collars that encircle the animal as they are secreted. Some species of pelagic *Ianthina* carry the egg capsules attached to their raft.[2]

Land operculates such as the Cyclophoridae have perforce lost the larvae altogether and deposit yolky eggs in tough envelopes. Most freshwater families such as the Hydrobiidae, Melaniidae and Valvatidae prefer to brood the young, rather than entrust veligers to the hazards of running streams. Incubation also takes place in many marine families and the types of brood pouch are very diverse. Thus the Siliquariidae, like some Ianthinidae, and the freshwater *Tanganyicia*,[127] have a spacious pouch in the head, opening beneath the right tentacle. The Struthiolariidae have a brood pouch in the mantle. *Viviparus* uses the oviduct as a uterus. The siliquariid *Stephopoma* carries the young freely in the mantle cavity, while the Vermetidae attach a row of capsules to the inside of the mother's shell.

The largest and finest veligers are those of Mesogastropoda. In three families, the Lamellariidae, Cypraeidae (Eratoinae) and Capulidae, the veliger is an *echinospira* (Fig. 16B) with the young definitive shell covered by a much larger secondary shell, the *scaphoconcha*, which has practically no weight and assists in flotation during the long swimming life.[120]

A few Neogastropoda, as the Nassariidae and Turridae, have also free larvae, but for the most part their eggs are placed in horny capsules, the majority serving as nurse eggs for the few canni-balistic survivors that hatch at the crawling stage. The Buccini-dae and their relatives produce an elaborately compacted spawn mass, but in the Muricacea the egg capsules are separate, and may be vase-shaped (*Nucella*), lens-shaped (*Ocenebra*), or cylindrical as in many species of *Thais*. Many of the Volutidae form spherical calcareous capsules attached to other shells. A great difference between mesogastropods and neogastropods is that in the latter the female employs her foot, which develops a ventral pedal gland, to mould the unfinished horny capsule that emerges from the capsule gland. Fretter has given a detailed account of the way the British *Buccinum*, *Ocenebra*, *Nassarius* and *Nucella* manipulate these cap-sules with the foot and attach them to the substrate.[80]

In male mesogastropods and neogastropods the glandular duct forms a so-called 'prostate'. Mixed with its secretion the sperms are carried from the mantle cavity to the head by a ciliated groove, which may sink in to form a shallow vas deferens. The head develops a muscular penis, attached behind the right tentacle. This is grooved by the male genital furrow and kept reflected into the mantle cavity when out of use.

In higher prosobranchs fertilization is always internal, but there are some species where this cannot be effected by copulation. First there are sessile forms like Vermetidae and Hipponicidae which may be out of reach of other individuals. In others, such as the Turri-tellidae, the mantle cavity is kept closed by a portcullis of pinnate tentacles against the entry of sediment—and thus also of the penis. Thirdly, in many tightly coiled or long-spired gastropods, such as *Bittium*, *Cerithiopsis*, *Clathrus* and *Cerithium*, the mantle cavity is very narrow and the female opening is too far up the spire for a penis to reach it. In all of these forms the male is aphallic and sperms are shed freely into the water and enter the mantle cavity of the female with the inhalant current.[80, 84] The genital duct is split like an open sleeve for entry of sperm, but how they finally reach it is a mystery. There is no authenticated cases in animals of sperms being guided by chemotaxis.

The strangest sexual phenomenon is the presence of two types of sperm in many families. The most numerous are small and normal *eupyrenic* sperms which fertilize the eggs. The others are much larger, reaching sometimes 100μ in length. They sometimes lack flagella and swim with an undulating membrane like spirochaetes. In *Viviparus* they bear a tuft of flagella at one end. The nuclei are degenerate and these *oligopyrenic* sperm evidently play no part in fertilization. The usual view is that they are nurse cells which disintegrate in the receptaculum to nourish the eupyrenes. But, as Ankel has shown, they can also have a transporting function. Huge numbers of normal sperms may attach by their heads to a vermiform sperm. The whole structure—known as a *spermatozeugma*—can swim strongly in sea water, and in aphallate genera—as *Clathrus* and *Ianthina* and probably *Cerithiopsis*—fertilization is achieved by the active entry of the carrier-sperm into the oviduct.[29]

SEX AND HERMAPHRODITISM

It has been widely believed that primitive gastropods are bisexual, and that hermaphroditism is the hall-mark of opisthobranchs and pulmonates. In 1909 Orton made his famous discovery that the slipper limpet, *Crepidula fornicata*, begins life as a male, passes through an hermaphrodite stage and finishes as a pure female.[148] It was gradually realized that in more and more groups scattered among the prosobranchs the sexes may—for a part of the life—be united in one individual. Sometimes, perhaps always, this hermaphroditism is of a protandric kind. Coe has called this *protandrous consecutive sexuality*, and it is perhaps best studied in the chains of sexual individuals formed by *Crepidula fornicata*. The first and youngest individual is a tiny male at the summit of the chain. It lies in the mating position on the right side of the shell of the young female lying next beneath it. The male has a large testis and a muscular penis which conveys the sperm. In older slipper limpets, lower in the chain, a hermaphrodite stage follows. Oocytes develop in the gonad, sperms cease to form, and the penis is partly absorbed. The oldest specimens, at the bottom of the chain, are mature females. The ovary and oviduct are functional, the penis is almost lost, and a brood of spat lies under the shell. Shorter chains—or associated pairs, small male and large female—are found in other Calyptraeidae, such as *Calyptraea*, *Janacus* and *Crucibulum*. With the change to female the animal becomes more sedentary, and merely broods over the eggs. Sex change can be modified by temperature, by food and by the influence of association. By removal of the female a young male can be induced to pass sooner into the neutral or female phase.

Consecutive sexuality—with protandry—has been found by Ankel in *Ianthina* and *Clathrus*. In the freshwater *Valvata tricarinata* there is a more complicated *rhythmical sexuality*, with a regular return to a male phase after the eggs are laid. The list of hermaphrodite forms—whether or not they are known to be protandric—includes some Hydrobiidae, the Omalogyridae, *Velutina* and *Puncturella*. Other hermaphrodites are the parasitic forms included in the Eulimidae and Entoconchidae, though some of the latter have minute dwarf males (*see* p. 179). A moderate male dwarfism occurs in *Lacuna pallidula*, where the male is one-tenth the weight of the female and lives attached to her shell.[50]

Orton and his colleagues have also investigated the sexuality of the limpets.[151, 152] In *Patella vulgata* 70·8% of the smallest individuals measured were males and only 4·4% females.* Of the oldest age group 34·7% were males and 64·2% females. In Italy, Bacci has had similar results with *Patella caerulea* and *Fissurella nubecula*.[33] This might suggest that the females grow larger than the males, but it also points to a change of sex within the lifetime of the limpet, and, as a further hypothesis, Orton considered there might be two types of male limpets, true males and temporary (protandric) ones. Most recently Dodd has further examined Orton's material and has in *Patella vulgata* found only a minute fraction of hermaphrodites (30 individuals in 60,000).[62] Among other limpets, however, Thorson has shown that *Acmaea rubella* is hermaphrodite and *ambisexual*—that is, with both ova and sperms produced side by side.

In Polyplacophora and Chaetodermomorpha the sexes are said to be always separate, though a detailed study of sex in a chiton, along the lines of the limpet work, would be of the greatest interest. The Neomeniomorpha are protandric, with a very short male phase.

All opisthobranchs and pulmonates are hermaphroditic. In higher forms of both groups—such as nudibranchs and helicid snails—eggs and sperm seem to mature simultaneously. In early members, consecutive sexuality with protandry is prevalent, a brief

* The rest were sexually immature.

male phase preceding a mixed or pure female stage, as in—for example—the pteropods (Limacinidae, Clionidae) in the opisthobranchs and the Ellobiidae and *Otina* among pulmonates, which
show a protandrous succession in a single season.[134] In the terrestrial
Carychium there is some evidence that a second male phase follows
egg-laying. Other established protrandic genera are the pulmonates
Physa and *Limax*, and the opisthobranchs *Aplysia* and *Aeolidia*.

Without more knowledge of sex genetics in gastropods it is
dangerous to speculate, but scattered evidence from many groups
indicates a deep-seated tendency in molluscs to protandry. It is perhaps an advantage that the sperms—metabolically less expensive—
should be formed earlier in the season, or by a younger animal. This
would leave a longer period—throughout the spring—for the eggs to
mature. In all three divisions of Gastropoda the younger and
briefer stage seems to be male, the later one female. Later prosobranchs have evolved towards separate sexes; so far as is known
there are no hermaphrodite Neogastropoda. The higher opisthobranchs and pulmonates—on the other hand—seem to have developed a true simultaneous hermaphroditism.

True parthenogenesis is very rare in the molluscs. In two mesogastropods, however, *Campeloma rufum* and *Hydrobia jenkinsi*,
males are unknown.[176] Self-fertilization is more common. Colton
and Pennypacker[51] have followed, for example, and isolated a self-
fertilized line of *Lymnaea* for twenty years over generations. In *Arion
ater* Williamson has found genetic evidence of cross-fertilization
and self-fertilization in the same individual. In some small land
snails, such as *Carychium* and *Vertigo*, the penis may at some
seasons be lost. Fretter found that in summer months the small tide-
pool gastropod *Omalogyra* produces a succession of self-fertilizing,
aphallate individuals. The original generation, matured in spring,
arises from copulation and normal fertilization.[81]

HIGHER GASTROPODS

Beginning from the simple pallial genital duct of prosobranchs the
Opisthobranchia have developed very complex genitalia. The male
and female portions separately represented in prosobranchs are here
united in one individual. The capsule gland has been replaced by a

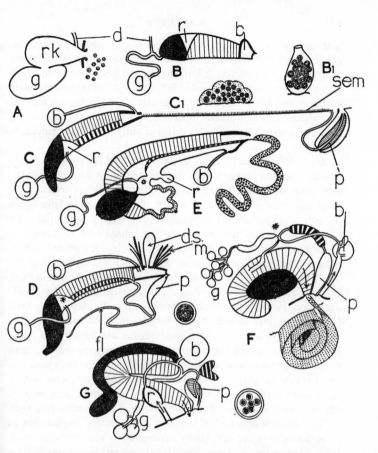

FIG. 14. Evolution of genital ducts in Gastropoda. The diagrams are schematic and somewhat generalized

A *Haliotis* (Archaeogastropoda), B *Nucella* (Neogastropoda), B1 Egg capsule, C *Ovatella* (a primitive pulmonate), c1 Egg mass, D *Helix* (an advanced pulmonate), E *Aplysia* (Anaspidea), F *Archidoris* (Nudibranchia), G *Acteonia* (Sacoglossa). Eggs or egg masses are shown with each; the albumen gland is black, the capsule gland or mucous gland lightly cross-hatched, the prostate heavily cross-hatched. *b.* bursa copulatrix, *d.* renopericardial or genitopericardial duct, *fl.* flagellum, *g.* gonad, *d.s.* dart sac, *m.* vaginal mucus glands, *p.* penis, *r.* receptaculum seminis, *r.k.* right kidney, *sem.* seminal groove or superficial vas deferens.

* Fertilization site.

spacious mucous gland secreting a jelly-like egg-mass or ribbon. This gland, together with the albumen gland, sperm receptacles and prostate, has sunken deeply into the general body cavity; and each gland may be elaborately subdivided, or cut off from the main path as one or more diverticula. The higher opisthobranchs—such as the Aeolidiacea and Doridacea—reserve a central part of the gonad for the formation of sperms, with a series of outlying follicles producing the eggs.

Early opisthobranchs have a ciliated seminal groove as in proso-branchs running forward from the common genital aperture to the penis (Fig. 14E). With the loss of the mantle cavity to contain it, the penis has become invaginated within the head, and in later forms the common aperture moves forward to lie near it on the right side of the head, so that both male and female ducts open together.

In most nudibranchs each partner fertilizes the other. Aplysi-oids, on the other hand, such as *Aplysia* and *Akera*, form a copu-latory chain in which each animal acts as a male to the one in front and a female to the one behind. The arrangement of the female ducts becomes very complicated indeed in the Doridacea (Fig. 14F). Here the vaginal section of the female duct separates from the oviduct to give a third genital aperture, the old female duct being reserved for secreting the egg-mass and discharging the eggs and the new duct forming a copulatory passage. This connects with two sacs for storing sperm, a bursa copulatrix which forms a temporary store after copulation, and—higher up—a receptaculum seminis which is the homologue of the same sac in prosobranchs (Fig. 14B).

The aeoliids and tritoniids retain an undivided vagina, but in some Sacoglossa the copulatory arrangements may be very novel. With *Limapontia*, *Actaeonia* and *Alderia* inward sperm travels by a more direct third passage, formed by the bursa copulatrix whose swollen tip rests close to the body wall (Fig. 14G). This bursa may acquire its own external opening, or—as in *Limapontia capitata* and *Actaeonia cocksi*—the body wall may be ruptured at copulation by a hollow spine, or *style*, on the penis of the partner, and sperm trans-ferred by hypodermic injection.[89] In *Alderia modesta* impregnation is reported to take place through almost any part of the body wall. The whole haemocoele becomes charged with sperm, some of which finds its way to the internally open bursa.

Opisthobranch egg-masses are easily recognized (Fig. 14E, F). The eggs are usually small, each with its own albumen coat and egg membrane, and the whole mass is enclosed in a thick matrix of clear mucus. The bulloids such as *Philine* deposit a jelly sphere through which runs a tangled string of eggs. Similar egg-masses of *Actaeon* are club-shaped. The aplysioids—including *Akera*—put out a long mucous string like yarn, which is deposited in a loose tangle. The pleurobranchoids, the dorids and the aeoliids produce a broad flat ribbon, studded with tiny eggs and attached in a coil or in folds to the substrate.

The Opisthobranchia are all marine, and nearly every species has small free-swimming veligers which hatch early and spend only a short time in the plankton. The best-known exception is the hightide pool sacoglossan *Actaeonia cocksi*. Here the eggs are large and yolky, enclosed in a spherical capsule (Fig. 14G), and the larva hatch at the crawling stage. *Alderia modesta*—a sacoglossan of even higher salt-marshes—might be expected to breed in the same way. Paradoxically it lays small eggs and has normal veligers. Like the supra-tidal *Littorina* (*Melaraphe*) *neritoides*, it evidently relies on the opportunities of distribution afforded by larvae. Further, yolky eggs are probably over-expensive to produce in a semi-terrestrial species living near the margin of its range.

The aquatic pulmonates have a hermaphrodite genital tract essentially comparable (Fig. 14c) with that of early opisthobranchs. The pallial genital glands have moved to the haemocoele, and the ciliated seminal groove has sunken to form a vas deferens, running to the penis within its sac in the head. Pulmonate eggs are much more yolky than in most opisthobranchs and free-swimming larvae are released only in such primitive marine forms as *Melampus*. *Amphibola* and *Siphonaria* have capsulate veligers in a jelly-like spawn coil as in opisthobranchs; for the most part—in Basommatophora—the eggs are clustered in a jelly resembling frog spawn, each having its own albumen layer and tough capsule.[137]

In the land pulmonates the eggs and genital system are adapted for new conditions. By comparison with other gastropods the eggs are few in number, extremely yolky and sometimes very large indeed. The largest species of the tropical *Achatina* lay eggs with limy shells, the size of thrushes' eggs. The typical egg shell is the tough elastic one—partly calcified—of garden snails and slugs, and this is laid down as the secretion of the mucous gland. Such shells protect the eggs from small predators but are not impermeable to water, that is to say, the eggs are not, as in land vertebrates, cleidoic. Their cytoplasm is adapted to tolerate considerable water loss rather than their shells to prevent it. Desiccation is also avoided by behavioural adaptations ensuring oviposition in damp and shaded places or beneath the soil.

The genital system of *Helix* (Fig. 14D) is an example often dissected. Most of its new features are adaptations to assist courtship and the successful transfer of sperm, a hazardous operation for a land mollusc. The sperms are enclosed by the male duct in a chitinous envelope, the *spermatophore*, secreted in the *flagellum*, a tubular outgrowth of the penis. Its transfer at copulation is assisted by the lubricating secretion of two clusters of branched mucous glands which open near the mouth of the vagina. The vagina develops also a muscular caecum, the *dart sac*, in which is produced a fine-pointed calcareous shaft, about 5/16 in. long, and delicately ridged. This is the *telum amoris*, or 'love dart', which is exchanged by the partners with some velocity before courtship, lodging in the integument and serving as a releaser stimulus for courtship behaviour. In some slugs the dart sac is lost as such, and is converted into an exsertile stimulating organ, the sarcobelum. Snails may remain several hours in coitus, and some species of *Limax* entwine themselves together in a sheet of mucus, performing a complicated 'Liebespiel' before pairing.

LAMELLIBRANCHIA

The reproductive system of bivalves—in contrast with the gastropods—is exceedingly simple. The gonads are paired or fused in the middle line. Their ducts are short and have no glands. In early bivalves such as *Nucula* they open into the kidneys and through them to the mantle cavity. In the higher forms they become separate, opening merely on a common papilla with the kidney, or finally through independent pores. Internal fertilization in the strict sense never occurs. In many bivalves, however, the sperms meet the eggs within the mantle cavity, and in two genera, *Xylophaga* and *Cuspi-*

daria, there are glandular patches near the genital opening that can act as sperm receptacles.[165]

The eggs are usually small and the larvae spend long in the plankton; but those that are incubated in the mantle cavity are provided with enough yolk to nourish the embryo till it is able to settle as a small replica of the adult. There is no 'placental' connection with the mother and the eggs develop morphologically outside the parent's body. The brood chamber is generally the interlamellar space of the inner or outer gill, as in the marine Erycinacea, *Teredo* and *Arca vivipara*. In the larviparous oysters the mantle cavity itself serves as a temporary brood chamber, and free-swimming larvae are then released, spending only a few hours in the plankton. In *Turtonia minuta* Oldfield has described gelatinous egg capsules, unique in bivalves, attached two or three at a time to the byssus and secreted by the glandular edge of the mantle.[147]

All freshwater bivalves appear to incubate the eggs, with the exception of the mussel *Dreissensia*, which is rather recently acclimatized in rivers and canals, and has free veligers.

The freshwater Sphaeriidae liberate small replicas of the adult from between the gills; but in the freshwater mussels of the Unionacea the young are released at a much earlier stage, and are incredibly numerous, from several hundred thousand to a million at one time! They begin life with a phase of parasitism on a freshwater fish, or sometimes a urodele. The larvae are known as *glochidia* (Fig. 15D), and are equipped with a small triangular-valved shell, and with attachment organs consisting of one or more hinged spines on the shell, or a long byssus thread. In some genera, such as *Unio* and *Anodonta*, the young attach themselves by the shell spines to the fins of the host. Species where the shell is unarmed are attached by the byssus thread to the gills. The glochidia soon become encysted by host tissues, which they proceed to liquefy and assimilate by the margin of their mantle. When the surrounding host tissues are exhausted the larvae undergo histolysis; the adult tissues and organs are then reconstituted, and the metamorphosed young mussel drops off to resume a free existence. European species of *Unio* and *Anodonta* all favour cyprinoid fishes; the American *Lampsilis* may live on the garpike *Lepidosteus* or the bass *Huro*, while *Hemistema* attaches to the gills of the mud-puppy, *Necturus*.[18]

Sex change in lamellibranchs has long attracted interest.[50] While hermaphroditism has been found in only 4% of the species studied, these have been well investigated, and have much theoretic interest. First, there is a group of *functionally ambisexual* bivalves, with sperms and ova formed in different regions of the same gonad, as for example in the majority of Pectinidae and in the Tridacnidae, *Sphaerium*, *Pisidium* and many *Anodonta* species. Or there may be a distinct ovary and testis opening separately on either side, as in members of the order Anomalodesmata, such as *Thracia* and *Pandora*. A second group consists of bivalves having one sex change in the life history, and these are generally protandric, as *Venus mercenaria* (with 98% of individuals being first males) and the wood-boring *Xylophaga dorsalis* and *Bankia setacea*.

In the oyster family, studied by Coe and his school in America and by Orton in England, we have two further sorts of sexuality, and two well-recognized groups of species. The larviparous oysters, typified by *Ostrea edulis* and *O. lurida*, show a *rhythmically consecutive sexuality*. They produce late, short-swimming larvae from the mantle cavity. The youngest gonads are predominantly male, and all individuals begin their breeding life as functional males. A residue of both male and female cells remains after the first season, and the rest of the life history shows a series of alternating sex phases. There is never a permanent change to female, but always a reversion to male after eggs have been shed.

The oviparous group of oysters is represented by *Ostrea virginica*, *O. angulata*, *O. gigas* and *O. cucullata* (i.e. those species which we are now bidden to refer to as *Gryphaea*). These oysters shed eggs which are fertilized externally and give rise to long-swimming veligers. They were classically thought to be bisexual, but are now known to be essentially hermaphrodite. For example Amemiya in Japan put *O. gigas* of two sexes into different tanks after boring holes in the shells to ascertain their sexual condition. After a year 28% of the females and 60% of the males had changed their sex. It was at first concluded that sex was redetermined every year by environmental factors regardless of previous history. More was learnt from Coe's work, from 1932 onwards, on *O. virginica*. Two months after spat setting the young gonad was potentially bisexual and its fate was determined by the water temperature and consequent supply of food. Thus, many more oysters became sexually mature in the first year in Carolina than in the colder waters of Massachusetts. The first dividing cells produced spermatids, but the young testis produced no sperms until the following spring. But this is not a case of strict protandry, as in larviparous oysters, since—in *O. virginica*—a small percentage—3% to 30%, depending on climate and food supply—first became female without any preceding male phase. Both sexes are to some extent intersexual: typical ovaries have a few sperms and *vice versa*, and at the end of the first year there are 1%–4% of true hermaphrodites. In warmer waters 70%–80% of first-year males were found, in cooler waters 95%. The small proportion of females always includes the largest of the age group. The oviparous oysters thus show *alternative sexuality*. In both groups of oysters there is, as in the molluscs at large, an inherent leaning to protandry; but the male phase may never be realized if nutritive conditions encourage femaleness from the first. The genetic rhythm must be very finely balanced, and the determination of sex so labile that nutritive conditions can tip it either way. And since primary gonads may differ widely in the proportion of male and female cells, there may be—as Orton suggested for limpets—a genetic distribution between races of pure males and potentially hermaphrodite males.

CEPHALOPODA

In the cephalopods the eggs are comparatively large and yolky, and do not completely cleave, that is to say the embryo is built up from a smaller disc of cells on the upper pole of the egg, and the larger part of the egg goes to form a yolk sac from which the young animal is nourished. In many species the eggs are relatively few, for example sixty in *Eledone*, a hundred or so in *Octopus maorum*. This is not always so: *Argonauta* lays many thousands of eggs at one time, and in the egg-piles of *Loligo*, which are communal, there may be 50,000 eggs. The behaviour of cephalopods is much more highly organized than in lower molluscs, and this is particularly so in reproduction. There may be complicated courtship and mating rituals, and very elaborate systems of parental care.

The sexes are always separate. A median ovary or testis lies at the apex of the body and opens straight into the coelom. The oviduct or male duct opens into the mantle cavity at the side of the anus. *Nautilus* has in both sexes a single functional duct (right) and a vestige on the other side. All other male cephalopods, and female Sepioidea, Loliginidae and Cirroteuthidae, have a single (left) duct, while most female Teuthoidea and Octopoda retain the primitive pair. The female duct is very simple; its only appendage is the so-called *oviducal gland* which secretes the coat of albumen round each egg. The outside egg membrane forms an elastic protein tunic, toughening in contact with sea-water. In squids and cuttlefish this is secreted by the *nidamentary glands*, of which there are one or two pairs, opening from the ventral body wall near the genital apertures. These pour their secretion over the eggs as they pass from the oviduct. In *Nautilus* it is the pallial wall itself that supplies the nidamentary secretion. Only in the octopods, where the shell gland is very highly developed, are the egg membranes secreted wholly in the oviduct.

In *Sepia* the eggs are very large (20 mm.) and are given a coating of ink as they are shed. They are attached like black grapes to suitable objects on the substrate.[186] *Loligo* encloses the eggs in two or three rows in large sausage-shaped egg-masses, attached at one end in clusters. *Octopus* and *Eledone* fix the single eggs together in clusters. The female *Octopus* expends a great deal of parental care on the eggs, brooding over them, and often flushing them with water from the funnel, or taking them up and cleaning them by passing them between the tips of the arms. In *Argonauta*, the paper nautilus, the brood is cared for in a very different way. The two most dorsal arms secrete the fragile calcareous 'shell' for which this genus is best known. The numerous tiny eggs—attached to branched egg strings—are carried in this shell, which thus has no homology with the true pallial shell of molluscs. It is not a house but a perambulator!

The cephalopod male duct is single and has become exceedingly specialized for the manufacture of the spermatophores (Fig. 15). The production and transfer of these sperm packets form the most elaborate features of cephalopod reproductive biology. Each spermatophore is a narrow, torpedo-shaped tube of chitin, containing a dense mass of sperm. The male conveys bunches of them to the female, after pulling them from his own genital opening by a specially modified arm known as the *hectocotylus*. After courtship and copulation they are attached to various parts of the body of the female or may be introduced into her mantle cavity. All cephalopods—*Nautilus* included—produce some type of spermatophore, and all possess some complication—it may be very intricate or relatively simple—of one of the arms, or of the tentacle crown, with which to transfer them. No cephalopod has a penis, properly so called.

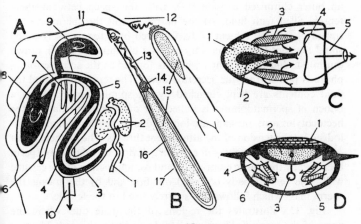

FIG. 15

A Male genital ducts of *Loligo* (Needham's Sac removed). 1) vas deferens from testis, 2) mucilaginous glands, 3) inner tunic gland, 4) middle tunic gland, 5) outer tunic gland, 6) waste duct, 7) caecum, 8) hardening gland, 9) finishing gland, forming cap and thread, 10) ejaculatory duct, with male opening into Needham's Sac (after Drew, simplified.)

B Spermatophore of *Loligo* before discharge and (right) after discharge has begun. 11) thread, 12) cap, 13) spiral filament, 14) cement body, 15) sperm mass, 16) inner tunic, 17) outer tunic).

C Diagram of the mantle cavity of *Sepia* in ventral view, showing 1) visceral mass, 2) ink sac, 3) gill, 4) anus, 5) funnel.

Arrows show direction of water circulation.

D Transverse section of pallial region of *Sepia*. 1) shell, 2) visceral mass, 3) rectum, 4) supporting membrane of gill, 5) afferent blood vessel, 6) efferent blood vessel.

We may describe the spermatophores in *Loligo*, where they have received the most careful study.[66] Each is about 16 mm. long, and a dozen or so may be produced in a day (Fig. 15B). A large individual may store up to 400 at one time, and they lie in a spacious pouch called Needham's Sac, which surrounds all the glandular parts of the genital duct. The rest of the duct in fact opens into Needham's Sac, which itself opens by the genital aperture into the mantle cavity. About two-thirds of each spermatophore houses the viscous mass of sperm (15). This is surrounded by an inner tunic (16) and an outer chitinized capsule (17), with the space between them tensely filled with fluid. At the narrower end the sperm mass is tipped by a small cement body, followed by a long, closely coiled spiral filament (13). At the very end is a chitinous cap (12), drawn out into a thin thread (thr.) which is formed as the soft spermatophore is pulled from the secreting ducts. The terminal cap and the fluid contents are kept stretched by the spiral filament. When a bunch of spermatophores is pulled out of Needham's Sac by the hectocotylus arm, the caps are loosened and the spiral filament dislodged by the tension of the attachment threads. The filament is not —as sometimes thought—an explosive device: ejaculation of sperm is caused by the elastic contraction and osmotic action of the capsule wall. The cement body is forced out first and by this means the sperm mass which follows it is securely fixed to the female.

Fig. 15A illustrates the regions of the male duct where the parts of the spermatophore are laid down and fashioned. The two *mucilaginous glands* (2) secrete the axial material, i.e. the mucous matrix of the sperm mass, the cement body and the filament. The inner and outer tunics come from the middle reaches of the duct (3, 4, 5). The whole structure is then thrust into a diverticulum which has been incorrectly called the 'prostate'. This serves as a hardening gland (8). Finally, in a terminal *finishing gland* (9), the cap and thread are secreted, and the spermatophore passes into the storage sac.

In *Loligo* the hectocotylus organ, on the fourth arm on the left side, is very slight. Several of the suckers are merely modified to form an attachment area for the spermatophores. Copulation is preceded by courtship ritual. The male swims alongside the female and displays at intervals, spreading his arms and assuming a dark red blush. There are alternative positions of copulation. The male may come to lie parallel to the female, lower sides in contact, grasping her by wrapping his arms tightly round her head. With a sweep of the hecto-cotylus arms he plucks out a bunch of spermatophores and inserts them into the female's mantle cavity, where they are attached near the oviduct. In the second position the male and female join head to head and the spermatophores are transferred to a glandular patch on the female's buccal membrane, which may be identified as a 'receptaculum'. The sperms are still immobile. They are acti-vated by contact with sea water when their reservoir is ruptured at the time the eggs are laid. Courtship and copulation are communal activities in the squid. Large numbers of males and females—which are at other times segregated—gather together at the spawning ground. The females contribute hundreds of egg-masses to the com-munity pile. As in a number of other cephalopods, oviposition appears to be rapidly followed by death.

Very interesting and diverse are the hectocotylus arms in other cephalopods. In *Nautilus* a special portion of the tentacle crown is hectocotylized, involving four tentacles of one of the lobes on the right side. This is called a *spadix*, forming a sleeved projection with a glandular tip. In some squids, such as *Rossia*, all the suckers of the hectocotylus arm are lost and are replaced by a glandular adhesive membrane. It is in the Octopoda that the hectocotylus is most elaborate. The third arm on the right is furnished with a spoon-shaped tip and this is connected with the base of the arm by a fold of skin which appears to form a sperm groove. The female is first caressed at the full arm's length by the male, and the tip is then put into her pallial cavity and the sperms deposited at the mouth of the oviduct. In Argonautacea (*Argonauta, Tremoctopus* and *Ocythöe*) the male is much smaller than the female and the hectocotylus is en-larged and autotomous. It has a long filament which remains coiled in a sheath until the arm is detached, after which the whole organ moves about freely for some time in the mantle cavity of the female. It was long regarded as a parasite, even by Cuvier, who gave it a special name, 'Hectocotylus octopodis'. Later and more imagina-tive workers endowed it with a gut, heart and reproductive system! Sex dimorphism is most extreme in *Argonauta*, where the female carries the papery shell. The male is a small dwarf one inch long, his largest organ being the detachable hectocotylus arm.

Two purposes may be served by larvae—finding new settling sites and gaining access to the rich food supply of the phytoplankton. Molluscan larvae are of different types according to the importance of the pelagic phase and the amount of planktonic food taken. The earliest larva was undoubtedly a trochophore like that of an annelid —a top-shaped creature with a tuft of cilia above and a ciliated band around the middle; and this is perhaps the closest resemblance that the Mollusca have ever borne to the Annelida.

Molluscan life histories do not perfectly correspond with taxonomy, but it is in general true that the archaeogastropods and the bivalves begin life as a trochophore and rapidly pass on to a veliger.[120] Fig. 15A shows the typical larval organs—most prominent a ciliated velum, drawn out into lobes in gastropods from the ciliated ring lying in front of the mouth. In the gastropods the early veliger goes through the critical episode of torsion, and its velum may later become very large (Fig. 16A), often subdivided in prosobranchs into four or six lobes, often ornamented by coloured spots. In bivalves a wheel-shaped velum projects from between the two valves of the larval shell. It is never deeply subdivided as in gastropods.

Thorson has recognized three ecological types of larvae, each represented in molluscs.[184] First there are planktotrophic larvae with a long larval life of up to two or three months, as in most lamellibranchs and many prosobranchs. These are the least modified larvae of all, and are small and cheap to produce on a large scale. (*Mytilus edulis* may spawn 12 million eggs, all capable of developing into larvae.) They are effective pioneers and the species which use them secure wide distribution. They will settle in great numbers in good years, and the stock of benthic adults is thus subject to great fluctuations according to seasonal conditions. Planktotrophic larvae are most usual in tropical and sub-tropical seas, and in high arctic seas the few molluscan larvae found are also of this type.

Such molluscan veligers are all ciliary feeders. The large velar cilia collect particles which are thrown on to a tract at the base of the velum leading to the mouth. Coarse or unsuitable particles are removed by rejectory tracts upon the foot.

Secondly, there are planktotrophic larvae with a short swimming life of never more than a week in the plankton. The velum is never elaborate, and planktonic feeding is of secondary importance, distribution being the main object of larval life. There is little growth between hatching and settling. Nudibranch larvae may be often of this type, and other British examples include *Gibbula cineraria*, *Hydrobia ulvae*, *Turritella communis* and *Bela trevelyana*. Such larvae are seldom if ever found in lamellibranchs. Being less dependent on

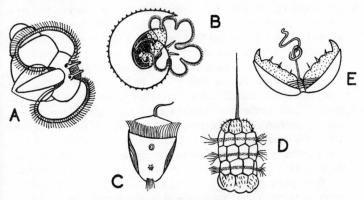

FIG. 16. Molluscan larvae

A Veliger of *Aclis* (Mesogastropoda), B Veliger of *Lamellaria* with *Echinospira* shell, C Trochophore stage of a bivalve, D Yolk larva of *Yoldia* (Protobranchia), E Glochidium of *Anodonta*.

food they are for small larvae surprisingly adaptable to unfavourable conditions, and serve mainly for dispersal.

The third type of larvae take no food in the plankton. They are *lecithotrophic*, hatching from very yolky eggs and developing into large, rather clumsy 'yolk larvae'. They swim little and are passively carried about in the plankton. Being independent of adverse conditions, species recruited in this way show very constant numbers from year to year. The chief disadvantage of yolk larvae is their small numbers and expensiveness to produce, and the small ability of the species to seize the chances offered by a good food year. Gastropods show few examples of yolk larvae, which are the normal type in three groups, the Amphineura, Scaphopoda and proto-branchiate Lamellibranchia. The yolk larvae of chitons are modified egg-shaped trochophores with a broad ciliary ring, spending only six hours to a few days in the plankton. In other yolk larvae, large flat velar cells surround the body like a girdle. *Neomenia* has three such rings, *Dentalium* four. In protobranchs such as *Yoldia* and *Nucula* they form a large barrel-shaped ciliated test, which is thrown off when the larva settles (Fig. 16D).

Not all molluscs have a planktonic life history. With the poor phytoplankton of arctic seas, few molluscs employ larvae, and yolk larvae are, surprisingly, absent. If larvae are to be liberated there at all, as in *Mya truncata* and *Saxicava arctica*, they must be numerous and planktotrophic, and the species must accept the hazards involved in taking advantage of the brief plankton bloom.

Many gastropods pass their whole development in the egg capsule. This is inescapable in land forms and is the rule in freshwater snails as well. In the sea too there are many examples of non-pelagic development. Most neogastropods (except Nassariidae and turrids) retain the larvae in the eggs, as do many mesogastropods and even some archaeogastropods. Free-swimming larvae are nearly always produced in that thoroughly marine group—the Opisthobranchia.

With some retained larvae the egg's own yolk is sufficient to carry it through development within the capsule, as in *Lacuna pallidula*, *Littorina obtusata* and *L. rudis* (*L. littorea* and *L. neritoides* are planktotrophic). But most non-pelagic prosobranchs are fed on nurse eggs which are enclosed in the same capsule but do not develop. *Natica catena* has usually fewer than 10 nurse eggs per embryo, and may sometimes produce pelagic young; *Nucella lapillus* has 20–30, *Buccinum undatum* 100, *Sipho islandicus* 7000 and the deep-sea *Volutopsis norvegica* up to 100,000!

A crisis in molluscan life must come at the settlement stage, when the pelagic larva metamorphoses. It was indeed once thought that only those that first touched down on a suitable ground could survive: those which fell by the wayside had no second chance. Recent work discussed by Gunnar Thorson on invertebrate larvae has shown, however, that the first choice may not be irrevocable. Larvae such as those of worms reared by D. P. Wilson and the echinoderms of Th. Mortensen were able actively to select a favourable substratum. Marie Lebour relates that the larvae of the molluscs *Nassa*, *Philbertia*, *Rissoa* and some *Natica* species passed through a short ambivalent swimming-crawling stage, when they could sample the substratum and select a site with great precision. Thorson also found that the larvae of the boring bivalve *Zirphaea* penetrated into the cork floats of collector bottles and settled there only. There is perhaps a critical trial period—not longer than a week—during which most larvae can postpone their final settlement while in search of a site. We find examples in sessile molluscs, as in oysters, of the settlement behaviour described by Knight-Jones and Crisp in barnacles and *Spirorbis*: here the larvae are strongly induced to settle by the presence of their own kind—even dead shells or persistently detectable traces of their own species previously on the site.

As we have seen, larvae are not always reliable guides to phylogeny, and may evolve many structures for their own needs as distinct from the morphology of the adult. This we call 'clandestine evolution'. The embryo shell can, however, give many clues as to both the relationships and the mode of life of its occupant. Thus the size and number of the embryonic whorls differ according to whether the larva had a long or short planktonic life. A multispiral protoconch with a small apex and many whorls denotes a long-swimming larva, and is thus characteristic of most gastropods of warm seas. A species with a yolky larva—more typical of high latitudes—has a simple protoconch with a large bulbous apex. By inspecting the protoconch of an adult (even a fossil) shell, we may thus deduce the mode of larval life. This rule, first discovered by Dall, applies even among the species of a single family. Thus the Naticidae and the Struthiolariidae both show alternative types of apex depending on different lengths of life history.

In a number of gastropods the embryonic shell is sinistral, and reverses its direction to coil to the right in the adult. Such an apex is evidently non-adaptive, and is found in both early opisthobranchs (bulloids and pyramidellids, while *Limacina* retains it as the adult shell) and in early pulmonates such as Ellobiidae and Chilinidae. It is an interesting confirmation of other evidence of the common origin and later divergence of these two groups of gastropods.

VIII

NERVOUS SYSTEM, SENSE ORGANS AND BEHAVIOUR

IN NO other phylum except the Chordata does the evolution of the nervous system cover such a wide span as in the Mollusca. An early mollusc such as a chiton is a slow-moving creature with a nervous system best compared with that of a flatworm; but the highest productions of the Mollusca—the cephalopod brain and sense organs—are rivalled only among the vertebrates themselves.

In the chitons—as no doubt in the first molluscs—neuromuscular action belongs chiefly to the head-foot; the muscles of the sole and the odontophore are from the first very complex. In the visceral mass and pallial cavity the chief effector organs are cilia and mucous glands, and these parts are hardly as yet brought under rapid control. In the primitive plan of the nervous system (Fig. 17A) there are few localized ganglia. The nerve ring round the oesophagus is built up of a dorsal cerebral band with scattered neurones, and a ventral labial commissure, sending forward connectives to a pair of buccal centres. These ganglia control the movements of the odontophore, and were probably the first to become distinct. Two pairs of parallel cords run back from the nerve ring, also with scattered nerve cells, and linked together by cross commissures in ladder fashion. These cords are the foundation of the viscero-pallial and pedal nervous systems respectively. The pedal cords run along the foot on the floor of the perivisceral space, and the two pallial cords lie laterally near the attachment of the mantle to the body. In addition, a simple stomatogastric or 'sympathetic' nervous system runs back from the nerve ring along the wall of the gut.

The nerve cells in the longitudinal cords soon become localized in distinct ganglia. In the earliest gastropods we find already a pair of *pleural* ganglia concentrated at the sides of the nerve ring at the head of the pallial cords. The cords themselves are reduced to connectives, forming a long *visceral loop* with a *parietal ganglion* becoming distinct on either side, and a single or sometimes paired *visceral ganglion* where the loop crosses the gut behind. *Haliotis* or *Trochus* (Fig. 17B) may be chosen to illustrate this early condition, with no distinct cerebral ganglia and the pedal ladder still unconcentrated. The cerebral ganglia are the next to appear, while in most mesogastropods the neurones of the pedal cords have been drawn into the nerve ring as a pair of ganglia; while the cords as such disappear. Thus we find the typical gastropod nerve ring, with two cerebral ganglia dorsally and two pleural and two pedal ganglia below. The cerebral and pedal pairs are linked in the middle line by cerebral and pedal commissures; and at either side the cerebrals are linked with the pleurals and pedals, and the pleurals with the pedals, by short connectives.

From the pleural ganglia springs the visceral loop, connecting to the nerve ring the parietal ganglia, from which nerves pass to the pallial organs. During torsion the gastropod visceral loop is twisted into a figure of 8, the condition known as *chiastoneury*. The right parietal ganglion now crosses above the gut to lie upon the left, being called the *supraintestinal ganglion* (though it really lies near the oesophagus). The original left parietal ganglion passes underneath the oesophagus to lie on the right as the *subintestinal ganglion*. In the Monotocardia (Fig 17C) the supraintestinal ganglion takes on the innervation of the remaining left side of the mantle cavity, including the surviving gill. It also supplies the osphradium, either directly or through an outlying *osphradial ganglion*. On either side the pleural and parietal ganglion may establish a direct link by a connective known as the *zygoneury*.

In the higher Gastropoda all the ganglia finally come to lie in the nerve ring, and the figure of 8 configuration of the visceral loop is lost. First—in the higher prosobranchs such as *Buccinum*—the subintestinal ganglion is withdrawn across to its original side to lie close against the left pleural ganglion. Then the supraintestinal ganglion moves back over the oesophagus to become attached to the right pleural member. In the pulmonates (Fig. 17G) the whole visceral loop is shortened with the incorporation of the visceral ganglion in the ring, which now consists of nine large ganglia, with the smaller buccal ganglia still attached by connectives. Torsion of the visceral mass has not been abolished in the pulmonates, but the evidence for it—in the twisting of the visceral loop—can no longer be clearly detected, and in *Helix* the nerve ring is very compact, with its ganglia in direct contact.

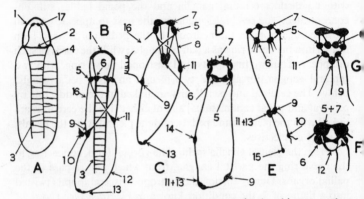

FIG. 17. Evolution of the nervous system in Amphineura and Gastropoda

A Amphineura (*Chiton*), B Archaeogastropoda (*Trochus*), C Meso-gastropoda (*Triton*), D Opisthobranchia (*Akera*), E Opistho-branchia (*Aplysia*), F Opisthobranchia (*Goniodoris*), G Pulmonata (*Lymnaea*). 1) cerebral cord, 2) labial commissure, 3) pedal ladder, 4) pleural cords, 5) pleural ganglion, 6) pedal ganglion, 7) cerebral ganglion, 8) zygoneury, 9) supra-intestinal ganglion, 10) branchial ganglion, 11) subintestinal ganglion, 12) visceral loop, 13) visceral ganglion, 14) accessory parietal ganglion, 15) genital ganglion, 16) dialyneury, 17) buccal ganglia (included in A only).

The Opisthobranchia (Fig. 17E), however, have completely re-versed torsion. During their phylogeny the mantle cavity has moved backwards along the right side towards its original site and the visceral loop actually untwists. All the ganglia lie in the nerve ring, usually (17G) above the oesophagus and united only by the pedal commissure below. The early opisthobranch *Actaeon* and the primi-tive pulmonate *Chilina* are interesting transitional forms in the re-duction of the visceral loop: they still display the well-marked figure of 8.

In chitons the mantle and girdle press close to the ground. Head tentacles or eyes would have little use, though the snout possesses tactile organs and the buccal cavity taste receptors, and there are rudimentary otocysts at the head of the pedal cords. The paired osphradia lie at the rear, usually near the last gill. The most important sensory area consists of tactile organs and light receptors, transferred where they are most needed, to the exposed surface of the shell plates. The valves are pitted with very numerous sense organs, like microscopic bright spots, and are of two kinds. The most abundant are simple epidermal papillae called *micraesthetes*. Moseley, who has studied them most closely, regarded these as merely touch receptors. The larger receptors, the megalaesthetes, lie at the centre of clusters of micraesthetes. These are much more complex, forming in many chitons, such as the non-British *Acanthopleura*, *Tonicia* and *Liolophura*, undoubted eyes, with a simple lens, a pigmented sheath and a retina. Their outer covering cuticle forms an elementary cornea. The megalaesthetes are innervated from the pallial cords and are densest near the growing points of the shell plates, where they have not yet been worn away. They are roughly arranged in rows, and one species, *Corephium aculeatum*, has some 3000 of them on the anterior valve, and on the other valves together about 8500.[141] The dorsal sense organs dominate the whole behavioural pattern of chitons, and even those species which lack true eyes are highly sensitive to light and shade. The animal wanders afield and grazes at night or when the tide is in, and on exposure to strong light retreats under stones, seeking a position of minimum light intensity, maximum humidity and maximum dorsal contact.[69]

With reorganization of the body, molluscan sense organs have often shifted to new locations. This is especially so of light receptors, which range from the simplest pigment spots to the intricate and beautiful eyes of heteropods, scallops and especially cephalopods. Like other sense organs the eyes have been many times lost, reacquired and rearranged, according to adaptive needs.

A gastropod like the top-shell *Monodonta* shows all the typical sense organs of the early mollusc. The cephalic tentacles are tactile and probably gustatory, and share their functions with the epipodial tentacles which come into wide contact with the ground. At the bases of the cephalic tentacles are paired eyes, and embedded in the foot are simple otocysts with calcareous otoconia. On the inhalant side of the mantle cavity lies the distinctive pallial chemoreceptor, the osphradium.

In later Gastropoda these organs have been emphasized or reduced according to habits.[25] The eyes are primitively simple in the limpets, forming open retinal pits with neither lens nor cornea. In other archaeogastropods, such as *Trochus*, *Haliotis* and *Turbo*, the optic vesicle has only a narrow opening and is filled with a watery humour; in higher gastropods it contains a spherical lens and is closed by a double-layered epithelial cornea. The majority of prosobranchs probably use their eyes for simple orientation in light, in the same manner as was demonstrated by Fraenkel with the sacoglossan opisthobranch *Elysia viridis*.[20] This small slug moves in a constant direction in horizontal light; the angle between the axis of the body and the line joining the eye to the source of light is known as the 'orientation angle'. Only light falling on the cup-like eye within 35° and 130° of the body can reach the retina, so that orientation angles outside these limits cannot be used. The eye thus serves as a 'light compass', a function which must be widespread, and has recently been described by Newell in the periwinkle *Littorina littorea*.[144]

The greatest visual powers are found in two groups of fast-moving gastropods. The pelagic Heteropoda have—as we have seen—tubular telescopic eyes, with a large lens, a tapetum and much-folded retinal surface. They find their direction and capture food by visual means, and the osphradium is quite vestigial. In the bottom-dwelling Strombidae, which progress with powerful leaps, the large eyes are mounted on long peduncles which dwarf the cephalic tentacles. The animal has an aspect of great alertness. Exploration is rapid and visual, no longer by the slow, tentative action of the tentacles, and the optic peduncles peep vigilantly from under the canopy of the shell, being moved actively to and fro.

In burrowing gastropods like the Naticidae, the Olividae and bulloids such as *Scaphander* and *Philine*, as well as in many nudibranchs, the eyes are small and buried in the skin, or altogether lacking. The passively drifting pelagic prosobranch *Ianthina* differs strikingly from the heteropods in being blind, and in having also lost the statocysts. In the Heteropoda the statocysts are highly developed as organs of balance. The sensory cells form a large macula and there is a single large otolith. After removal of one statocyst, *Pterotrachea* is at first unable to orient, developing a pronounced roll towards the operated side.

One or two pelagic opisthobranchs have compensated for the sacrifice of the eyes during their earlier benthic history. Thus the shelled pteropod *Corolla* has special adaptive eyes, complete with lens and retina, appearing as pigment spots round the edges of the wings. The bottom-dwelling onchidiid slug *Peronia* has followed the chitons in shifting the light receptors to the dorsal surface, which is studded with small tentacles bearing eyes remarkably like the pallial eyes of some lamellibranchs.

The land pulmonates explore much more by sight. The eyes are carried at the tips of long inversible head tentacles, and some snails are found to turn aside from an object at a distance of 10 cm. Such eyes are, however, small and simple in structure, and form perception is probably lacking, as in all molluscs except cephalopods. The tactile and chemosense has shifted in pulmonates from the large tentacles to a pair of small secondary tentacles developed from the oral lappets.

The forward-facing mantle cavity in prosobranchs becomes— rather in the manner of the protochordate pharynx—the centre of all those functions depending on the passage of a water current: respiration, olfaction, detection and removal of sediment, and in a few cases feeding as well. The mantle is highly sensitive to inborne particles, and Hulbert and Yonge have held that the osphradium, as well as being a chemoreceptor, may also be a mechanoreceptor detecting particles suspended in the water current. Herbivorous gastropods such as trochids and littorinids, even those like *Aporrhais* and *Turritella*, that dwell near silt, have nevertheless relatively simple osphradia. This organ is largest in the carnivores, becoming broad and filamentose like a subsidiary gill (p. 71). The inhalant siphon, which leads the water current to the osphradium, now becomes the anterior out-post of the body, acting as a moving nostril continually sampling the environment ahead. Copeland[55] has shown that the whelks *Alectrion* and *Busycon* begin to crawl or accelerate in the direction of oyster juice, and find their prey by a directed reaction or klinotaxis. *Nassarius reticulatus*, according to Hentschel,[100] has the same ability. Whelks such as *Cominella* can detect carrion from a distance of six feet, and the Conidae (p. 96) use their siphon and osphradium for stalking live prey.

With the lack of a pallial water current in opisthobranchs and pulmonates the osphradium ultimately disappears too. The typical olfactory organs of opisthobranchs are a pair of modified head tentacles, the rhinophores, which become clubbed and finely plicate to increase the sensory area. The tactile sense reaches a new importance in naked nudibranchs, the whole dorsal with its processes being highly sensitive to contact.

Both chitons and limpets show a homing behaviour, involving a wonderful power of orientation. After a feeding sortie, at night or during high tide, they return with great precision to their permanent resting site. Many limpets excavate a deep scar, its edges eroded by the shell and conforming exactly to it in outline. The distance of the possible journey varies with the species. Stephenson—*see* Thorpe (1956)[24]—finds that *Patella granularis* travels and returns from as far afield as five feet. Accuracy of performance falls off with distance. Chitons, *Onchidium* and the marine pulmonate *Siphonaria* make similar journeys and, sometimes at least, may return by a different route. On reaching the scar or resting site the animal turns and manœuvres till an exact fit is obtained. This happens even after the scar has been reversed in position, or when the whole rock has been lifted out and re-oriented. Such behaviour implies a space memory and a subtle appreciation of topography not yet explained by the available sense organs. *Siphonaria* and *Onchidium* are said to use touch, the one with the edges of the mantle, the other with the buccal lips. Removal of the tentacles with the eyes in limpets does not prevent homing. Tactile information must play a large part, but any detailed registering of the substratum by a 'touch memory' would seem to be ruled out by the experiments of re-orienting the scar, and by the different homeward path sometimes taken. The problem is complicated, and obviously a wide appreciation of many aspects of the environment is involved. To formulate this in terms of classical neurology is not easy, since a gastropod mollusc has only relatively few neurones available in its total 'brain'.

The lamellibranch nervous system is essentially simple. Paired cerebral ganglia lie above the oesophagus and—with the exception of the protobranchs—the pleural ganglia are completely fused with them. Pedal connectives lead to the pedal ganglia embedded in the base of the foot, and long visceral connectives run back to a pair of visceral ganglia lying beneath the posterior adductor muscle. The cerebropleural ganglia innervate the palps, anterior adductor muscle and part of the mantle, as well as the otocysts and osphradia. The visceral centres control a large territory: they innervate the gills, heart, pericardium, posterior adductor muscle (sometimes the sole adductor remaining), as well as part or all of the mantle, the siphons and pallial sense organs. Where concentration of the nervous system has taken place, as in *Pecten*, *Spondylus* and *Lima*, it is the visceral ganglia that provide the new centre and the cerebrals that move back to join them, forming a 'visceral brain' of an elementary sort, sometimes with distinct optic lobes receiving nerves from the pallial eyes.

No bivalve has a head and most of the sense organs have withdrawn from the anterior end. Vestigial eyes are found here only in Mytilidae and *Avicula*. The otocysts are very simple, deeply embedded in the foot near the pedal ganglia. In protobranchs and the Mytilidae they have the primitive form of otocrypts, opening narrowly to the exterior. In the sedentary Ostreidae they lack otoliths. The paired osphradia are simple sensory patches lying near the attachment of the gill close to the visceral ganglia, though they are innervated by cerebral nerves running through the visceral connectives.

The rest of the exteroceptors have come to lie at the edge of the open mantle or—in burrowing bivalves—are concentrated at the tips of the siphons. Thus *Cardium* possesses sensory tentacles round both siphons and these are equipped with small but rather complex eyes, with a retina, hyaline lens and cornea. Few other eulamellibranchs have eyes, but the siphons commonly have pigmented light sensitive spots, as in pholads, some venerids and in *Mya*. In sessile or surface-dwelling lamellibranchs, pallial eyes are often abundant, distributed

151

like the tactile tentacles along the free middle lobe of the mantle edge. In the Arcidae the individual eyes are of simple structure, but gathered together in facetted groups, like a compound eye.

By far the most alert of bivalves are the swimming Pectinacea. Here the pallial tentacles are highly developed, forming sensitive fringes of tactile organs or guarding tentacles for the exclusion of sediment. Most beautiful of all are the several rows of long coloured retractile tentacles in the Limidae. In *Pecten* and *Spondylus* the tentacles are shorter, many of them tipped with small but elaborate eyes, with a metallic blue sheen from the tapetum or light-reflecting layer behind the retina. The dioptric apparatus is a corneal lens, with sometimes a dome of hyaline cells lying outside it. The retina, as in vertebrates, is inverted, that is, the light must pass first through a nervous layer to the sensitive receptors beneath—an outer layer of rods and an inner layer of cones. The complexity of these eyes is something of a puzzle, since they seem to be at a surprisingly low functional level. They can detect movement or a shadow, but make no satisfactory definition of shapes. A scallop will detect a starfish predator or starfish juice by its chemosense alone, and will make no response by flight to a model of a starfish. The pallial eyes must how-ever have contributed to the speed of response involved in the de-velopment of swimming (p. 55). Horizontal swimming in *Pecten* with left side down has led to an asymmetric development of the statocysts: though both are present the orientation and control of all swimming reflexes are initiated from the left one alone.

A few small bivalves such as *Kellya* and *Lasaea* are able to crawl relatively fast with the foot over a hard or soft substrate. *Lasaea* can orient away from light by a klinotaxis. Here the inhalant aperture is anterior as in *Nucula*, and together with the foot is photosensitive.

Apart from the foot, the muscular activities of bivalves are few and stereotyped. First there are movements of the mantle edges and siphons, largely directed by respiratory needs. Second, and univer-sally important, are the powerful contractions of the adductor muscles, by whose action the valves are tightly closed or allowed to gape. By these muscles the bivalve controls its whole relations with the world outside.

The nervous control of adductor movements has recently been studied by Barnes in *Anodonta*.[34] Here there is a regular alternation of bursts of activity and periods of quiescence that seems to be rather a general feature of bivalves. Every six hours or so the valves are for a short period rapidly opened and shut. Between these times they are held tightly closed, by a portion of each adductor muscle capable of prolonged contractions or *tonus*. Another portion contains fibres producing rapid or *phasic* contractions, but unable to keep up tonus. Both the tonic and the phasic parts of the rhythm are controlled from the ganglion nearest the muscle, either cerebropleural or visceral. The phasic rhythm is intrinsic and fast contractions continue all the time. They can be observed, however, only when the simultaneous tonic contractions are inhibited, which takes place from time to time by impulses arising in the cerebropleural ganglia. The cutting of the visceral connectives thus produces permanent tonus in the posterior adductor. The inhibition of tonus does not appear to be reflexly induced by lack of oxygen or food or accumulation of faeces, and Barnes concludes it is probably spontaneous.

In most lamellibranchs the two parts—tonic and phasic—of the adductor muscles cannot be separately identified. But they are histologically distinct in *Anodonta* and are especially well-marked in those surface-dwelling Anisomyaria, like *Pecten* and *Ostrea*, that retain only the posterior adductor. Here the single enlarged muscle is attached to the centre of the shell and produces the rapid opening and closing so important in expelling sediment in bivalves lying on a silted bottom, with a widely open mantle. The slow tonic fibres of the adductor are smooth, while those of the fast portion are spirally striated. There has been much controversy about the way the slow fibres act. It is now generally thought that repeated tetanic contractions are brought about by sustained impulses from the ganglia,[123] though others have suggested a passive 'catch mechanism', whereby the viscous components in the muscle catch the contractile elements at constant length in the manner of a rachet.

Sustained tetanic contractions must be best developed in intertidal bivalves like *Mytilus* that stay closed for long periods. By contrast the fast muscle is most useful in forms like *Pecten* that expel sediment or swim by the clapping of the valves. The swimming habit —an unusual accomplishment in a bivalve—has thus arisen merely by emphasis of one phase of the normal adductor rhythm. The

Pectinacea are especially pre-adapted for it by the shape of the shell, the widely open mantle, the fast adductor and the pallial light organs.[215]

CEPHALOPODA

The cephalopod brain has become so highy differentiated that it is well not to look for too precise homologies with the ganglia of other molluscs. The nautiloid brain (Fig. 18B) consists of three half hoops of nervous tissue, a wide cerebral band above the oesophagus, connecting with paired optic lobes, and two bands below, an anterior pedal and a posterior pleurovisceral. The whole brain lies within a widely fenestrated cartilage capsule.

In later cephalopods the brain is much more concentrated and more completely enclosed by cartilage. The diagram (Fig. 18c) of the brain of *Octopus* will serve to identify the chief parts.[42, 223] There is first an upper supraoesophageal region, divided up into eight separate centres, certain of which receive sensory nerves, as well as connectives from the buccal ganglia. The dorsal region connects at the sides with very large stalked optic lobes (10), which lie at the bases of the eyes and constitute a separate part of the brain. The lower supraoesophageal region of the brain consists of a pedal centre in front (11) and a pleurovisceral centre behind (15), continuous with each other and linked with the supraoesophageal brain above. The pedal centre sends eight large nerves to the arms (in decapods ten nerves arise from a more or less separate brachial ganglion) and also supplies the funnel. From the pleurovisceral centre run back the two great pallial nerves to the stellate ganglia (Fig. 18A, 6) on the inside of the mantle. These ganglia innervate the circular and longitudinal pallial muscles that contract to expel water in swimming. Two large visceral nerves also run back to the visceral mass.

Considering the motor functions of the cephalopod brain first, we shall examine the pallial innervation in a squid like *Loligo*, a much faster swimmer than *Octopus* and with a rather less modified nervous system. In *Loligo* (Fig. 18A) the pleurovisceral centre has a median ventral bulge, the giant fibre lobe (3), and it is from here that the contractions of the mantle are ultimately controlled. Im-

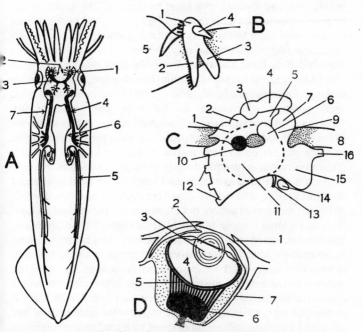

FIG. 18.   Cephalopod nervous system and eye

A Pallial innervation of *Loligo*. 1) lobus magnocellularis, 2) giant cell body, 3) first order giant neurone, 4) second order giant neurone, 5) third order giant neurone, 6) stellate ganglion, 7) pallial nerve (after Young).

B Brain of *Nautilus* in side view. 1) supraoesophageal centres, 2) pedal band, 3) pleurovisceral band, 4) optic lobe, 5) buccal mass.

C Brain of *Octopus* in side view. 1) lobus olfactorius, 2) frontalis inferior, 3) frontalis superior, 4) verticalis, 5) subverticalis, 6) basalius, medius, 7) basalis posterior, 8) oesophagus, 9) position of laterally placed basalis lateralis, 10) optic stalk, 11) pedal mass, 12) brachial nerves, 13) nerve to funnel, 14) position of otocyst, 15) pleurovisceral mass, 16) pallial nerve (after Boycott and Young).

D Section of the eye of *Sepia*. 1) cornea, 2) iris, 3) lens, 4) retina, 5) optic nerves, 6) optic lobe, 7) optic capsule.

pulses are set up in one or other of a pair of giant neurones situated in this lobe, and studded with some hundreds of cell bodies. Other large motor neurones have their cell bodies here and motor axones proceed from them to the arms, especially the long tentacles which make lightning capture of the prey. Of the two largest neurones in the giant fibre lobe, known as *first order giant neurones* (1), each sends a stout axone to the main palliovisceral centre, and these, after making a fusion in the mid-line(a very unusual condition in neurones), make synapses with several *second order giant neurones* (4). These have cell bodies in the palliovisceral centre, and send axones to the funnel and by way of the pallial nerves to the stellate ganglia. In these ganglia lie the cell bodies of *third order giant neurones* (5), whose axones in turn run directly to the pallial muscles.[222]

Such a giant fibre system is an ideal one for producing rapid movement rather than the prolonged contractions of tonus. There is little fine gradation of action, but excitation is synchronized on both sides and a large number of muscle fibres contract simultaneously, reaction time being greatly accelerated. Giant fibres are hence found in, for example, annelids, nemertines, crustaceans, as also in molluscs, in situations where quick escape or attack is required. In *Loligo* the mantle contractions are mediated from the brain with the fewest possible units, namely one pair of giant fibres, and with a rapid conduction rate, attaining up to 20 m./sec. One combination not achieved by cephalopods is that of speed with gradation or precision of movement; this is possible only in vertebrates, with rapid conduction by numerous nerves of normal size, by virtue of the special properties of the myelin sheath.

In the slower-moving *Octopus* there are no giant fibres to the stellate ganglion, and impulses travel to the mantle by axones of ordinary size. In addition some of the neurones within the stellate ganglion produce a series of neuro-secretory processes, ending blindly in a glandular *epistellar body* attached to the ganglion. If this gland is removed locomotion is impaired, the body becomes limp and the chromatophore muscles lose tonus as well. Direct nervous control of muscle tone seems in part replaced by neuro-secretion.[220]

There are four areas in the suboesophageal brain whose impulses produce expansion of the chromatophores. These—as we have seen —are microscopic bags of pigment, expanded by extrinsic muscles under nervous control, and contracting by their own elasticity. Two anterior chromatophore lobes—for the head and arms—are found in the pedal mass, two posterior lobes for the mantle lie in the visceropedal mass. The bottom-dwelling *Sepia* is outstanding in its speed of colour change, and *Octopus* also has a well-developed chromatophore effector system. In pelagic *Argonauta* and *Loligo* these lobes are smaller than in *Sepia* and *Octopus*, and the fibres of their neuropil seem less regularly arranged.

All these effector systems—pallial, brachial and chromatophoral—are located in the suboesophageal part of the brain, collectively comprising the *lower motor centres*. They are, however, connected with and closely supervised by the higher centres of the brain, and these we must now examine. Lying immediately over the oesophagus, and so forming the lower part of the supraoesophageal region, are the areas known together as the *higher motor centres*. There are three lobes (Fig. 18c, 6, 7, 9), the *lobus anterior basalis* supervising the movements of the head and arms, the *lobus posterior basalis*, concerned with mantle and funnel movements, and the *lobus lateralis basalis*, supervising the expansion of the chromatophores.

Above the higher motor centres and lying thus at the top of the brain are five centres which are functionally as well as topographically the highest in the brain. Of these the *lobus inferior frontalis* (2) is the collecting centre for tactile information, especially from the arms, and is larger in *Octopus* than in decapods. The two olfactory lobes are small centres in cephalopods, lying upon the optic stalks. Above all the others lie the *lobus superior frontalis* (3) and the *lobus verticalis* (4), with the *subverticalis* (5) beneath it, which receive no direct sensory nerves.

The dominance of the higher centres is less obvious in *Sepia* than in *Octopus*. In a cuttlefish with the whole of its supraoesophageal brain removed the lower motor centres can still produce a sustained forward ripple of the fins, driving the animal backwards, for as long as three days. This movement is—in itself—independent of reflex stimulation, though it can be stopped by reflexes, as set up for example by gentle touch. It appears to originate from a rhythmic flow of impulses from the lower motor centres: a simple innate behaviour is thus initiated in the brain itself—influences from sensory inflow from the world outside may modify or inhibit it, but do not

promote it. It is the role of the supraoesophageal brain to regulate
such elementary behaviour, chiefly by suppressing parts of it. Thus,
in *Sepia*, if the lobus anterior basalis of one side is alone removed, a
spinning movement results, with the operated side outwards. The
impulses promoting fin movement on this side are now free of
inhibition by the higher motor centres.

In *Octopus* the lower brain is much less autonomous. The supraoesophageal brain and the optic lobes together exert a close control
over behaviour. If both these regions are removed, the animal becomes limp and loses all definite posture, performing only simple
acts such as breathing and proprioceptive reflexes. It behaves in
some ways like a 'spinal vertebrate'. If the supraoesophageal centres
are so removed that the optic lobes are left connected with the lower
brain, normal posture is maintained, but walking or food capture is
impossible; the picture is one of 'decerebrate rigidity'. If both optic
lobes and one half of the supraoesophageal brain are removed, the
octopus when prodded walks in circles, the side with the intact supraoesophageal brain being on the outside. Removal of both optic
lobes with the supraoesophageal brain left intact prevents any
walking: the two halves of the supraoesophageal brain appear to
inhibit each other. The flow of impulses from the optic lobes evidently determines the balance of activity here. If the optic lobe stalk
on the left, for example, is cut, and the nerves between the retina and
the optic lobe are severed on the right, the animal circles with the
left side outwards. The intact right optic lobe inhibits the supraoesophageal brain on its own side. If the retinal nerves are intact on
both sides the animal never circles. Boycott and Young suggest that
the retina may set up a continuous discharge of impulses that act to
inhibit the inhibitory effect of the optic lobe.[40]

Removal of the five highest supraoesophageal lobes does not
seem to interfere with normal movements. Only if the three basal
lobes, or higher motor centres, are damaged is behaviour abnormal.
Young compares these three areas to the tegmentum of the mammal-
ian mid-brain: they are distinct from and functionally intermediate
between the lower motor centres and the higher or associative centres.
By the basal lobes innate or rhythmic behaviour is integrated into a
total behaviour pattern. Visual information, for example, may be
received from the retina, and the resulting impulses pass from the

optic lobes to the higher motor centres. These centres, by their control of the lower brain, regulate and co-ordinate the elements of innate behaviour, in the light of the sensory appraisal of the animal's present environment.

In almost all cephalopods the recognition of food or enemies depends primarily upon sight. *Nautilus* alone retains osphradia, while all cephalopods have a simple olfactory pit beneath the eye; but—in contrast to gastropods—the olfactory sense is poorly developed, particularly in cuttlefish and squid. Touch is however highly important, especially in the Octopoda, which have sensitive exploratory tentacles and live in intimate contact with the bottom. While a cuttlefish will follow a prawn by eye, once detected, round an opaque screen, the octopus will make a detour round the screen only if a tentacle has reached there first. Octopods thus explore space by tactile information from the tentacles. These arms also perform quite complex manipulations. Various authors have described the elaborate building behaviour of *Octopus*; by picking up and shifting stones with the tentacles elaborate retreats or 'villas' are put together. In the fast-swimming squids—by contrast—vision is all-important: the two long tentacles are normally kept retracted and sheathed. It is possible because squid behaviour has become so highly geared to the light sense that these cephalopods must produce their own bioluminescence as a condition of life in abyssal waters. In abyssal octopods on the other hand there are few luminescent species; chromatophores are lacking and in *Cirrothauma* even the eyes are reduced.

If the superior frontalis and verticalis lobes of *Octopus* are removed, much of the behaviour is left unimpaired. Activities such as the reflex behaviour of mating and the associative behaviour involved in food capture still continue. But the animal will no longer search actively for food and will hunt objects only within its immediate vision. The frontalis and verticalis provide, in the words of Young and Boycott, 'a system of action wider than that dictated by the immediate environment'. Here the animal stores experience of the past, that can be called upon to modify present behaviour. These lobes are in fact 'learning centres'.[41, 42]

In their now well-known experiments Boycott and Young presented octopuses with alternative situations: a crab alone and a crab associated with a small white disc. A 'punishment' of a mild electric shock was administered when the crab with the disc was seized, and the crab shown alone was allowed to be eaten. After a period of training, the animals learned to discriminate against crabs shown with a white disc, and the normal pattern of attack was in such situations restrained. How long this learned inhibition can be retained is not certain; temporary anaesthesia with urethane did not abolish it. On removing the lobus verticalis, or severing it from the frontalis superior, the inhibition was, however, lost, and crabs with white discs were again freely attacked. Inhibition seems to depend on these two lobes or the interaction between them. Removal of the other higher centres did not affect it, nor did the loss of one half of the verticalis. Moreover, operated animals had some power to relearn and to store experience in some part of the brain left intact. In similar experiments with removal of the verticalis in *Sepia* relearning began quite rapidly; the inhibitory area seems much less localized than in *Octopus*.

From such experiments with associative learning in *Octopus*[42] Boycott and Young have also investigated the recognition of different shapes. An octopus will learn to avoid a crab shown with a square of one size associated with a 'punishment', while continuing to attack crabs with larger or smaller squares. This discrimination is independent of the distance at which the squares are shown. Distinct reactions are made to certain figures of different shapes, but with the same area (i.e. the same amount of light reflected) or with the same length of perimeter. There are distinct reactions also to crosses and squares, and—less accurately—to figures with internal differences, thus—■ and □. That the relation of the shape of the object to the rest of the background, or to gravity, may be important is suggested by the ability to distinguish ▬ from ▌ or ◣ from ◆. Discrimination of squares from circles is poor.

Wells and Wells have recently made similar experiments to test the powers of tactile discrimination in blinded *Octopus*. Rewards and punishments were associated with small plastic cylinders of Perspex marked with grooves cut at different distances apart and running in different directions. The touch receptors of the arm suckers were unable to register differences in the spatial arrangement of the grooves. They could discriminate only between the varying amounts of total surface left ungrooved and thus coming in contact with the suckers, regardless of the direction or pattern of the grooves themselves. *Octopus* could, however, also discriminate with the tentacles between objects differing in non-surface or chemical characteristics, such as different species of shellfish. They have, as the Wells describe it, an efficient 'chemotactile' sense.[192]

'Intelligent' learning has modest beginnings in cephalopods, but it represents nevertheless the greatest triumph of the molluscan nervous system. J. Z. Young has used the arrangement of neurones in the frontalis and verticalis lobes of the octopus as a model of how an elementary system might develop for storing experience. These two lobes in *Octopus*, he points out, have characteristically small neurones without axones, an arrangement broadly comparable with the vertebrate cerebral cortex. Memory could have its neurological basis in activity between such neurones 'dynamically maintained by means of some simple, reverberating self-firing circuit'.

The *Octopus* brain is a territory of great promise where the neurologist has only begun to work; continued experiment will contribute much more to our understanding of the mechanism of learning.[192]

F

IX

THE EVOLUTION OF THE GASTROPODA

THE Gastropoda are by far the largest class of the Mollusca. Modern classification breaks them into three primary divisions, the subclasses Prosobranchia, Opisthobranchia and Pulmonata. The Prosobranchia are the most numerous, widely distributed and diverse; the Opisthobranchia reach the highest level of specialization; and the Pulmonata—while more conservative in structure—show the most ambitious physiological adaptations.

The 230 families and 1640 genera* of Gastropoda form a material too rich for any tidy arrangement. Few main evolutionary lines with side-branches can be picked out. The picture is rather one of bushes branching from the base; with new shoots springing from each subsidiary stock, as the appearance of new characters provides preadaptations for still further evolutionary pathways. The classification given in the Table (Appendix) largely follows Thiele (1931),[15] with modifications introduced from Odhner's arrangement of the opisthobranchs.[145]

In reviewing the various systems in earlier chapters we have had a good deal to say about prosobranch evolution. We shall devote this chapter to certain aspects of the Gastropoda not yet treated, namely land and freshwater evolution, the radiations of the opisthobranchs, and the evolution of parasitism.

LAND AND FRESHWATER GASTROPODA

The first requirement of a land mollusc is a mantle cavity that can be turned into a lung, and the true Pulmonata are by no means the only Gastropoda that have left the water. The prosobranchs them-

*According to the conservative list of Thiele (1932).

selves have produced many lines of land operculate snails, and they must indeed have given rise to the pulmonates as well. To become terrestrial a gastropod must also have possessed internal fertilization and devices for storing the sperms and secreting egg capsules. This rules out most of the Archaeogastropoda, but as soon as these requirements were met, first in the Neritacea, land evolution became very persistent. Right through the Mesogastropoda, at least in those that had a reasonably unspecialized microphagous diet, every major group has had its terrestrial offshoots. Once on land, the diet could vary, even becoming carnivorous. The shell could be lost, and the respiratory arrangements altered. But the forms that made the original crossing to land were those that had not already become too committed to any specialized marine habit.[110] [135]

The most primitive true pulmonates we know are the South American family Chilinidae and the very widespread Ellobiidae,[137] represented in Britain by *Ovatella*, *Leucophytia* and *Carychium*. *Ovatella myosotis* lives in salt marshes, *Carychium minimum* on land and *Leucophytia bidentata* is secondarily intertidal. The Ellobiidae are not found fossil till the Jurassic, but preservation of land pulmonate remains was probably hazardous, and many technical points link this family with the prosobranchs and the earliest opisthobranchs. We must think of the Opisthobranchia and Pulmonata —widely different as they were soon to become—as having struck out originally from very similar ancestors, probably before the Carboniferous.

The headquarters of modern Ellobiidae are salt marshes and estuarine mudflats, and the largest species live in the tropical Indo-Pacific. Waters of muddy estuaries are often turbid and poor in oxygen, and it may have been much easier for molluscs to breathe air with a lung by rising to the surface than to obtain oxygen from the water by a gill. The original lung was probably a preadaptation in aquatic ancestors that made later land life possible. Other early air-breathing groups such as the Dipnoi and the Amphibia may have acquired their lungs in similar habitats in the same way. The ellobiids themselves are rather unprogressive.[135] There are only three fully terrestrial genera: *Pythia*, which lives in tropical coastal forests in Australia and Malaya, and *Carychium* and *Zospeum* in the Northern Hemisphere. *Carychium minimum* is very minute, and a member of

the litter fauna of beech forests and other damp places. It can survive submersion and probably always lives in a saturated atmosphere, tied—like terrestrial copepods and ostracods—to a narrow
sub-aquatic micro-climate. The related genus *Zospeum* is very little
known: *Z. spelaeum* is blind, and burrows in limestone soil in the
Karst District of Yugoslavia.

Most terrestrial molluscs have early relationships with estuarine
or freshwater species, and they may share similar adaptations, especially in respiration and reproduction. Carter[46] has suggested that
freshwater life may lead to preadaptations making the transition to
the land easier than by a direct path from the sea. Thus, lack of
oxygen in estuarine waters may first lead to aerial respiration. Many
tropical prosobranchs living in stagnant inland waters, such as *Pila*
and *Ampullarius* (=*Pomacea*), have the mantle cavity partitioned
into both a gill chamber and a lung. Air-breathing in aquatic snails
in turn allows aestivation in response to occasional drought. This
leads to further adaptations against desiccation, and a fully amphibious habit develops. With this come changes in the mode of excretion (p. 116), leading finally to a complete terrestrial life. On the
other hand, cases of direct evolution from the sea to the land are
rather few. A near approach is the sub-genus of high tidal periwinkles, *Melaraphe*. The British *Littorina* (*Melaraphe*) *neritoides* attaches by dry mucus to sun-baked rocks above high water spring
tide. It grazes on sparse algae and lichens when the rock is wet and
is very responsive to splash. After five months' drought it can emerge
from the shell in two or three minutes on return to water. *Melaraphe*
is, however, tied to the shore by a free-swimming veliger stage, and
this line of evolution seems to have led no further.

A flourishing group of land and freshwater prosobranchs is the
Neritacea, the highest of the Archaeogastropoda and the only ones
with a special genital duct. *Nerita* itself is an amphibious high-tidal
genus. *Theodoxus* (=*Neritina*) lives in gently running fresh water. It
has given rise to a series of snails living in fast streams where the shell
has become progressively flattened and elongate: in *Navicella*, for
example, we have a freshwater slipper limpet, retaining a functionless operculum upon the upper surface of the foot. On the other
hand, *Neritodryas*, of the East Indies, is a neritinid that has become
almost terrestrial.

The next family, the Helicinidae, are entirely terrestrial Neritacea, and are equipped with a pallial lung. There are twenty-six genera, twelve of which live in the West Indies and South and Central America.[2, 110] The East Indies and Malaya are a second headquarters of this family. These snails live in damp places, in tropical forests, in leaf-sheaths, at the bases of epiphytes and in ground litter, and have become very diversified. *Proserpina*, evolving from *Helicina*, has lost the operculum altogether, developing like many pulmonates a series of ridges and lamellae guarding the aperture. Its shell is smooth and polished, partly enveloped by the mantle. And to underline the truth that evolution to the land is seldom one-way, we find in the genus *Smaragdia* a terrestrial neritinid that has gone back to marine life.

The land operculate family Cyclophoridae with sixty-seven genera has arisen from the most primitive stock of the Mesogastro, poda, the Archaeotaenioglossa. They are rather small, trochoid-conical or discoidal snails, living in tropical and subtropical forests like the land Neritacea. As we have seen (p. 46), the shells of some genera (*Opisthostoma* and the tubed land operculates) may evolve in very characteristic ways. The freshwater representatives of these snails are large and well known. They include the amphibious apple-snails, *Ampullarius*, of South America and *Pila* of India and S.E. Asia. A related family is the Viviparidae, represented in slow-running muddy streams in Britain by two species. *Viviparus viviparus* is a ctenidial ciliary feeder.[54]

From near the periwinkles (Littorinacea) has arisen a further series of land snails. The Pomatiasidae, with twenty-six genera, has geographical headquarters in tropical forests of the E. and W. Indies, but has one British representative, *Pomatias elegans*, burrowing in calcareous soils. Our only other land operculate belongs to a second family, the Acmidae; *Acme fusca* is minute and long-spired like *Carychium* and lives under logs and litter in beech woods.[55A]

The Valvatidae are a small and isolated family, derived at about the same level, and living in slowly running fresh water. We have three British species with small conical to trochoid shells. Uniquely among Mesogastropoda, *Valvata* has a bipectinate ctenidium, projecting freely from the mantle cavity.[49A]

Of the next super-family, the Rissoacea, the Rissoidae are marine, with numerous genera and species, having a small crystal-line style and grazing on algae in tide pools. Further up the shore, in salt swamps, occurs a small rissoid snail *Assiminea*; while in fresh waters in almost every part of the world occur members of the Hydro-biidae, a most numerous family with fifty-eight genera. Most are completely aquatic and like the British *Hydrobia* and *Bithynia* pos-sess a gill.[121A] A few, such as *Geomelania* in the West Indies, are land-dwellers in tropical forests.

Land operculates—according to Winckworth—account for some 4000 species of snails, as compared with more than 15,000 for land pulmonates. Operculates are poorly represented in Europe, most of Asia, N. America and Africa. They come into their own in Central America, the Antilles, the West Indies, and also S.E. Asia and the East Indies. In the island of Jamaica they in fact outstrip the pul-monates in numbers. Russell Hunter[110] gives for Jamaica the ap-proximate figures:

Land Operculates (species)		Pulmonates
Helicinidae	120	
Cyclophoridae	30–36	approx. 215 spp.
Pomatiasidae	60	
Hydrobiidae	20–25	
Total	230–241	

The super-family Cerithiacea is represented in Britain by such thoroughly marine genera as *Cerithiopsis* and *Turritella*, all with elongate shells. In subtropical shores many species of *Cerithium* live on estuarine mud between tides, and the family Potamididae is as a whole amphibious, browsing and trailing long shells on delta muds in Malaya and N. Australia. *Telescopium, Pyrazus, Terebralia* and some species of *Potamides* are—like the Ellobiidae—almost ter-restrial and replace the gill by a pallial lung. The freshwater Ceri-thiacea belong to the large family Melaniidae, with thirty-nine genera (none British), which show a most interesting evolution. They are richest and most spectacular in Lake Tanganyika, an inland sea where low selection pressure has made possible a fauna of eighty-four species of snails. Of these, seventy-two are prosobranchs and sixty-six are endemic; the Melaniidae include fifty-eight of them. Their shells are variously shaped and ornamented, resembling marine genera in solidity and sculpture. Gunther, and later Moore,[127] regarded these Tanganyika snails as a relic of a halolimnic fauna, originally marine and surviving in a cut-off arm of the Jurassic Indian Ocean. Pelseneer clearly disproved this, and showed them to form an adaptive radiation of a single melaniid stock, and Yonge has later reviewed their adaptations.[206] Though so varied in shell form, all species are herbivores or deposit feeders with a crystalline style. Some genera, such as *Typhobia*, *Bathanalia* and *Bythoceras*, live at a depth of 100 fathoms on mud. *Typhobia* bears long spines like a muricid. *Tanganyicia* and *Nassopsis* are littoral genera, living on rocks where the surf breaks. *Spekia* and *Tanganyicia* are smooth and naticoid, *Chytra* and *Limnotrochus* are of trochoid shape, and *Paramelania* and *Nassopsis* are spindle-shaped, like a marine nassid.

Land prosobranchs live in a favoured environment of high temperature and high humidity. Outside these conditions operculates are not found very widely. The true Pulmonata, however, have had a more spectacular evolution and enjoy a much fuller terrestrial life. After the arthropods they are perhaps the most widely speciating and successful of land invertebrates. If pulmonates lack the structural variety shown by opisthobranchs, this is because they have made a much more subtle use of physiological adaptations. The Helicacea and the Limacidae are at once the most familiar pulmonates in this country, and the most specialized and progressive. The Helicacea are generally accounted the 'highest' group of pulmonates. The distinguishing feature of terrestrial pulmonates (order Stylommatophora) is the mounting of the eyes at the tips of inversible tentacles. In the aquatic order Basommatophora, on the other hand, they lie at the tentacle base as in prosobranchs. The family Ellobiidae are classed at the foot of the Basommatophora, and from snails at least comparable with these it is likely that both orders of pulmonates arose. Land pulmonates belonging to the primitive Endodontidae are however known from the Carboniferous, long before ellobiid fossils first appear. The order Stylommatophora is a huge assemblage, running to fourteen super-families and some 600 genera. The order Basommatophora is much smaller, with forty-eight genera grouped into four super-families.

In land evolution the water problem was probably the first and greatest. The smallest and earliest Stylommatophora are restricted like operculates to habitats where the atmosphere is moist. Most Endodontidae and Zonitidae, for example, live in leaf mould or litter, under dead bark, or in dark and damp places. The Succineidae are permanently amphibious and hardly able to resist desiccation. Many pulmonates, however, can tolerate intermittent dry seasons. British species of *Helicella* are found in summer, sealed by a dry mucus film and hanging from grass blades in the heat of the sun. Such African species as *Helix lactea* and *H. desertorum* congregate in thousands on dry scrub, in a mid-day temperature of 43°C. With rain they become active and creep out in marauding swarms. By burrowing in the soil where the temperature a few inches deep is many degrees cooler, various snails are able to aestivate in the dry season. The heartbeat is reduced and respiration greatly slowed down. Some species can enter a prolonged state of diapause or suspended activity when conditions are unfavourable. A famous example is a specimen of *H. desertorum* in the British Museum which after four years fixed to a tablet emerged and crawled about when taken into damp air. Comfort cites a six-year diapause in *Buliminus pallidior*, and even a claim of twenty-three years for *Oxystyla capax*.[52A]

Hibernation, aestivation and tolerance of dehydration are achievements of the higher Stylommatophora. *Helix*, *Arion* and *Limax*, for example, were found by Howes and Wells to show a regular hydration and dehydration cycle, marked by large and irregular fluctuations in weight, as in internal osmotic pressure. In dry weather they lose water and tend to aestivate when weight is low. Aestivation is thus tied up with the natural water cycle and can also be induced experimentally by desiccation.[105] Feeding and digestion are confined to the weight peaks and are incompatible with aestivation. The immediate mechanism of reactivation is not hydration, but a sensory stimulation effect: 'the raindrops knock at the door and the snail comes out. Hydration follows after, when it has eaten and drunk' (Wells).[191] Unlike most terrestrial animals, slugs have no structural protection against desiccation and show a probably unique range of fluctuation in water content. Thus *Limax variegatus* was found to lose by evaporation 2·4% of its initial weight per hour (58% in twenty-four hours) while still; when actively crawling it lost by mucus secretion and evaporation 16% in one hour! This is normally replenished by feeding and drinking. Helicidae can conserve water by retiring into the shell and forming an epiphragm; when active they expend water as rapidly as slugs.

Arion and *Limax* have a diurnal cycle: their activity reaches a maximum at night, being stimulated, below 21°C., by falling temperatures. Above this point activity rises with temperature, enabling a more rapid moving away from harmful or lethal temperatures.[59]

Uricotely (p. 116) is another adaptation to conserve water. Uric acid can also be stored in the eggs, though this is little evidence that snail eggs are truly impermeable or 'cleidoic' as in reptiles and birds. They may lose by evaporation 40% of their water, a fowl's egg only 15%. Some snails however develop normally after a loss of as much as 85% (Needham). Safety is secured partly by indifference to desiccation, partly by behavioural adaptations such as burying the eggs or laying them in the shade.[143]

The sea is never lacking in calcium, but many land habitats may be so. Land gastropods have a calcium store in the digestive gland upon which they draw for shell-building. Their shells are never as massive as marine ones, and in most pulmonate groups we find evolutionary series leading to complete loss of the shell. Thus—in the Zonitidae—we have a progressive lightening of the shell in the series *Zonitoides*, *Retinella*, *Oxychilus* and *Vitrea*. In the neighbouring family Vitrinidae, the shell is extremely thin and fragile, sometimes overgrown by the mantle, and evolution leads on to the slugs of the family Limacidae (*Limax*, *Agriolimax* and *Milax*). By a parallel trend, the slugs of the Arionidae are derived from primitive endodontid pulmonates. Tolerance of water loss and economy in calcium are both preadaptations to the slug habit, and we have seen as well (p. 43) the mechanical advantages of the tapered and compressible body.

Of his ninety-five British Stylommatophora, Boycott lists twenty snails as obligate calciphiles, and a further sixteen as strongly preferring calcareous soils. Only one species—*Zonitoides excavatus*—is

F*

an obligate calcifuge, restricted to acid heaths and woodlands. In the fifty-eight indifferent species are included all the slugs and only one snail with a substantial shell. In analysing habits, twelve species were found to be obligate hygrophiles, thirteen to be xerophiles, eleven—including eight slugs—anthropophiles near human cultivation, the remainder preferring woodlands.[38]

There are, however, few land habitats where some land pulmonates have not spread. There are numerous desert xerophiles, and several burrowing forms, for example in Britain, *Caecilioides acicula* and the testacellid slugs. Like the land operculates, the Pulmonata are most diverse and of largest size in the hot, moist forests of the tropics, with a rich food supply and high metabolic rate all the year round. Our most characteristic European families are the Helicidae, Limacidae, Arionidae and Clausiliidae; and every warmer region has its recognizable stamp: Africa with its giant Achatinas, South America with large and highly coloured snails more numerous than anywhere else, including herbivorous *Bulimulus* and *Bulimus*, and carnivorous *Glandina* and *Streptaxis*. In Malaya, China, the E. Indies and N. Australia the tropical Helicidae have their headquarters. A peculiar region is New Zealand, with its large fauna of primitive endodontids, large species of carnivorous *Paryphanta* and lack of helicids. Hawaii is the centre of the Achatinellacea, and in the Pacific are also centred the bulimulids, *Partula* in the Polynesian area and *Placostylus* on the islands of Melanesia.[2]

Some fine accounts of the ecology and habits of British pulmonates are to be found in the works of Boycott,[38, 39] Quick,[169] Stratton[182] and Ellis,[3] and in the detailed treatise by Taylor.[14]

EVOLUTION IN THE OPISTHOBRANCHIA

Thiele has recognized some sixty-nine families of opisthobranchs, yet this is a smaller group than either the prosobranchs or pulmonates. Opisthobranchs are the most typically marine of gastropods, and the sacoglossans of tide-pools, such as *Actaeonia*, or of salt marshes, as *Limapontia*, are almost the only high tidal representatives. In evolutionary enterprise, however, the opisthobranchs rank first among the Gastropoda: they are a living museum of adaptive morphology, nearly every family having some distinctive pattern to show. Like the pulmonates, the opisthobranchs must have early arisen from a prosobranch stock and the evolution of shelled opisthobranchs was well under way by the end of the Carboniferous. A primitive shelled form like *Actaeon*[87] has much in common with both prosobranchs and early pulmonates, but thereafter the three classes become widely different.

We have already seen the way the opisthobranchs escaped from torsion and dispensed with the spiral shell; and how with the disappearance of torsion the mantle cavity was reduced and eventually lost, along with the ctenidial gill. With the slug-like body, the way was set for a rich evolution of new forms, both bottom-dwelling and swimming. The loss of the shell and gill is the basis of the old division into 'tectibranchs' and 'nudibranchs'. This unfortunately cuts across several natural series; the opisthobranchs cleave rather into a number of radial lines, independent almost from the beginning. Odhner's standard classification uses as many as seven ordinal divisions,[145] and in adopting it here we shall go further, and regard the two series of 'pteropods' as distinct orders, Thecosomata and Gymnosomata.

	Odhner (1932)[145]				Pelseneer (1906)[9]
				1. 'Sub-order'	TECTIBRANCHIA
Order	1. CEPHALASPIDEA			'Tribe'	BULLOMORPHA
	2. ANASPIDEA	..	..	—	APLYSIOMORPHA
3. THECOSOMATA	.. .. ..		..	(with Bullomorpha)	
	PTEROPODA				
4. GYMNOSOMATA	.. .. ..		..	(with Aplysiomorpha)	
	5. NOTASPIDEA	..	..	PLEUROBRANCHOMORPHA	
				2. 'Sub-order'	NUDIBRANCHIA
	6. ACOCHLIDIACEA ..	..	..	—	
	7. SACOGLOSSA	..	..	ELYSIOMORPHA	
				(part with Bullomorpha)	
	8. NUDIBRANCHIA				
	Super-family				
	Dendronotacea	..	—	TRITONIOMORPHA	
	Doridacea	..	—	DORIDOMORPHA	
	Arminacea				
	Aeolidiacea..	..	—	AEOLIDIOMORPHA	

The Opisthobranchia are a good example of what has been styled 'programme evolution', with several independent groups each running through a series of broadly similar changes. At the lower reaches of several orders we find opisthobranchs with a spiral shell, a mantle cavity and a ctenidium, and detorsion only beginning. Thus in the Cephalaspidea we have the fully shelled *Actaeon*, an ideally primitive type, with an operculum, full torsion including a figure of 8 nerve loop, and generalized mantle cavity, gut and reproductive organs. It is matched among the Sacoglossa by shelled 'bulloid' forms of a similar kind, though without an operculum, such as *Cylindrobulla*, *Arthessa* and *Oxynoe*. The Anaspidea or aplysioids begin with the fully shelled bulloid-like *Akera*. The first of the Thecosomata—the Limacinidae—are spirally shelled, with an operculum, though all have lost the gill*; and in the Notaspidea or pleuro-branchoids the earliest members have a large external limpet-like shell. The various groups show different degrees of progress: the Cephalaspidea, the most primitive, seldom lose the shell, while in the 'highest'—the Nudibranchia—it is never present, and the naked body may become very specialized.

Some early steps in opisthobranch evolution are illustrated in the Cephalaspidea (bulloids) and the Anaspidea (aplysioids), the first group chiefly burrowers, the second living mainly on algae at the surface. The bulloids culminate in types such as *Philine* with a flattened wedge-like body, internal shell and strong calcified gizzard adapted for crushing the shelled prey.[77] The later aplysioids are larger and plump-bodied, with a vestigial internal shell and a gizzard employed for triturating and straining algal food. A remarkable side theme in both groups is swimming, best developed by *Akera* among aplysioids, which is very exactly matched by *Gasteropteron* among the bulloids.

The swimming habit is well exploited by the pteropods of the order Thecosomata, generally held to be derived from early cephalas-pids. These are of modest size, entirely pelagic and ciliary feeding, being an incredibly numerous component of the plankton. The least modified family, Limacinidae, well reveal how thecosomes may have been derived from neotenic bulloid larvae;[133] they have still a sinis-tral spiral shell and an operculum, and, apart from its long para-podial wings, the foot retains a wide sole. The Cavoliniidae have acquired bilateral symmetry, with the shell produced into a narrow

* *Peracle* is said to have a true ctenidium.

cone, or a flattened case, variously equipped with spines (p. 41). The Cymbuliidae show a different trend, with the development of a boat-shaped pseudoconcha; with them should be mentioned the curious genus *Peracle*, which has all the appearance of a *Limacina*, with its coiled shell and operculum, but is in fact ancestral to the Cymbuliidae.[11]

The other order of pteropods—the Gymnosomata—are some of the most advanced and isolated opisthobranchs. They are all active swimmers, lacking an adult shell, mantle cavity and ctenidium. The larval shell is fragile and thimble-shaped. The body is fusiform, sometimes with secondary 'adaptive gills', and like the heteropods the gymnosomes are rapacious carnivores. They feed mainly on thecosomes, with which they usually swarm, and specialize in large batteries of prehensile buccal tentacles, hooks and suckers. Their buccal armature gives them some of the advantages of both cephalopods and chaetognath worms.[11]

The Acochlidiacea are a small and little-known order of opisthobranchs, all minute and dwelling in coarse sand and silt. There are four genera, *Acochlidium*, *Hedylopsis*, *Microhedyle* and *Strubellia*. *Hedylopsis suecica* was described by Odhner from shell sand, along with Amphioxus, *Caecum* and *Polygordius*. It is about 2 mm. long, with the anterior end narrow and extensible for burrowing. The naked visceral sac projects well behind the foot and is covered with spicules. The animal is a deposit feeder, and is shy in habits, hiding in small empty shells, or rolling itself into a ball.[146]

The order Sacoglossa we have already characterized (p. 99) by their peculiar suctorial feeding, extracting the cell fluids of green algae by the piercing radula and force-pump pharynx.[71] Their diet commits them to a small size, never longer than about three-quarters of an inch. In the buccal organs the Sacoglossa stand apart from all the rest of the class, but in other characters they seem to follow the opisthobranch 'programme' fairly completely. There are seven families, of which the first two, the Arthessidae and the Oxynoidae, are primitively shelled and ctenidiate, broadly comparable to *Actaeon* or to prosobranchs. They develop, however, large swimming parapodia. With the Elysiacea we reach the nudibranch sacoglossans, with the dorsum usually coloured green, brown or black, from derivatives of chlorophyll in the food or from symbionts.

In the Hermaeidae (*Stiliger, Alderia* and *Hermaea*), living in tidal pools on algae, the digestive gland has ramified into dorsal appendages as in aeoliids. In the Caliphyllidae and the Elysiidae the body is flattened, with leaf-like lateral expansions; and the high tidal Limapontiidae (*Limapontia, Actaeonia* and *Cenia*) have a narrow body, smooth and slug-like.

The Notaspidea are rather generalized opisthobranchs, foreshadowing the true nudibranchs, to which they have almost certainly given rise. In *Pleurobranchus* the body is flat and slug-like, the mantle covering the dorsal surface and projecting as a skirt. From beneath it in front extend grooved rhinophores; on the right side it shelters a true ctenidium and an osphradium, though there is no mantle cavity. In *Tylodina*, the most primitive-looking of all Notaspidea,[145] there is a broad limpet shell, covering the animal entirely. In *Umbraculum* the external shell is circular and sits aloft like a chinaman's hat. Feeding is by microphagous grazing on sponges or deposits. The radula is very broad, with numerous, primitive, simple teeth. *Umbraculum* has the record number of 150,000 teeth.

The true Nudibranchia are grouped into four super-families. They are the dominant section of the opisthobranchs, and the most colourful and extravagant of all gastropods. Detorsion is complete, the shell, gill and mantle cavity are wholly lost, and rhinophores as in other opisthobranchs replace the head tentacles and osphradium, standing up club-like on the front of the dorsum. As we have already seen, each super-family carries its special stamp. Some trends are pushed ahead in different groups in a roughly parallel way, such as the reduction of the mantle edge and its replacement by various dorsal outgrowths; the adaptation of the naked surface for protective and respiratory functions; and the breaking up of the digestive gland and its deployment in the dorsal body wall. The reproductive organs become very complex, especially in the Doridacea; and the digestive organs become adapted for a grazing carnivorous life, and finally for suctorial habits.[74, 97]

In some ways the Dendronotacea, especially, for example, the Tritoniidae, are the most primitive nudibranchs; but this super-family has become variously specialized. They are technically distinguished by the rhinophore having a basal sleeve, formed from part of the mantle. A very common feature is the lavish outgrowths of the dorsal surface, such as branching gill tufts in *Tritonia*, or spoon-shaped processes in the Lomanotidae. In the Dendronotidae these processes are richly branched, and in the Dotonidae they resemble cerata, provided with branch tubercles arranged in rings. Among the swimming Dendronotacea are both the large-cowled, heavy-bodied Tethyidae[27] reaching twelve inches long (p. 40) and the delicate pelagic Phyllirhoidae.

The hall-mark of the Aeolidiacea is the habit of feeding on coelenterates and storing their nematocysts in cnidosacs in the cerata. With this means of protection they may develop very bright warning coloration. The cerata may be tapered or club-shaped, and develop various patterns of arrangement. *Coryphella* is a rather primitive British form with short cerata. *Facelina* and *Aeolidia* are other well-known genera. *Glaucus* and *Fiona*, which feed on siphonophores, are pelagic Aeolidiacea; and one family, the small worm-like Pseudovermidae, represent simplified aeoliids probably living on sand-dwelling interstitial hydroids.

In the super-family Doridacea the body is typically flat and the foot wide. The anus lies posteriorly at the middle of the upper surface, and around it is a circlet of pinnate secondary gills. The mantle is often provided with spicules, but the digestive gland does not ramify in it and cerata are never found. Early Doridacea, such as *Gnathodoris* and *Bathydoris*, are probably derived from tritoniids, and like them have jaws and a broad radula, being grazing carnivores or deposit scrapers. The Dorididae (*Archidoris*, *Jorunna*, etc.) have a similar broad radula, and graze on sponges. They have also a wide mantle brim. Higher families show two trends: the retreat of the mantle brim, with its replacement sometimes by tentacular processes, and the narrowing of the radula (sometimes its total loss) with the development of suctorial feeding (p. 98). In the Notodorididae the mantle is a good deal reduced, and in the Polyceridae (*Polycera* and *Triopa*) long marginal 'horns' develop. The Onchidorididae (*Onchidoris* and *Acanthodoris*) and the Goniodorididae (*Goniodoris* and *Ancula*) are suctorial feeders with buccal pumps (Fig. 10), and in the latter family the mantle brim is narrow or lacking.

The best-known British representative of the Arminacea is the yellow and black striped *Pleurophyllidia*, with secondary gill-lamellae

crowded beneath the mantle skirt. The buccal mass has no radula
and feeding is entirely suctorial. This is a mixed group, classed
together from technical anatomical features not at once obvious;
Janolus—another British genus—has an aeoliid appearance, with a
dorsal covering of cerata.[145]

PARASITIC GASTROPODA

Most of those gastropods that have become parasitic have been
generally placed in the prosobranch order Mesogastropoda. They
show two very different types of habit: some are ectoparasites with
a normally shaped body and a long spiral shell, others have adopted
a more permanent attachment to the host, which may culminate in
complete endoparasitism, with the normal molluscan characters
quite discarded. The most advanced members of this group are even
more simplified than tapeworms. It is only by their veliger larva, with
a spirally coiled horny shell, that we can recognize them as molluscs
at all.[18, 19]

   To the first group belong two main families, the Eulimidae[85] and
the Pyramidellidae.[86] The eulimids are ectoparasites of echinoderms.
The shell is usually smooth and highly glazed, and sometimes—as in
the British *Balcis devians* (Fig. 19A), a parasite on *Antedon bifida*—
the tip of the spire slants a little to one side. The Pyramidellidae, like
the Eulimidae, are generally tiny, seldom more than two-thirds of
an inch in length, with slender shells, often ribbed or strongly sculptured. They associate chiefly with bivalve molluscs, sedentary worms
and coelenterates, crawling over or hanging by the proboscis from
the soft body of the host. They insert the slender proboscis into the
body wall, sucking blood or tissue fluids—in *Turbonilla interrupta*,
for example, from the mantle edge of bivalves, in *Turbonilla elegan-
tissima* from the blood gills of cirratulid worms (p. 93). Both eulimids and pyramidellids are fairly host-specific. Though usually overlooked by collectors they can often be taken plentifully by careful
searching in the neighbourhood of the known host. Fretter and
Graham have added much to our knowledge of British species;
the following is a list of some pyramidellid parasites and their
hosts:[97]

Odostomia rissoides . . .	*Mytilus edulis*	
O. scalaris	*M. edulis*	
O. lukisii, O. unidentata, O. plicata .	*Pomatoceros triqueter*	
O. eulimoides	*Pectinidae*	
O. trifida	*Mya arenaria*	
Chrysallida spiralis . . .	*Sabellaria spinulosa*	
C. obtusa	*Ostrea edulis*	
Turbonilla interrupta . . .	*Ostrea, Pecten, Venus*	
T. elegantissima	*Cirratulus, Audouinia,*	
	Amphitrite	
T. jeffreysi	*Halecium* and other	
	hydroids	
Angustispira spengeli (Indo-Pacific) .	*Meleagrina*	

Both these families were until recently placed in the mesogastropod super-family Aglossa, but, as we have seen (p. 93), there are fundamental differences in their feeding organs. The Pyramidellidae have chitinous jaws exquisitely adapted as piercing stylets, while the Eulimidae have an unarmed proboscis, evidently softening the host tissues by secreting enzymes. The Eulimidae—and perhaps indirectly the Pyramidellidae—are descended from the less modified family Aclididae, with long-spired shells but only moderately long proboscis and normal jaws and radula.

Fretter and Graham believe that the pyramidellids are not prosobranchs at all, but opisthobranchs specialized at an early level. Though the external structure gives little hint of it, there is good evidence for this view. The Pyramidellidae appear geologically at about the same time as the Actaeonidae (Carboniferous) and much earlier than most mesogastropods. They show many quite circumstantial resemblances to opisthobranchs, of a kind that are unlikely to be adaptive, and can thus be more reliably used as taxonomic features. As in early opisthobranchs and pulmonates as well, the larval shell is at first sinistrally coiled, later reversed to dextral. The shell aperture, the tentacles and the structure of the hermaphrodite genital system and of the gut point to opisthobranch connections. The same holds good—as was found recently—for cytological details of the sperm. If, in spite of first appearances, we are to rank the pyramidellids with opisthobranchs, we shall need a separate order, quite distinctive from bullomorphs and showing some likenesses to prosobranchs. At this point in the classification, the three sub-classes Prosobranchia, Opisthobranchia and Pulmonata undoubtedly draw very close together.[135]

In the ectoparasite *Thyca* (Fig. 19D), which lives permanently attached in the ambulacral grooves of starfish, the shell is depressed and cap-shaped, the foot reduced, and the proboscis, with neither radula nor jaws, is permanently plunged through the integument of the host. *Thyca* is generally classed with the Capulidae. From here, or from Eulimidae, may have arisen the next family—Stiliferidae—which are still more intimate parasites of echinoderms. The first genus, *Mucronalia* (Fig. 19C), has a long spiral shell like the euli-

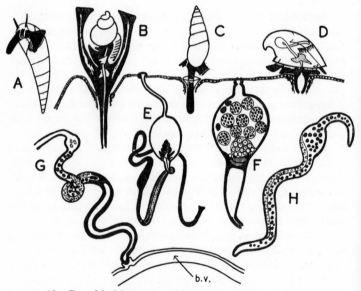

FIG. 19.   Parasitic Mesogastropoda, grouped to show position in relation to their various hosts

Suctorial ectoparasites: A *Balcis* (Eulimidae), B *Stilifer*, C *Mucronalia*, D *Thyca*.
Endoparasites: E *Gasterosiphon*, F *Entocolax*, G *Entoconcha*, H *Enderoxenos* (mature adult free in body cavity). *b.v.* blood vessel of host.

mids, a vestigial foot with a small operculum, and a proboscis striking deeply into the host—urchin, brittle star, starfish or holothurian. At the base of the proboscis is a fleshy frill, which in *Stilifer*
(Fig. 19B) is destined to grow up round the spiral body of the animal
to form an enclosing sac, the *pseudopallium*. The parasite now sinks
deeper into the host (a starfish or urchin) and the flask-shaped pseudopallium opens by an external pore through which respiratory
water is pumped. In the pseudopallial cavity lies the spiral body with
its horny shell. *Gasterosiphon* (Fig. 19E) is completely internal. Its
swollen pseudopallium still conceals a small visceral mass and communicates by a narrow siphon with the world outside. Most of its
length—about five inches—consists essentially of a tubular proboscis lying freely in the body cavity of a holothurian.

The family Entoconchidae, endoparasites of holothurians, has
evolved further still. The first genus, *Entocolax* (Fig. 19F), still possesses a dilated pseudopallium opening by a siphon through the
body wall of the host. Within it lodge several tiny cellular spheres,
which are the dwarf males, consisting of little more than a testis.
The visceral mass of the female is reduced to an ovary and short
oviduct, the rest of the body being a long proboscis containing the
simplified gut. *Entoconcha* (Fig. 19G) is a worm-like creature three
or four inches long, fixed by its proboscis mouth to the ventral blood
vessel of its host. Most of its length is occupied by a tubular cavity
(probably a pseudopallium in origin) containing the eggs, and in a
slight terminal swelling a cluster of fifteen to twenty dwarf males.
Enteroxenos (Fig. 19H) reaches a final simplicity. It is a pale white
worm up to six inches long, attached to the gut of *Stichopus* when
young, afterwards free in the coelom. The body cavity is a spacious
uterus filled with developing eggs, and there is neither mouth nor
gut, food being freely absorbed through the body wall.

There are two little-known genera of parasitic mesogastropods placed
by some near the Lamellariidae: *Ctenosculum* living on the arms of the
starfish *Brisinga*, where it produces a kind of gall, and *Asterophila* living
immersed in the arm tissues of *Pedicellaster*. Each has a globular body,
with vestiges of gastropod organization, enclosed in a pseudopallial
capsule. In addition there is *Paedophoropus* living in the Polian vesicles
and respiratory tree of holothurians. The proboscis is very enlarged and
the female has a dilated brood sac formed by the foot (*see* Caullery
(1952)).[19]

X

THE LAMELLIBRANCHIA AND THEIR CLASSIFICATION

THOUGH the bivalves are wonderfully diverse in form and habit, their basic pattern is unmistakable. No lamellibranch has a head, buccal mass or radula. In nearly all of them the mantle encloses the whole body, and is itself covered by a two-piece shell. The role of food-catching has passed from the head to the gill, and the main sense organs have moved to the edge of the mantle. In higher forms the mantle cavity may be closed to the world outside, except for the siphons and the foot-gape, and the animal burrows deeply into the substrate. Great emphasis is placed on mucus and cilia in the life of bivalves, and the pallial organs and the stomach are especially elaborate. The chief muscular organs—besides the foot—are the all-important shell adductors.

Of the first group of lamellibranchs, the Protobranchia, only a few living genera remain, all—as we have seen—rather specialized. The Nuculidae and Malletiidae for example feed on surface deposits by means of peculiar palp proboscides (p. 77). *Malletia* and *Yoldia* have highly enlarged pumping ctenidia. The Solenomyidae, with their long, tubular, mainly periostracal shell, have developed a power of darting and swimming with the piston-like foot.[209] But in spite of these peculiarities, which the most primitive ancestors of lamelli-branchs could not have possessed, palaeontology and comparative morphology agree in pointing to the protobranch bivalves as the forerunners of all the rest. The Nuculidae already existed in the Silurian and related shells are found in the Cambrian.[10] In living forms the ctenidia, arrangement of the mantle cavity, and structure of the gut and reproductive organs, have an indelible primitive stamp. In all their characters—whether primitive or specialized—

180

protobranchs stand clearly apart from other bivalves; in many ways they deserve to be separated into their own sub-class.

Above the Protobranchia we run into difficulties in classification. With such a constant basic structure we shall expect to find much parallel evolution in lamellibranchs, and there are three different types of character of which we must take account. First, there are 'adaptive' characters, which are immediate modifications for a particular mode of life, and thus dangerous to use in classification. Secondly, there are 'progressive' characters, those which usually show a definite trend of advance, often running parallel through several unrelated groups; and thirdly, 'conservative' characters— those that persist unchanged or stable over long periods. It is the last that will be most useful in showing real affinities.[128]

In the last half century there have been two main bases of classification of lamellibranchs, employing either gills or the hinge characters, neither by themselves fully satisfactory. Pelseneer's system (1889)[159] attached particular importance to the condition of the gills, whether 'protobranch', 'filibranch', 'pseudolamellibranch', 'eulamellibranch' or 'septibranch'. To lay stress on these characters Pelseneer made them the basis of his five orders. In 1906[9] he discarded the order Pseudolamellibranchia, distributing some families to the Filibranchia, others to the Eulamellibranchia. In 1911 he revived this order. He failed to realize that the condition of the gill is a progressive character, passing through successive stages of evolution in several parallel lines. It leads to a 'horizontal' classification rather than a natural or 'vertical' grouping.

European workers such as Thiele (1935)[15] and American and recent British conchologists, such as Winckworth[196] in his British List, have in part replaced Pelseneer's system by drawing on various classifications that use the structure of the hinge, such as that of Cossmann (1914) and Dall (1895 and 1916).[60] This has the advantage of keeping the palaeontologist in harmony with the zoologist. Its great weakness is in the neglect of soft parts: for example, the obviously distinct order of protobranchs is placed in one group with some or all of the filibranchs. Most single-based systems break under strain at some points; what is needed is a more liberal classification blending evidence from as many reliable sources as possible.[112]

One such arrangement was attempted by the French conchologist Douvillé, who in 1912 sketched a provisional classification without proposing any formal names.[63] His work was largely overlooked until Morley Davies[128] brought it to notice again in 1932. Douvillé's division of lamellibranchs strikes an ecological note: he recognizes three broadly parallel streams based on predominantly different modes of life. At the same time he aspires to a truly phyletic arrangement, being on the watch for pitfalls due to convergent evolution, and keeping ecology subordinate to structure. In seeking to adapt Douvillé's system for these pages I have had in mind the want of any other system quite so natural, and have tried to harmonize his groupings as far as possible with names familiar from the standard work of Thiele.

Douvillé's three major lineages begin with separate stocks of prosobranchs, perhaps only distantly related among themselves or to any protobranchs living today. Each line is in turn like a many-stranded rope, the strands in general advancing together, but spreading out from time to time in adaptive radiations. The first, or so-called *normal branch*, must have begun with free-moving bivalves, dwelling on the surface or actively burrowing. They had rather solid, white porcellanous shells, perhaps not too unlike a modern *Nucula*. They gave rise to most of the modern eulamellibranchs. Typical shell forms are those of the plump *Cardium, Venus* or *Astarte*, but—as in the Tellinacea—the shell may become light and streamlined for rapid burrowing.

The second lineage is the *sessile branch*, neither free on the surface nor burrowing, but attached to the ground by a byssus. This branch is derivable from no living prosobranchs and incorporates most of Pelseneer's Filibranchia and Pseudolamellibranchia. The structure of the animal is far more modified than in the normal branch, and the shells are rather thin and often highly pigmented. The nacreous as well as the prismatic layer is highly developed. Douvillé's third series is the *deep-burrowing branch*. This has produced modern bivalves with long fused siphons, a closed mantle cavity and a gaping shell with a poorly developed hinge. Such forms are *Panopea* and *Mya*, and the piddocks which burrow into firm substrates. Protobranchs such as the burrowing *Solenomya* were suggested as a starting point, but this is very problematical, and to identify a definite ancestor is not really important. Further work will show whether Douvillé's branches form even the foundation of natural groups: a great deal of evidence seems at present to point in their favour.

I. THE SESSILE BRANCH OF LAMELLIBRANCHS
Orders: Taxodonta and Anisomyaria

These, after the protobranchs, are the oldest bivalves. They became fashionable in the middle and later Palaeozoic and early Mesozoic, when most of the living families were established. The majority are filibranchs but *Ostrea* and *Lima* develop pseudolamellibranch gills (*see* p. 78). They vary greatly in appearance but all agree in the widely open mantle and lack of siphons, the importance at some stage at least of the byssus (except in the oysters), and the tendency to asymmetry between the anterior and posterior parts of the body. In a detailed study Jackson (1890)[113] united the 'Aviculidae and their allies' with the Arcidae; and Douvillé included here the Mytilidae, which Atkins[32]—from the ciliation of the gills—would leave apart. From Graham's study of the stomach there appears a general similarity in all the members of Douvillé's sessile branch. We may regard these forms as constituting a level of 'mesolamellibranchs' in contrast with the 'eulamellibranchs', which include Douvillé's normal and burrowing branches.

In all but the earliest of this series the primitive symmetry is greatly modified. The most ancient super-family is the Arcacea (noah's ark shells and their relatives), which may be placed alone in the order Taxodonta. These have *taxodont* dentition, a long row of uniform teeth as in *Nucula*. The two adductor muscles are equal and the anterior and posterior halves of the body approximately equally developed, as in the British *Glycymeris*, which has the rounded shape of a venus-shell. *Glycymeris* and *Limopsis* burrow shallowly but *Arca* (Fig. 20A) rests at the surface with the dorsal side uppermost, attached by a byssus springing from the whole edge of the foot.

In the remaining families (order Anisomyaria, if we may there include the Mytilidae), the sessile habit has caused profound changes.[215] With the mussels (Mytilidae) the byssus and foot have moved to the anterior end, restricting the anterior adductor muscle to a small size (the *heteromyarian* condition). In *Modiolus* and *Mytilus* (Fig. 20B) the animal is still attached upright to the substrate, and—especially in *Mytilus*—the anterior end is small and pointed, the posterior end broad and rounded, with a large posterior adductor. The Mytilidae show considerable adaptive radiation. The genus *Modiolaria* contains small nut-shaped bivalves, embedded in a nest of their own byssus threads or in ascidian tests. Two genera have become narrow and elongate, burrowing in rocks. *Botula* is attached by byssus threads within its burrow in soft non-calcareous rocks, the ridged shell valves abrading the rock by opening thrusts of the ligament. *Lithophaga*, the date mussel, bores by rotating the shell in calcareous rocks; the fused inner lobes of the mantle are glandular and appear to secrete an acid mucus.[218]

In more advanced Anisomyaria the shell usually lies upon its right side, becoming flattened, with the two valves no longer quite alike. The pearl oysters, Pteriidae (super-family Pteriacea), have a short byssus emerging by a deep notch in the right (lower) valve. The anterior adductor muscle has been lost, the foot is very small and functionless, and the whole anterior half of the animal is now of minor dimensions. The single posterior adductor muscle lies at the centre of the valves, in the *monomyarian* condition. The mantle cavity lies widely open and water enters around two-thirds or more of the rounded margins of the shell. The pearl oyster itself (*Pinctada*) (Fig. 20C) has almost circular valves, but with a long straight hinge. Later genera, such as the wing shells (*Pteria* or *Avicula*) (Fig. 20D) show a strong tendency to elongate along the hinge-line. In the Vulsellidae—by the same emphasis of the hinge—the exhalant point is carried posteriorly on a long salient, until in the hammer-oysters (*Malleus*) (Fig. 20E) the shell finally becomes T-shaped or hammer-like.

The fan shells, Pinnidae, also belong to the Pteriacea, but show a quite different trend of evolution Fig. 20F). They have long and wedge-shaped equal valves, and are unique in being embedded upright in the sand and secured there by a byssus. Each byssus thread is attached to a sand particle, and the whole structure gives great stability in a soft substrate. The fan shell is immobile and the foot and anterior end are greatly reduced. The posterior or uppermost part of the shell is broad and triangular, composed of horny con-chiolin, only thinly calcified. There is a wide mantle gape at the broad end, with thickened lips, and—as in other Pteriacea—there are efficient ciliary and mucous tracts for cleansing the mantle cavity of sediment. The greater part of the mantle in *Pinna* is free of attachment to the shell, and its edges can be deeply withdrawn and protected from injury by special pallial retractor muscles.[216]

Like the pearl oysters, the Pectinacea or scallops (Fig. 20G) lie upon the right side.[171] [215] Both valves may be concave and similar or the left one may be flat. Here, however, the valves have again become symmetrical about the hinge and beak. In the viscera distortion resulting from anterior fixation by the byssus remains, but the shell and mantle have been emancipated from the rest of the body, and—unlike the Pteriacea—have a new superficial symmetry.

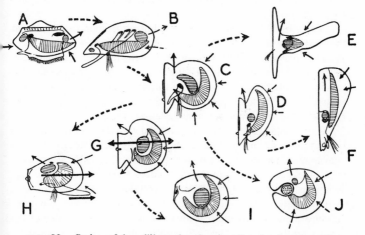

FIG. 20. Series of lamellibranchs showing the development of various monomyarian forms. (The arrangement is not strictly phyletic.) The small entire arrows show the direction of inhalant and exhalant pallial currents. Heavy arrows show the directions of swimming in *Pecten* and swimming and crawling in *Lima*. Each diagram shows the gill, the foot with byssus (where present), the adductor muscle (hatched) and the pedal muscle insertions (black).

A *Arca*, B *Mytilus*, C *Pinctada*, D *Avicula*, E *Malleus*, F *Pinna*, G *Pecten*, H *Lima*, I *Ostrea*, J *Anomia*.

(*After Yonge*)

An early representative such as *Chlamys varians* still shows a slight asymmetry, with a byssus as in *Pteria* passing through a notch in the right or lower valve, and the squared 'lugs' at either side of the hinge unequally developed. The exhalant current is expelled at these points, immediately to the sides of the narrow hinge. Incoming water can thus enter right round the rest of the circumference and flow straight through to the hinge side. Attachment by the byssus may soon be lost, as in *Hinnites* and *Spondylus*, and in *Plicatula*, in favour of direct cementation. Such forms lie in a deep, cup-shaped right valve. Though the mantle is widely open to sediment, the silt-ing up of this valve is prevented by the great development of the 'quick' part of the adductor muscle. The shell can be rapidly opened and closed and the sediment falling on the mantle edge so removed. In the Pectinacea the mantle edge carries a profusion of sense organs, with tactile tentacles sensitive to sediment and complex eyes (p. 152).

Pecten itself was never cemented, but on gaining freedom from the byssus developed the swimming habit (Fig. 21F). For this—as in *Chlamys opercularis* and still more so with the thin circular shell of the related genus *Amussium*—the body is admirably adapted. The 'quick' muscle forms a mechanism for clapping the valves, and the pallial margin with its light sense and velar curtain controlling the exit of water are important preadaptations for swimming.[171, 202]

The Limidae or file shells are classified with the Pectinacea. Some species such as *Lima excavata* are attached by the byssus from which they may spin a nest of dense threads. Others such as *L. hians* swim, though less efficiently than the Pectinidae. The direction of the foot is uniquely reversed (Fig. 20H); it protrudes between the rounded shell margins, so that the animal may crawl actively with the hinge hindmost. In this direction it also swims, taking a bite out of the water and then closing the shell with the mantle edges apposed ex-cept postero-dorsally where the exhalant current issues.[215] *L. hians* has long, brilliantly orange pallial tentacles; in some species the gills and mantle are scarlet and the tentacles white.

The most remarkably altered of all byssus-attached bivalves are the saddle oysters, Anomiacea (Fig. 20J). In *Anomia* and *Monia* the byssal notch seen in *Pteria* and *Chlamys* is now very deeply em-bayed in the right valve. The byssus threads coalesce into a calcified cable, which emerges near the centre of this thin lower valve. The upper valve is convex and moulded to the substrate, producing a strong bilateral asymmetry. The byssal retractor muscles are attached to the upper valve only, and serve, like the shell muscles of a limpet, to pull the animal down against the substrate. There is thus virtually only one functional valve, fitting close to the ground like a limpet shell. Since this is adducted by the byssal muscles, the true adductor is tiny and without function. The tropical saddle oyster, *Placuna*, has lost its byssus and lies freely on the ground. Uniquely it has turned over to lie on the concave left valve, whose upturned margins raise the edges of the mantle clear of sediment.

The oysters, Ostreacea, are also highly modified for sedentary life. The byssal stage is early abandoned, the spat becoming cemented by the right valve immediately on settling. The foot is lost entirely, and the gill has become crescentic, extending round a wide part of the mantle circumference. Adult oysters may lie attached to objects on muddy ground, as *Ostrea edulis*, or may be zone-forming on rocks, as *O. cucullata*. None of this group swim, but the 'quick muscle' is highly developed for expelling sediment (Fig. 20ı).

II. THE EULAMELLIBRANCHIA

i. *The 'normal branch' of lamellibranchs*
Orders: Heterodonta and Schizodonta

On the whole the lamellibranchs of the 'normal branch' have flourished later than the sessile forms, in the later Mesozoic, Tertiary and Recent times. A majority of species lie freely at or near the surface, or burrow actively in sand or mud. Although the normal branch has a number of sessile members, its name is a fair one in that most genera have avoided the extreme specializations due to attached life. Though in such a large group any general statement will oversimplify, their earliest habit is probably the shallow burrowing we have met with already in the cockles (Cardiacea) and the venus-shells (Veneracea).

An early group well represented in Britain is the Astartacea, also with a heavy, strongly sculptured shell, a widely open mantle and short siphons. The foot is sometimes very powerful, as in Cardiacea (p. 51) and Cyprinacea (with one British species, *Cyprina islandica*) and in the Isocardiacea. *Isocardia cor* has a large orbicular shell, heart-shaped in end view, with the umbones spirally coiled, and with short siphons.[155] The super-family Mactracea are better adapted for burrowing, having smooth light shells, moderately streamlined, the two siphons fused and the mantle lobes partly united. They may also, like the cockles, use the foot for leaping. A deeper burrowing group is the Lucinacea. A British example, *Loripes lucinalis*, has a rounded shell, laterally compressed, and uses the thin extensible foot to construct a separate mucus-lined exhalant tube.

The most adept burrowers are, however, the Tellinacea, where—as we have seen—the shell becomes thin, smooth and very narrow from side to side. The foot expands to a wide thin-edged blade and the separate siphons are very long. While most bivalves are suspension feeders by filtering off particles from the water current, the Tellinacea have become specialized for feeding on the surface deposits (p. 82).[212] Many of the Tellinidae and the Semelidae (e.g. *Scrobicularia*) have almost elliptic shell valves, but the group includes also the Donacidae, with wedge-shaped, triangular shells, and the Asaphidae, where the shell valves become wafer-thin, sometimes gaping and elongate. The British genera are *Gari*, containing the sunset shells, some of the most beautiful of bivalves, and the razor-shaped *Solecurtus*, which, with *Tagelus*, runs parallel with the razor-shells (Solenacea) of similar fast-burrowing habits.

All the above families are members of the order Heterodonta. The hinge teeth are well developed and important in classification, forming well-marked sets of cardinals and laterals (for details, *see* Piveteau[10]). We may consider now some of the more specialized offshoots which the heterodont lamellibranchs of the normal branch have produced.

First, in the super-family Erycinacea, are some bivalves of very small size. Their primitive habit is to nestle in crevices, as with *Lasaea rubra*, reaching to high water of spring tide, and *Kellya suborbicularis* at low tide. In some ways they recall nuculoids in habits, crawling freely on the surface, taking in their inhalant current by a special anterior siphon and expelling it behind. More advanced members of the Erycinacea show leanings to commensal and even parasitic life. The foot may reacquire a flattened sole and the shell becomes thin and transparent, gaping widely and partly enveloped by the mantle. Such bivalves typically frequent the burrows of marine invertebrates, such as crustaceans and particularly sand-dwelling echinoderms. There are a number of such commensal pairs in the British fauna, the bivalve always very specific to its chosen host. *Devonia perrieri* lives with the holothurian *Leptosynapta inhaerens*, *Mysella bidentata* with the sand-dwelling brittle star *Acrocnida brachiata*. *Montacuta substriata* is found in the neighbourhood of the heart urchin *Spatangus purpureus*, and *M. ferruginosa* with *Echinocardium cordatum*. All these appear to feed in the normal way, collecting food by the gill. They may temporarily attach to the host with the byssus, but the exact economy of these partnerships still needs careful study.[162]

The British *Lepton squamosum*, with its very compressed shell, lies against the wall of the burrow of the crustacean *Upogebia stellata*. A Japanese commensal, *Peregrinamor oshimae*, attaches beneath the body of another *Upogebia* species. Its ventral surface is drawn close to the host by byssus threads, and the shell is peculiarly flattened dorsoventrally, making it heart-shaped in dorsal view. The burrows of the Australian prawn *Axius plectorhynchus* harbour no fewer than six species of commensal bivalves. One of these, *Ephippodonta macdougalli*, keeps its valves permanently agape at 180°. It clings to the substrate by the fused mantle edges, which resemble the foot of a limpet but with a fissure for the true foot to emerge.

In *Chlamydoconcha* the mantle wholly surrounds the shell, leaving narrow siphons in front and behind, while *Entovalva* is parasitic —or perhaps inquiline—in the gut of synaptids. Unlike gastropod parasites it is not suctorial, appearing to absorb ready-digested food through the gill and mantle.

The true giants of the lamellibranchs are the clams of the family Tridacnidae, from the tropical Indo-Pacific coral reefs. These are a surface-dwelling offshoot of the Cardiacea or cockles and have become very specialized in their structure and nutrition. *Tridacna gigas* reaches three feet in length and may weigh 300 lb. *Tridacna fossor* embeds in coral fragments, while the smaller *Tridacna crocea* actively bores. The genus *Hippopus* differs in having no byssal gape. These clams live in the shallow waters of the reefs, and, like some of the Alcyonacea, owe their great success to augmenting their food supply by farming immense numbers of zooxanthellae, or unicellular symbiotic algae.[209A] As Yonge has shown, the symmetry of the shell and body is radically altered (Fig. 21G). In *Tridacna* a strong byssus emerges through a gape on the lower side of the shell valves which rests close against the ground. The dorsal and ventral aspects are very likely to be confused, since the umbones and hinge have migrated through a full 180° to lie on the ventral side close to the byssal gape. The up-facing open side with the interlocking toothed margins lies in fact—by reference to the

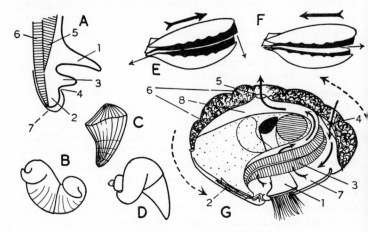

FIG. 21. Lamellibranchia

A Transverse section of mantle edge of a bivalve (from Yonge). 1) inner lobe, 2) outer lobe, 3) middle lobe, 4) secretory groove of periostracum, 5) inner layer of shell, 6) outer layer of shell, 7) periostracum.

Shells of Mesozoic *Chamacea*. B *Diceras*, c *Radiolites*, D *Caprina*, E, F *Pecten* in swimming posture, velum shown in black, E 'Forward' swimming by expulsion of water at hinge side, F 'Hinge-first' swimming by expelling water at free edge with velum raised, G Structure of *Tridacna*, showing migration of hinge and siphonal areas, by broken arrows. 1) foot with byssus, 2) hinge, 3) gill, 4) inhalant siphon, 5) exhalant siphon, 6) enlarged pigmented siphonal lips, 7) inhalant chamber of mantle cavity, 8) exhalant chamber. Adductor muscle hatched, pedal retractor muscle black.
(*After Yonge*)

viscera—at the dorsal aspect. The anterior adductor muscle has disappeared, and the siphons have migrated upwards from the posterior end to fill the whole dorsal gape. The siphons stay fully expanded in sunlit waters, and their lips are enlarged and fleshy, superficially pigmented with green, brown and yellow to form a screen protecting the symbiotic algae from too intense light. The algae lie in the deeper siphonal tissues, in blood sinus, enveloped by amoebocytes. Light for photosynthesis is focussed upon them from groups of hyaline organs acting as lenses, and derived from the well-developed siphonal eyes of the typical *Cardium*. The products of circulation become available by the digestion of the zooxanthellae within the amoebocytes. The kidneys are abnormally large, for getting rid of the waste products of this digestion, carried to them by amoebocytes. Notwithstanding this special source of food, the Tridacnidae retain typical gills, stomach and crystalline style, and normal ciliary feeding is obviously possible as well.[217]

The super-family Chamacea have adopted a permanently attached mode of life, cemented upright by the deeply conical right valve, to which the left valve, usually smaller, forms a lid. The Jurassic and Cretaceous representatives are extremely numerous, known chiefly from the large conical Rudistae, such as *Hippurites*. There is only one surviving genus, *Chama*, an oyster-like bivalve, with the foot greatly reduced, and a flat opercular valve. It shows a strong parallel with the gastropod *Hipponyx* (p. 32),[115] which has reached a similar end from very different beginnings. The most ancient Chamacea, the family Diceratidae of the Jurassic, had equal right and left valves, both spirally coiled like ram's horns. In the derivative form *Requiena* the free valve has become operculiform, while *Chama* has been derived in the same way from *Matheronia*. The rudistid family, Radiolitidae, was derived from the Caprinidae, with *Caprina* showing the free valve much larger than the fixed and spirally coiled. *Caprinula* shows an intermediate stage in which the fixed valve has much elongated. As in the fossil oysters, *Gryphaea*, orthogenesis seems to have been rife among the Chamacea, and a flourishing Cretaceous stock has left behind it only a single living form.[10]

Lamellibranchs have spread into lakes and rivers along several separate lines. These have radiated rather little in basic structure, but with geographical isolation have undergone great speciation. The Unionidae, the largest freshwater family, containing the familiar *Unio* and *Anodonta*, are important if only for containing eighty-five genera and some 1000 species, accounting for one-fifth of all living lamellibranchs! We have already referred to their peculiar life histories, with parasitic glochidia larvae. Their three sub-families are the Lampsilinae, with *Lampsilis* and other genera chiefly N. and C. American, the Anodontinae of Europe, America and E. Asia, and the Unioninae, mainly Asiatic and E. Indian though found also in America and Africa. A second family is the Mutelidae, with *Diplodon* and *Hyridella*, the freshwater mussels of the southern hemisphere. The small family Aetheriidae has three genera of specialized freshwater 'oysters' in the Amazon basin, tropical Africa and India. *Acostaea* is monomyarian, becoming cemented by the right valve, after which the posterior end alone continues to grow, the anterior end with the umbones remaining as a claw-like appendage.[215]

The above three families form the super-family Unionacea, belonging to the order Schizodonta. Classification is based on the hinge teeth, with two-limbed Λ-shaped teeth, arranged inside each other in a fan shape. In some Unionidae—such as *Anodonta*—they are lost; but they are well shown in the related Trigoniacea, a filibranch group chiefly found fossil,[10] but with a few living species in the Australian genus *Neotrigonia*.

The remaining freshwater lamellibranchs are chiefly heterodonts. Most successful—after the unionids—are the Sphaeriacea, with the two families Corbiculidae and Sphaeriidae. The world-wide genera *Sphaerium* and *Pisidium* are well represented in Britain, small colourless orbicular bivalves, usually less than half an inch long, found burrowing shallowly in nearly all types of freshwater habitat. They have short siphons, paired in *Sphaerium*, fused in *Pisidium*, and the mantle lobes almost unfused. The Cardiacea have established a freshwater line in *Adacna* and *Diadacna*, the cockles of the Caspian Sea. In *Dreissensia* we have a mussel from the Caspian Sea (allied by some to *Mytilus*) which has acclimatized itself in English rivers, and still possesses veliger larvae. The W. African *Egeria* is a river-dwelling donacid, *Gnathodon*, a brackish water mactrid of the Gulf of Mexico, *Glaucomya* and E. African freshwater razor shell and *Nausitoria* a freshwater Teredo of the Ganges.

ii. The 'deep-burrowing branch' of lamellibranchs
Orders: Adapedonta; (?) Anomalodesmata

The third division of Douvillé's arrangement is the *deep-burrowing branch*—not, as we have seen, that the normal branch has not produced innumerable burrowers; but in the present line the strongest evolutionary force has been to modify the shell for deep penetration, often with permanent sacrifice of mobility. The mantle is extensively fused, the hinge is always weak and the valves generally gape freely. In the first order, the Adapedonta, the hinge teeth are degenerate or unrepresented. The immobile habit is frequently obvious from the shell, which is thin and fragile with nothing of the streamlining or solidity of the Heterodonta.

Only in the super-family Solenacea do we find great mobility. Here the shell is long, light and razor-shaped (Fig. 6D). The siphons are rather short but the foot is an elongated plug that can be thrust downwards from the gape at the anterior end of the shell. The uniform cross section of a razor shell well adapts it to sliding through sand, and speed with depth of burrowing is the keynote of the Solenacea. In many ways they converge on the razor-shaped Tellinacea, such as *Psammosolen*, *Pharus* and *Solecurtus*, just as in *Petricola pholadiformis* we have an elongate venerid that has evolved parallel to the pholads.

In the Myacea the trend of evolution is quite different (Fig. 6E). The deep-burrowing clams *Panopea*, *Mya* and *Platyodon* have a very small foot, together with long, fused leathery siphons and a closed mantle cavity. Some species (*see* p. 52) can burrow in stiff mud by rocking the shell valves sideways to abrade the wall of the burrow. The Myacea show also considerable adaptive radiation. Adult *Mya* has a vestigial foot and is almost stationary, but *Platyodon cancellatus*, a Californian myid, continues throughout life to bore efficiently in hard clay. *Sphenia* and *Saxicava* have short siphons and nestle in shallow crevices. One small species of the American *Cryptomya* reaches with its siphons not to the surface, but into the deep burrows of the ghost shrimp, *Callianassa*. *Aloidis* is bilaterally asymmetrical with a larger right valve. It has returned to shallow burrowing and fixation with a single byssus thread.[210]

The main habit of the Myacea, that of deep and permanent burrowing, has been passed on to the super-family Adesmacea (p. 53). This consists of the Pholadidae or piddocks (Fig. 6H) (boring in hard rock or clay), and two families of wood-borers, the less-modified Xylophaginidae and the very specialized shipworms, Teredinidae (Fig. 6I). The ligament is much reduced in the Adesmacea, and the shell valves rock upon their hinge points in the transverse plane. The foot is used as an attachment disc whilst rotatory boring movements are made. Evolution culminates in the extraordinary modifications of the genus *Teredo*. The naked siphon dominates the whole morphology of the animal; the visceral mass is small and anterior, the shell being used only as an abrading tool.

The last of the lamellibranch series are those forming the order Anomalodesmata. They fit less well into Douvillé's 'burrowing branch' but, from the weakness or loss of their hinge teeth and the fusion of their mantle margins, may be suspected of having abandoned a former deep-burrowing habit. This group is still imperfectly understood, and may be found to be polyphyletic; its members agree however in being hermaphroditic and in having the outer demibranch reduced and upturned dorsally. As in *Aloidis* among the Myacea, the two shell valves may become unequal. Some species may lie recumbent on one side. In the Pandoridae and Myochamidae the valves show the asymmetrical *pleuroconch* condition, with a deeply convex right valve and a flatter left one.[28] *Pandora* and *Myodora* may burrow shallowly by inserting the shell horizontally or obliquely into the sand. The fragile valves of the burrowing family Laternulidae (*Cochlodesma*, *Laternula* and *Periploma*) are also unequal, the right being more convex. British *Cochlodesma praetenue* embeds in sand to a depth of three inches (Fig. 6B) and lies horizontally on one or other side. Its siphons are long and separate, making mucous tubes as in Thraciidae; the inhalant one alone reaches the surface, the exhalant opening into a blind horizontal gallery.[28A] The Lyonsiidae show a progression towards sessile life: *Lyonsia* lives freely at the surface, *Entodesma* attaches by its byssus in crevices, and the American *Mytilmeria* nestles deeply in ascidian tests, becoming spherical and heteromyarian.[213] The Thraciidae have returned to deep burrowing, and line their siphonal tubes with mucous secretion. The Australasian Chamostreidae have—like the Chamidae—become firmly cemented to the substrate by the deep right valve, the left forming a lid.

A strange offshoot is seen in the family Clavagellidae, the watering-pot shells, surely the least recognizable of all bivalves. As in *Teredo* the conjoined siphons are much the largest part of the animal and secrete a strong calcareous tube. *Clavagella*, which may reach three feet in length and two inches in diameter, is embedded but cannot actively burrow. The valves are functionless and excessively small, the left one in *Clavagella* and both in *Brechites* being fused to one side of the tube. *Brechites* is of smaller size and rests loose on the surface. Inhalant and exhalant currents both pass through the open posterior end. The anterior end, the place of the original pedal gape, is convex and perforated by small holes like the rose of a watering-pot. Of the evolution and adaptive significance of this family we yet know little.

The three genera *Cuspidaria*, *Cetoconcha* and *Poromya* are by Pelseneer given the status of a separate order, Septibranchia. They are evidently derived from surface-living Anomalodesmata. The septibranchs are little known at first hand, but are very beautifully specialized. As we have seen (p. 83), they are 'lamellibranchs without gills'. They replace these with a perforated muscular septum used for pumping water through the pallial cavity. In many ways the septibranchs are the most peculiar of the bivalves, retiring from a filter-feeding life to become scavengers or carnivores, ploughing through the plantless ooze at unlighted abyssal depths.[200]

Ecologically it cannot be said that the 'deep-burrowing branch' is a well-assorted group. Most of the Anomalodesmata do not burrow deeply and it is in respect of these that Douville's scheme is weakest. The Adapedonta and Anomalodesmata are both taxonomically advanced groups of eulamellibranchs, especially in their pallial fusion and the weakness or lack of the hinge. Further knowledge, particularly of the less familiar Anomalodesmata, will help to decide whether the two groups are fundamentally related. For a tidy classification, there is much to be said too for keeping the septibranchs as a distinct order.

XI

THE FIRST AND LAST CEPHALOPODS

THIS is the only class of molluscs as a whole pelagic. Its members are the largest, most active and most delicately specialized. Cephalopods are organized upon a more stereotyped pattern than gastropods or lamellibranchs; but this is a pattern of high success, for which advances in nervous co-ordination are supremely responsible. Stillmann Berry—speaking of the exquisite adjustment of modern cephalopods to their environment—cites their complex chromatophore systems, colour change and light organs; their interplaying systems of finely balanced musculature with few or no skeletal hard parts; the delicate balance between eye, sucker and chromatophore, or mantle arms and fins; and the innumerable types of hectocotylus and spermatophore, often involving most astonishing modifications in sexual behaviour.[36]

The great majority of cephalopods are now extinct, known only from the shells they have left in the rocks. The nautiloids ran unchallenged through the early Palaeozoic, the most active carnivores in the seas; and were then outstripped in numbers by the ammonoids which—with the belemnoids—continued abundant until the end of the Mesozoic. Very different methods are needed to study the living and the extinct cephalopods, and we must be content with a very partial understanding of the fossil forms. There is only one genus surviving that can tell us much about the way of life of Palaeozoic cephalopods: by good providence the living *Nautilus* has preserved a very ancient organization, and—after setting aside possible specializations and peculiar features—we still have in the three recent *Nautilus* species living fossils of enormous value.

Nautilus, as we have seen, is very unlike all other living cephalopods. It has a large, many-chambered external shell, and its funnel

196

is formed of two overlapping lobes. The tentacles are represented by numerous retractile filaments, with neither suckers nor hooks. The eye is of the simple pin-hole camera type, an open vesicle without cornea or lens. There is no ink-sac and no vivid play of chromatophores. There are two pairs of ctenidia and osphradia, as well as of auricles and kidneys. Most of these features in *Nautilus* are surely primitive; but it may not be safe to regard the modern survivors as typical in every way of the Palaeozoic cephalopods. In particular this may apply to the duplication of the palliopericardial organs. Rather than class all fossil ammonoids and nautiloids with the 'Tetrabranchiata' as was once the practice, we should remember that this condition may be an aberrant feature of *Nautilus* and its immediate relatives only. It could—on the other hand—have been widespread in the past, but this we shall probably never know. Flower has recently brought some evidence that the structure and large number of the tentacles of modern *Nautilus* may be a specialized character, not representative of most extinct forms.

The Nautiloidea and the Ammonoidea are each vast groups. The modern practice is to regard them as separate sub-classes and to rank the belemnoids and the modern cephalopods together in a third sub-class, the Coleoidea. Nautiloids first appear in the Upper Cambrian, ammonoids in the Upper Silurian. The former almost, and the latter entirely, die out at the end of the Cretaceous. A recent reckoning allows some 300 genera of nautiloids with about 2500 species. Flower and Kummel have grouped these into 75 families, forming 14 so-called 'orders'. The ammonoids were even more numerous, with 163 families and about 600 genera, divided into two main orders and six sub-orders. The largest members of the Ammonoidea are the Cretaceous giants *Pachydiscus septemarodensis*, like cartwheels two metres across. The greatest of the nautiloids must have been the straight forms of the genus *Endoceras*, some of which reached fifteen feet in length.[10, 16]

The Nautiloidea possessed smooth, simply sculptured shells with gently curved septa attached to the wall of the shell by straight sutures. The Ammonoidea often bore heavy sculpture and in most genera the septa were wrinkled and deeply convoluted at the edges, forming intricate sutures, folded and refolded with incredible complexity. Such a septum—it has been suggested—served to increase the animal's surface of attachment in the body chamber of the shell; or it may have strengthened the shell against alterations in external pressure on changing depth. But of the real adaptive significance of ammonoid sutures we know almost nothing. The initial chamber of the nautiloid shell is a short cone, situated opposite the blind end of the siphuncle; in ammonoids—as also in belemnoids and *Spirula*—it is spheroidal. There may have been fundamental differences between the ammonoid and nautiloid animals; but in many features the two groups have evolved on parallel lines, and we shall constantly meet with convergent adaptations in each.

Limited as our evidence may be, we can make some reconstruction of the life and habits of these mighty groups; and in certain interpretations the most cautious may agree.[35] The first nautiloids in the Upper Cambrian were no doubt also the first cephalopods. They had a cap-like, slightly curved shell, which increased in height as its apex first became occupied by gas-filled chambers. The siphuncle was widely open and some of the viscera probably extended into it. The foot may at first have retained its flat sole for creeping, but—as the distinctive cephalopod pattern emerged—it soon spread forward to surround the mouth and its edge became divided into a fringe of tentacles. As the growth of the chambers increased and the shell lightened, locomotion by water jets became possible. The animal could take short spurts upwards or backwards and dart nimbly off the ground.

Early nautiloids with short conical or cap-shaped shells may have swum upright. The first really fast pelagic forms were probably, however, the long, straight 'orthocones' of the *Orthoceras* type, moving horizontally like squids. Many of these species must have lurked close to the bottom, like modern sepioids, as we are sometimes able to deduce from the countershaded markings on the upper side of the shell alone, long and parallel stripes in the Ordovician *Geisnoceras*, zigzags in *Kionoceras*. A few early nautiloids such as *Gonioceras* (Ordovician) became strongly adapted to the bottom, with a flat wide-spreading shell and close-spaced septa, superficially resembling a cuttle-bone.

The long orthocones varied from a few inches in length to fifteen feet in *Endoceras* (Ordovician).

Flower has recently described some shell trails and supposed tentacular impressions of the orthoconic nautiloid *Orthonybyoceras*; if his interpretations are correct, they give a fascinating insight into the habits of these creatures. The shell trails are straight and shallow, a little more than the length of the shell (Fig. 22P). Some are rounded behind and end abruptly in front; these—it is suggested—were made by the animal alighting after swimming horizontally. Other trails are rounded at both ends, as by the animal touching down briefly before swimming away again. Their arrangement makes it clear that the orthoconids could swim forward, as does a modern squid with the funnel pointed back, or could swing on their apex through a wide angle to change direction by steering with the funnel. Some shorter trails, as of the nautiloid *Fucoides graphica*, were radially clustered, suggesting congregation about a mass of food debris, or even a concourse of animals for mating as is found in the modern *Loligo*. In front of many trails of *Orthonybyoceras* was found a crescentic

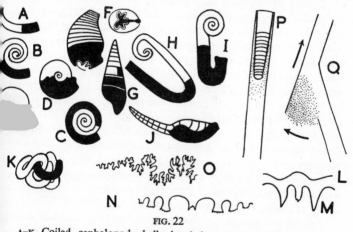

FIG. 22

A–K Coiled cephalopod shells in their natural postures. The terminal chamber, occupied by the body of the animal, is shown in black. A A cyrticone, B A gyrocone, C An ophiocone, D An ammoniticone, E A nautilicone, F *Hexameroceras*, also shown in apertural view, G *Turrilites*, H *Lytoceras*, I *Macroscaphites*, J *Ascoceras*, K *Nipponites*, L–O Sutures of cephalopod shells, L Nautiloid type, M Goniatite type, N Ceratite type, O Ammonoid type, P, Q Trails of *Orthonybyoceras* (after Flower), P Straight trail with shell in situ, Q Trail showing change of direction.

group of impressions attributed to short curved arms, apparently six to fourteen in number. These nautiloids may therefore have had a relatively small number of quite strong tentacles, which could be used for grasping the bottom or holding the animal steady.[73]

Even the longest of cephalopod shells must have been extremely buoyant, inconveniently so when resting near the bottom, since an apex filled with gas would tilt the head and body against the ground. Various expedients seem to have been employed by the straight nautiloids to keep the centres of gravity and buoyancy at about mid-length throughout life, and to maintain a horizontal position. For instance calcareous deposits secreted in the ventral part of a widened siphuncle could form a stabilizing ballast, partly filling the empty chambers. Or, as in the curved Silurian Ascoceratidae (Fig. 22J), a dorsal saddle of air cells could be incorporated in the body chamber from the forward growth of diverticula from earlier closed chambers.

Coiling of the shell in a plane spiral allowed more elegant swimming and a freer power of manœuvre (Fig. 22). This was initiated very early, soon after the rise of the orthocones in the Ordovician; and once begun it seems to have been pushed further, as the most feasible method of holding the body chamber horizontal above the ground, rather than thrusting the head on to the substrate by the buoyancy of the apex. Forward migration of the centre of gravity could be retarded by coiling; and more rapid growth on the ventral side of the shell produced an openly coiled *gyrocone* (Fig. 22B). Even here increasing body weight would still lead to a forward tilt. The final solution was either a many-coiled *ophiocone* (Fig. 22C) with numerous volutions all in contact, or a *nautilicone* (Fig. 22E), found in many Palaeozoic genera and in modern *Nautilus pompileus*. Here the later chambers completely invest the previous whorls, and the centre of gravity is shifted to the centre of the coil.[35, 187]

Curved and straight nautiloids (*cyrticones*) (Fig. 22A) and *orthocones*) had run their course by the Triassic, and long before that— in the Devonian—had been outnumbered by coiled forms.

The first ammonoids evidently arose from coiled nautiloids in the later Silurian, the earliest representatives being the goniatites. They soon became much more varied than the nautiloids in the details of the siphuncle and sutures. The shell differed too in having the aperture closed by a form of operculum, either a single horny plate (*anaptychus*) or two calcareous plates (*aptychi*). The siphuncle generally lay 'ventrally', towards the lower side of the shell. Fig. 22L–O illustrates some types of sutures, beginning with the *goniatite* form, folded into simple *lobes* and *saddles*. These were succeeded by *ceratite* sutures (Permian to Triassic), with the saddles smooth and the lobes crenulated, and finally by the *ammonite* type, with both lobes and saddles intricately crenulated.[10]

The advent of the ammonoids saved the Cephalopoda from decline: they ensured a continued abundance of coiled shells until the end of the Mesozoic, and they exploited many of the shell adaptations that the nautiloids had already begun. In lightening, streamlining and irregular coiling they went much further. Most nautiloids —as indeed the modern *Nautilus*, though still a good swimmer—are blunt-prowed, and the shell is typically rounded in cross section. Ammonoids are often more compressed, often with angled edges, and sharp cut-water keels. Such keeled forms—as *Oxynoticeras*, *Oxycerites* and *Prionodoceras*—are referred to as *oxycones*, and were obviously the most active swimmers. There is an analogy among the small pelagic gastropods, with the rounded shell of the slow-swimming *Limacina* making leisured vertical migrations, and the keeled, compressed shells of *Oxygyrus* and *Atlanta* which are fast swimmers. The heavier shells with strongest sculpture probably belonged to ammonoids dwelling close to the bottom. All coiled species must, however, have been able to swim with the funnel in the manner of *Nautilus*. The ventral edge of the aperture has always a 'hyponomic sinus' or notch presumably for the passage of a funnel.

Almost from the beginning of the nautiloids passively floating types developed. Thus in the Silurian we find plump vase-shaped *brevicones* (Fig. 22F), derived from orthocones, that must have drifted head downwards from the gas in the apical chambers. Their apertures are much contracted, often reduced to a mere slit, with a median exit for the funnel, and side notches for the eyes, which were perhaps borne on long stalks. Several pairs of arms probably issued by further side notches, of varying number, as in *Pentameroceras*, *Hexameroceras*, *Septameroceras* and many others. The coiled *Ophidioceras* and the horn-shaped *Phragmoceras* have also apertures like these. Much later, in the Jurassic, we find the coiled ammonoid *Morphoceras*, with only a narrow opening for the funnel, and

H

separate side fenestrae for the arms and eyes. Such animals must have been unable to capture or ingest bulky food. They were almost certainly slow-moving, and were very possibly plankton feeders. They perhaps had a thin widespread arm web for ciliary food collecting, or developed slender tentacles for deposit feeding. Such microphagous habits have been developed in several other carnivorous groups, as for example in anemones, jellyfish, starfish, pteropods and even basking sharks. Alternatively the narrow-mouthed cephalopods may have been predators with a suctorial proboscis, breaking down food externally as do many modern decapods by salivary enzymes.

In the latter half of the Mesozoic there appear many advanced ammonoids whose mode of life is even more difficult to reconstruct. *Scaphites* (Fig. 211) begins as a coiled ophiocone, is then straight, and has a final recurved part where the adult lives. In *Hamites* the immature shell is also straight, and sharply recurves in the adult. In *Ptychoceras* the recurved limb lies in contact with the previous straight part of the shell. *Heteroceras* has an open corkscrew spiral, the later part recurved, and *Spiroceras* has reverted to an open gyrocone. Such latter-day ammonoids were once regarded as 'degenerate' evolutionary lines, foretelling extinction. But it is surely unsafe to apply these quasi-moral judgments to populations still flourishing and numerous, and we may be pretty sure that the Jurassic and Cretaceous seas were populated by no handicapped or inefficient race of cephalopods. These ammonoids must have given up active swimming; and Trueman, by calculating the axis joining their centre of gravity and centre of buoyancy, has shown the posture in which many species floated.[187] Like normally coiled ammonoids, they rested with the aperture raised above the bottom. Here they may have drifted almost passively, with the head conveniently tilted for catching sluggish prey. They could make leisured saunters, or up and down movements by the use of the funnel, and their buoyancy would increase when the animal was expanded, and be lowered when the soft parts lay compactly in the body chamber. The funnel must have given them active control of posture, and we need not consider such species in any sense as victims of an air-filled shell, mechanically restricted to any one attitude.

From early times helicoid nautiloids and ammonoids began to re-invade the bottom. Already in the Devonian the nautiloids had produced the flatly trochoid shell *Trochoceras*. In the Triassic appeared the long spiral-coiled ammonoid *Cochloceras*, and in the Jurassic came *Turrilites*, with a shell like a sinistrally coiled *Turritella*. Such shells may have been trailed on the substrate, or if air-filled and unballasted would have been light enough, though rather clumsy, to carry aloft. The animals probably lived rather like octopods, crawling nimbly with the arms, and having the same facility for taking quick funnel spurts off the ground. A final aberrant stage is the Japanese *Nipponites* (Fig. 21κ), coiled in a complicated series of Us in varying planes. Whether or not it was sessile, it must have been immobile and possibly—like the irregular vermetid gastropods —trapped its food with mucus or cilia.

The phylogeny of fossil cephalopods must be approached as cautiously as their ecology. Spathe's review of the history of the Cephalopoda sharply challenges many of the older views, particularly the belief in 'programme evolution', with a grand evolutionary progress through straight, curved, open-coiled, tightly coiled and secondarily straight shells. The first nautiloids of all were in fact small, slightly curved cyrticones. Alongside the straight orthoceratids of the Ordovician and Silurian existed already a wealth of coiled shells of all grades. Straight shells, though earlier more abundant, co-existed with coiled until the end of the Palaeozoic; there was no successive replacement in time by cyrticones, gyrocones and nautilicones. Most open gyrocones and some cyrticones are in fact secondarily uncoiled nautilicones.[181]

The first ammonoids were already coiled. As well as by forms like *Hamites* and *Scaphites*, they were overtaken in the Cretaceous by the secondarily straight ammonoids of the Baculitidae, extremely similar to early orthoconic nautiloids. The ammonoids have left no descendants. The nautiloids, though they dwindled earlier, have persisted longer, having a short renaissance in the Tertiary with coiled genera such as *Aturia*. *Nautilus* itself remains living. The last of the straight orthoceratids gave rise as well to a vigorous straight-shelled line that expanded in the Mesozoic. These were the belemnoids, from which modern cephalopods have sprung; and it is to their descendants that we must now turn in our survey of the sub-class Coleoidea.

The Coleoidea (Fig. 7) fall naturally into two main orders: the first and larger, the Decapoda with ten arms, body fins and an internal shell or a vestige of one, and the second, the Octopoda, with eight arms of equal length, no shell and usually no fins.* The modern coleoids have fewer species than most other molluscan sub-classes. They are not, however, a dwindled relict group, but rather a new expansion of the Cephalopoda into molluscs of superior power and activity to all others. Metabolic rate, sensory and locomotor powers have vastly improved, and the average body weight has increased a hundredfold. Only a few genera live in restricted habitats on the

* *See* Vampyromorpha, p. 212)

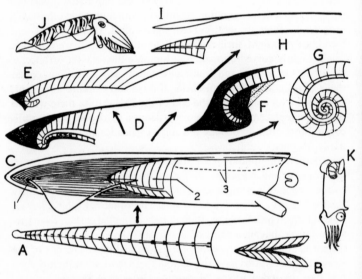

FIG. 23.   Evolution of the cephalopod shell

A A primitive orthocone, B *Piloceras* (L. Ordovician), c A belemnoid, D A primitive sepioid *Belosepia*, E *Sepia*, F *Spirulirostra*, G *Spirula*, H *Conoteuthis*, I *Loligo*, J *Sepia* (entire animal), K *Spirula* (entire animal). 1) guard, 2) phragmocone, 3) pro-ostracum.

bottom, and it is this greater mobility and wider range that explains their relative lack of speciation. Ecologically as well as physiologically we are dealing with molluscs at a new level of independence.

The Belemnoidea (Fig. 23c)—the first sub-order of the Decapoda —arose in the Triassic, and disappeared, apart from one Tertiary family (Neobelemnitidae), in the Cretaceous. They are distinguished from their straight nautiloid ancestors by the shell being internal. As we have already seen in Chapter III, the belemnoid shell had three parts: a small chambered *phragmocone* corresponding to the whole nautiloid shell, a solidly calcified *rostrum* which is the cigar-shaped part usually found fossil, and, extending forward, a broad shield, the *pro-ostracum*. The belemnoids were evidently rapid funnel-swimmers like a modern *Loligo*, the rostrum giving them an arrow-like rigidity, the phragmocone giving buoyancy at the centre of the body, and the pro-ostracum providing attachment for the mantle. The external mantle would allow improved jet-locomotion, and its tough muscles have in a few cases made possible the preservation of impressions of soft parts that we never obtain from the delicate tissues of ammonoids and nautiloids. Traces survive of triangular fins as in *Loligo*, of the head with rather feeble jaws, of the funnel and of the ink-sac. Most interesting, the arms were provided with one or two rows of hooks instead of horny suckers. Whether all belemnoids were hooked is not known, nor is there general agreement on the number and relative length of the arms. Some authors figure six, others eight, apparently of equal length. Later forms at least appear to have had ten, and so—in the strict sense—can be admitted as 'decapods'.

Belemnoids were generally of modest size, the animal probably about a foot in total length. The largest probably reached six to eight feet. There were numerous species, grouped in a recent classification[10] into sixty-three genera and five families. They seem to have shown rather little adaptive radiation, though genera like *Hibolites* with a light spear-shaped rostrum must have contained fast swimmers. Others—such as *Belemnites giganteus*, with a heavy conical rostrum—were slower and benthic. Belemnoids are thought to have fed on fish, crustaceans and at times on each other. From the finding of 'grave-yard' formations of fossils, they must at times have swum together in immense swarms.

Living decapods are classed in two sub-orders, the Teuthoidea and the Sepioidea. In all of them, as we have seen, the shell is reduced in importance. The main existing types are the open-coiled phragmocone of *Spirula*; the 'shell' of *Sepia*, with the upper side of the phragmocone wide and flat and with a small rostrum; and the 'pen' of *Loligo*, uncalcified and with a horny gladius and shaft representing the pro-ostracum. Various Tertiary fossils provide annectant forms leading down to these modern survivors. *Spirulirostra*, with a curved phragmocone and persistent rostrum, foreshadows *Spirula* (Fig. 23G); *Belosepia* (Fig. 23D), with the lower side of the phragmocone reduced leads to *Sepia*; and from *Beloteuthis* and *Palaeololigo*, with large pro-ostraca, was produced the pen of the squids (Fig. 23I).

The Sepioidea, together with the addition of the Loliginidae from the Teuthoidea, correspond to the formerly recognized group Myopsida, distinguished from other families (Oigopsida) by their closed external cornea. The sepioid families Sepiidae, Sepiadariidae and Sepiolidae are on the whole coastal in distribution, adapted to benthic life and of comparatively small size. The little *Spirula*—three or four inches long—is probably a representative of an isolated bathypelagic group of sepioids. Bruun, who has studied it alive, finds it to float or swim actively in a slightly oblique position with its head downward. It is kept upright by the small gas-filled shell, surrounded by soft tissues.[43]

Both the sepioids and the octopods show more speciation than the oceanic Teuthoidea, but the latter easily predominate in numbers of families and genera. Only the coastal Loliginidae show many species. The loliginids and sepioids are certainly much better known than the squids of deeper water. The majority of the Teuthoidea can indeed have been seen alive only by fishermen. Some of the deeper-water Teuthoidea are giants of the seas; others—as the Cranchiidae—are relatively small. We shall mention in turn some of the families of greatest interest.

The mightiest of the cephalopods are the several species of the Architeuthidae,[177, 188] with such proud names as *Architeuthis princeps* and *Architeuthis dux*. These may exceed fifty feet in total body length. Three-quarters of this is accounted for by the tentacles, the shorter arms reaching fifteen feet. The fins, though large, are not excessively developed, and the locking apparatus of the mantle (p. 59) is feeble. This suggests that the architeuthids are not rapid swimmers; they may be taken off the continental slope in depths of only 100–200 fathoms, where they seem to feed on the larger benthic animals. They are also known as larvae, being the small squids once called *Rhynchoteuthis*, with the two tentacles joined in the form of a spout.

Much more accomplished swimmers are the medium giants of the family Sthenoteuthidae. *Sthenoteuthis caroli*, occasionally entering the northern North Sea from the Atlantic, may reach three feet in body length and seven feet overall. It is exceedingly active, with a strong locking apparatus and broad rhomboidal fin vane and can shoot from the water like a rocket, sometimes landing on shipboard. Hardy remarks that this species is 'very adept at summing up a situation and quickly taking the only way out . . . it thus skilfully avoids traps and nets'.[21] A smaller related species, *Ommastrephes sagittatus*, is sometimes stranded in large numbers on British coasts. The most adept 'flying squids' we have already mentioned (p. 61) as belonging to the family of hooked squids, Onycoteuthidae (Fig. 7B), using their fin vane and funnel for shooting from the water and gliding like flying fish. Even larger vanes are found in the deep-water Octopodoteuthidae: in species of *Cucioteuthis*, the eight arms and two tentacles are all short and the two fins together form a circular expanse many times larger than the rest of the body. In the family Thysanoteuthidae the tentacular arms have two rows of filaments, as well as suckers, running their whole length. Two triangular fins are attached the whole length of the body, giving it a rhomboidal shape like a ray.

Still greater specializations are found in the bathypelagic family Chiroteuthidae (Fig. 7C). These small squids are thin-bodied and cylindrical, specializing, as the names *Chiroteuthis* and *Mastigoteuthis* suggest, in extraordinarily long, whip-like tentacular arms. These are non-retractile and are equipped with suckers spaced all the way along; they may reach six times the body length, or—in *Chiroteuthis veranyi*—some twenty-four inches. Of the short arms, the ventral two are very flat and wide. The fin vane lies right behind the body, forming a flat, circular expanse; in *Grimalditeuthis* there is a double vane, from a pair of semi-circular fins at either side.

Doratopsis vermicularis, with a terminal circular vane, is theslenderest of all cephalopods, with a flexible body the thickness of a pencil.

Some weirdly adapted squids belong to the two deep-water families Histioteuthidae and Cranchiidae. The first are of smallish size, less than a foot overall, sometimes much smaller, and studded with light organs. In *Calliteuthis* the eyes are asymmetric, the right one smaller and sunken with a circlet of light organs which the left one lacks. *Histioteuthis* species are reddish-purple to black and resemble small vampire squids (*see* p. 212) with the six dorsal arms united by a membranous web, whose medusoid movements virtually replace the funnel in swimming as in the cirroteuthoid octopods.

In the Cranchiidae we have about twenty genera of small squids, on the whole planktonic within about 100 metres of the surface, though some go much deeper. They present some odd shapes and many of the described species are probably larval. *Cranchia* itself has a plump, vase-shaped body, narrowest at the mantle edge, with two long tentacles and the other arms very short. In *Bathothauma* (Fig. 7D), a deep-water genus, these short arms are carried up in a small rosette on a long peduncle which bears the mouth. In most cranchiids the posterior fins are small and rounded, but *Galiteuthis*—which is a fast swimmer—has a slender body about eight inches long, tipped with a large triangular fin vane. The eyes of cranchiids are always prominent and sometimes mounted on stalks. In the small *Sandalops melancholicus* the stalks are bent down at right angles, and the eyes look ahead with an unmistakable air of sadness which has given rise to the specific name.

Many cephalopods show a striking bioluminescence.[22] [36] This is especially a property of the oigopsids, found in three-quarters of the known species, particularly those living in deep waters. Relatively few myopsids are luminescent, and in the Octopoda only two deep-water species—*Melanoteuthis luceus* and *Eledonella alberti*. In four families of squids every species possesses light organs, namely the Lycoteuthidae, Lampadoteuthidae, Bathyteuthidae and Enoploteuthidae, as well as most if not all of the Cranchiidae and Histioteuthidae. In these families light is produced by the photogenic tissues of the animal itself, and special light organs may be distributed in almost every part of the body. In the cranchiids they occur—as well as elsewhere—on the lower surface of the eyeballs, where they can be covered by movable folds of skin. Other families may have optic light organs without lids. They are generally found widely on the integument of the mantle, head and arms, especially in circlets around the eyes. In luminescent Chiroteuthidae they extend right down the long tentacles. There may also be intrapallial light organs on the visceral mass. These rely for the effect on the transparency of the tissues; and the animal must resemble the apocalyptic beast, 'full of eyes within'. The histology of the light organs has had much attention from authors such as Joubin, Hoyle, Chun and Stillmann Berry.[36] They become extraordinarily complicated and diverse, especially in the Enoploteuthidae and Histioteuthidae. There is usually a nest of primary photogenic tissue, to which may be added 'reflector mechanisms, pigment cups, lenses, diaphragms, directive muscles, windows, colour screens and accessory photophores'. For descriptions of the light produced, the old expedition reports are full of interest. To quote from Hoyle's translation of Chun's Valdivia Report on *Lycoteuthis diadema*:

Among all the marvels of colouration which the animals of the deep sea exhibited to us, none can be even distantly compared with the hues of these organs. One would think that the body was adorned with a diadem of brilliant gems. The middle organs of the eyes shone with ultramarine blue, the lateral one with a pearly sheen. Those towards the front of the lower surface of the body gave out a ruby red light, while those behind were snow white or pearly, except the median one which was sky blue. It was indeed a glorious spectacle.

Then Watase's description of the Japanese inshore squid *Watasenia scintillans*, the *hotaru-ika*, fortunately common at times in shallow water:

When the animal is about to produce light the chromatophores covering the spots will concentrate and remove themselves, thus opening a way for the light. The light is so brilliant that it seems like a sunbeam shot through a tiny hole in a window curtain.

Luminescent myopsids employ a different means of lighting by an association between the animal and symbiotic luminiscent bacteria. In Loliginidae and Sepiidae—as well as luminescent bactera harboured on the skin—the ducts of the accessory nidamental glands are filled with masses of photogenic bacilli or cocci. Light may be produced by internal illumination, or emission of the contents into the water. The bacteria are transmitted to the next generation intimately attached to the egg membrane. In the Sepiolidae (*Sepiola* and *Rondeletia*) there are more complex light organs, formed by specialization of part of the accessory nidamental gland, and the provision of a pigment sheath, reflector and lens. In the deep-water sepiolid *Heteroteuthis dispar* (1200–1500 fathoms) the light is not finally proved to be due to bacteria; instead of a cloud of ink, an attacking fish receives a 'veritable bombardment of liquid light' in greenish clouds of faint cobalt patches.[22]

What is the significance of bioluminescence? A. C. Hardy gives an interesting discussion of light production in deep-water crustacea, and finds it associated with migrations over a long depth range rather than with a permanently deep habitat.[21] This seems true of cephalopods as well—the permanently abyssal octopods, for example, do not produce light at all. As well as repelling predators, light may be of direct use to the animal itself, though whether—as has been suggested—it is especially employed in courtship display, for hunting food, or for recognition of fellows, we do not know. As we have suggested before, cephalopod life is so fundamentally centred round the visual sense that it may have been difficult—at all events for deep-migrating oigopsids—to substitute any other sense in darker waters. Perhaps only by taking with them their own light supply have such essentially visual animals as squids been able to penetrate the unlighted depths.

THE OCTOPODA

The octopods have lost all trace of the shell, except for a last vestige of it in the fossil *Palaeoctopus*. The two tentacular arms have disappeared and the other eight arms themselves form long tentacles, arranged in a circlet linked by a web around the mouth. *Octopus* and *Eledone*, with rounded body, no fins and leisured swimming, are very typical of inshore Octopoda. They have much more contact with the bottom than most decapods. The eight arms no longer merely hold the captured prey. They themselves are organs of attack, and are exploratory and tactile members as well. The Octopoda have a finely developed sense of touch, and those that live at the bottom employ colour change as well, though never with such subtlety as in the cuttlefish. We must not regard all Octopoda as like *Octopus* in habits. There are three other very distinctive modes of life shown by offshore genera—the surface-dwelling, the bathypelagic and the permanent abyssal-benthic.

The Argonautacea are the typical octopods of the upper waters of the open sea. They are found from the surface to 500 fathoms, being proficient but not fast jet-swimmers. Above all other cephalopods they exhibit sex dimorphism. In *Argonauta* (Fig. 7G) itself the sex difference is greatest, with two of the arms in the female modified to secrete a graceful papery 'shell'. This contains the bunches of eggs, which are small and extremely numerous. The males are dwarfed with an elaborate and often autotomous hectocotylus arm. In *Ocythoe*, a pelagic form without a 'shell', the dwarf male is tiny enough to shelter in empty salp tests like the amphipod *Phronima*.

In very deep waters, but not usually living at the bottom, occur the bathypelagic octopods such as *Eledonella*, *Vitreledonella* and *Amphitretus*. These have a long depth range and no particular modifications for benthic life. The greatest depth record of any cephalopod is that of *Eledonella*, reaching 2949 fathoms. Another genus, *Japetella*, is interesting in having a pelagic larva, supported at the surface by a cuticular test produced into irregular filaments. *Amphitretus*, which has the arms half-webbed, possesses 'telescopic' eyes raised on stout peduncles from the dorsal side. The whole body is clad in a loose sheath of transparent jelly.

The deep benthic octopods of the super-family Cirroteuthacea are the most strangely modified of all.[175] They are web-swimmers, a logical development of the octopod pattern of eight radial arms joined by a basal web. In *Cirroteuthis*, *Cirrothauma* and *Opisthoteuthis*, as we have seen, the web is very large, reaching almost to the arm tips. Within the web the arm suckers are modified as a double row of filaments, used as tactile organs and for collecting fine particulate food. *Cirroteuthis* and *Cirrothauma* have a high conical body and swim slowly by opening and closing the web.

Opisthoteuthis is flattened, rather like a webbed starfish, with mouth below, bulging eyes, small funnel and a pair of fins above (Fig. 7H).

The cirroteuthids and many of the bathypelagic octopods have lost most of their firmness and muscular power. They develop a thick coat of jelly-like subcutaneous connective tissue, and the muscles themselves are sometimes degenerate and invaded by this jelly. *Cirrothauma* is as fragile in texture as a jellyfish, and one can read newsprint through its transparent body. With the slower web-swimming there is reduced muscular effort and no doubt a lower metabolic rate. In the Cirroteuthidae the branchial hearts are consequently very small, and the structure of the gills is simplified. The pallial aperture and the funnel are likewise very reduced. Feeding is microphagous, and though the jaws are retained, the radula—never of major importance in cephalopods—is quite lost in *Cirrothauma*. In total darkness the chromatophore system and the ink-sac are valueless, and they seldom survive. Light organs are unusual in any octopods. Finally—strange culmination for a cephalopod!—*Cirrothauma* has almost lost its eyes as well. In *Opisthoteuthis*, of the shallower continental shelf, these are still well developed.

With the webbed octopods were once classed the small deep-water vampire squids (*Vampyroteuthis*) (Fig. 7F) for which—since the work of Pickford (1946)—we must recognize a special third order of living Coleoidea, the Vampyromorpha. The animal is deep purplish-black in colour, the female eight inches long and the male a little smaller. They swim by an arm web, beneath which the tentacles bear short cirri. The conical body bears large terminal fins and is covered with light organs, the one at the base of either fin having a large 'eyelid'. There appear at first to be eight equal arms, but close inspection reveals a unique character in two small retractile filaments like coiled tendrils, homologous not with the long tentacles of decapods but apparently with the second dorsal pair of arms.[161]

CLASSIFICATION OF RECENT MOLLUSCA

CLASS	SUB-CLASS	Order
I. MONOPLACOPHORA	.	Tryblidiacea (1 species living)
II. AMPHINEURA	*APLACOPHORA* ⎤	Neomeniomorpha Chaetodermomorpha
	POLYPLACOPHORA ⎤	Lepidopleurida Chitonida
	PROSOBRANCHIA	Archaeogastropoda (= *Aspidobranchia* = *Rhipidoglossa* + *Docoglossa*) Mesogastropoda (= *Pectinibranchia* (in part) = *Taenioglossa*) Neogastropoda (= *Pectinibranchia* (in part) = *Stenoglossa* = *Rachiglossa* + *Toxoglossa*)
III. GASTROPODA	*OPISTHOBRANCHIA*	Cephalaspidea (= *Bullomorpha*) Anaspidea (= *Aplysiomorpha*) Thecosomata ⎤ Gymnosomata ⎦ (= *Pteropoda*) Sacoglossa Acochlidiacea Notaspidea (= *Pleurobranchomorpha*) Nudibranchia
	PULMONATA ⎤	Basommatophora Stylommatophora

CLASSIFICATION OF RECENT MOLLUSCA—*Cont.*

CLASS	SUB-CLASS	Order
IV. SCAPHOPODA · · · ·	·	(4 genera)
		Protobranchia
V. LAMELLIBRANCHIA **(BIVALVIA, PELECYPODA)**	*(Filibranchia +* *Pseudolamellibranchia)*	Taxodonta Anisomyaria
	(Eulamellibranchia)	Schizodonta Heterodonta Adapedonta Anomalodesmata (including *Septibranchia*)
VI. CEPHALOPODA · · ·	*NAUTILOIDEA*	Nautilida (13 extinct orders)
	AMMONOIDEA	(2 large extinct orders)
	COLEOIDEA	Decapoda Vampyromorpha Octopoda

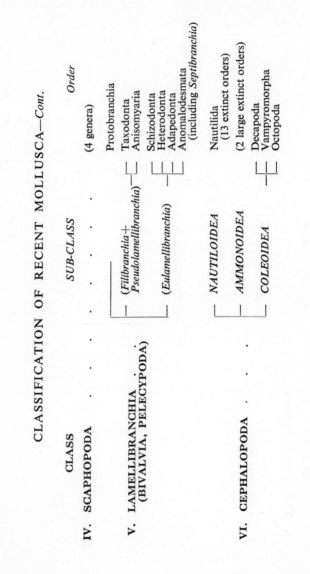

APPENDIX 1

Classification of the Mollusca, with the Super-families and principal families, based with modifications upon Thiele (1931–35)

CLASS AMPHINEURA
SUB-CLASS POLYPLACOPHORA

		Families
Order Lepidopleurida	(p. 65)	Lepidopleuridae
Order Chitonida ..	(p. 65)	Lepidochitonidae, Mopaliidae, Cryptoplacidae, Ischnochitonidae, Chitonidae

SUB-CLASS APLACOPHORA
Order Neomeniomorpha

(p. 18) Lepidomeniidae, Neomeniidae, Proneomeniidae, Parameniidae

Order Chaetodermomorpha

(p. 18) Chaetodermatidae

CLASS GASTROPODA
SUB-CLASS PROSOBRANCHIA
Order Archaeogastropoda

Super-families		*Families*
Zeugobranchia ..	(p. 67)	Pleurotomariidae, Haliotidae, Scissurellidae, Fissurellidae
Trochacea	(p. 30)	Trochidae, Turbinidae
Patellacea	(p. 70)	Acmaeidae, Patellidae
Neritacea	(p. 164)	Neritidae, Helicinidae

Order Mesogastropoda

Archaeotaenioglossa	(p. 165)	Cyclophoridae, Ampullariidae, Viviparidae
Valvatacea	(p. 165)	Valvatidae
Littorinacea ..	(p. 165)	Littorinidae, Pomatiasidae, Acmidae
Rissoacea	(p. 166)	Rissoidae, Hydrobiidae, Assimineidae
Cerithiacea	(p. 166)	Cerithiidae, Potamididae, Cerithiopsidae, Melaniidae, Turritellidae (p. 73), Silquariidae Vermetidae (p. 33)
Ptenoglossa	(p. 33)	Ianthinidae, Scalidae
Aglossa	(p. 177)	Aclididae, Stiliferidae, Eulimidae, Entoconchidae

Calyptraeacea	..	(p. 32) Calyptraeidae, Capulidae, Xenophoridae
Strombacea..	..	(p. 33) Aporrhaidae, Struthiolariidae, Strombidae
Heteropoda..	..	(p. 34) Atlantidae, Carinariidae, Pterotracheidae
Naticacea ..	..	(p. 34) Naticidae
Cypraeacea	..	(p. 35) Cypraeidae, Lamellariidae
Doliacea ..	..	(p. 32) Cassididae, Cymatiidae, Bursidae, Doliidae, Pirulidae

Order Neogastropoda

Buccinacea ..	..	(p. 35) Buccinidae, Nassidae, Galeodidae, Fasciolariidae
Muricacea ..	..	(p. 35) Muricidae, Thaididae, Coralliophilidae, Magilidae
Volutacea ..	..	(p. 35) Volutidae, Harpidae, Mitridae, Olividae, Marginellidae
Toxoglossa ..	..	(p. 96) Conidae, Turridae, Terebridae

SUB-CLASS OPISTHOBRANCHIA

Order Cephalaspidea

Bullariacea ..	..	(p. 172) Actaeonidae, Bullariidae, Retusidae
Philinacea ..	..	(p. 172) Scaphandridae, Philinidae, Atyidae, Runcinidae, Gastropteridae
*Pyramidellidae	..	(p. 176)
Order Anaspidea		(p. 172) Aplysiidae, Akeratidae
Order Thecosomata ..		(p. 172) Limacinidae, Cavoliniidae, Cymbuliidae, Peraclidae
Order Gymnosomata		(p. 173) Pneumodermatidae, Cliopsidae, Clionidae

Order Sacoglossa

Oxynoacea ..	..	(p. 173) Arthessidae, Oxynoidae
Elysiacea ..	..	(p. 174) Hermaeidae, Elysiidae, Limapontiidae
Order Acochlidiacea..		(p. 173) Acochlidiidae

Order Notaspidea

Umbraculacea	..	(p. 174) Umbraculidae
Pleurobranchacea ..		(p. 174) Pleurobranchidae

Order Nudibranchia

Dendronotacea	..	(p. 174) Tritoniidae, Iduliidae, Lomanotidae, Dendronotidae Scyllaeidae, Phyllirhoidae, Tethyidae
Aeolidiacea..	..	(p. 175) Coryphellidae, Aeolidiidae, Facelinidae, Calmidae, Glaucidae
Doridacea ..	..	(p. 175) Dorididae, Bathydorididae, Notodorididae, Polyceridae, Onchidorididae, Goniodorididae
Arminacea ..	..	(p. 176) Arminidae

* Provisionally placed here by Fretter and Graham (1949).

SUB-CLASS PULMONATA

Order Basommatophora

Actophila ..	.. (p. 163)	Ellobiidae, Otinidae, Chilinidae
Amphibolacea	.. (p. 75)	Amphibolidae
Patelliformia	.. (p. 75)	Siphonariidae
Hygrophila ..	.. (p. 75)	Lymnaeidae, Physidae, Planorbidae, Ancylidae

Order Stylommatophora

Onchidiacea	.. (p. 44)	Onchidiidae
Soleolifera ..	.. (p. 76)	Vaginulidae
Succineacea	.. (p. 75)	Succineidae
Tracheopulmonata ..	(p. 76)	Athoracophoridae
Achatinellacea	.. (p. 170)	Achatinellidae
Vertiginacea	.. (p. 43)	Cochlicopidae, Vertiginidae, Enidae, Valloniidae, Clausiliidae
Achatinacea	.. (p. 170)	Achatinidae, Ferussaciidae, Subulinidae
Oleacinacea	.. (p. 44)	Testacellidae
Endodontacea	.. (p. 169)	Endodontidae, Arionidae
Zonitacea ..	.. (p. 169)	Zonitidae, Limacidae, Vitrinidae, Polygyridae
Acavacea ..	..	Acavidae
Bulimulacea	.. (p. 169)	Bulimulidae, Urocoptidae
Helicacea ..	.. (p. 170)	Helicidae, Pleurodontidae, Fruticicolidae
Streptaxacea	.. (p. 101)	Streptacidae, Paryphantidae

CLASS LAMELLIBRANCHIA

Order Protobranchia

Super-families		*Families*
Nuculacea ..	.. (p. 78)	Nuculidae, Malletiidae
Solenomyacea	.. (p. 78)	Solenomyidae

Order Taxodonta

Arcacea ..	.. (p. 183)	Arcidae, Glycymeridae

Order Anisomyaria

Mytilacea ..	.. (p. 184)	Mytilidae
Pteriacea ..	.. (p. 185)	Pteriidae, Vulsellidae, Pinnidae
Pectinacea ..	.. (p. 186)	Pectinidae, Limidae
Anomiacea ..	.. (p. 186)	Anomiidae
Ostreacea ..	.. (p. 187)	Ostreidae

Order Schizodonta

Trigoniacea ..	.. (p. 192)	Trigoniidae
Unionacea ..	.. (p. 192)	Unionidae, Mutelidae, Aetheriidae

Order Heterodonta

Astartacea ..	.. (p. 188)	Astartidae
Carditacea ..	..	Carditidae
Sphaeriacea	.. (p. 192)	Sphaeriidae, Corbiculidae
Isocardiacea	.. (p. 188)	Isocardiidae
Cyprinacea ..	.. (p. 188)	Cyprinidae
Cyamiacea ..	..	Cyamiidae
Gaimardiacea	..	Gaimardiidae
Dreissenacea	.. (p. 192)	Dreissenidae

Lucinacea .. .. (p. 188) Lucinidae
Erycinacea .. .. (p. 188) Erycinidae, Galeommatidae
Chamacea .. .. (p. 191) Chamidae
Cardiacea .. .. (p. 189) Cardiidae, Tridacnidae
Veneracea .. .. (p. 51) Veneridae, Petricolidae
Mactracea .. .. (p. 188) Mactridae, Amphidesmatidae
Tellinacea .. .. (p. 188) Donacidae, Asaphidae, Semelidae,
                          Tellinidae
Order Adapedonta
Solenacea .. .. (p. 193) Solenidae, Glaucomyidae
Myacea .. .. (p. 193) Aloididae, Myidae, Saxicavidae
Adesmacea .. .. (p. 194) Pholadidae, Teredinidae,
                         Xylophaginidae
Order Anomalodesmata
Pandoracea .. (p. 194) Lyonsiidae, Pandoridae,
                       Myochamidae, Chamostreidae,
                       Thraciidae, Laternulidae

Clavagellacea .. (p. 195) Clavagellidae
(Order Septibranchia)
Poromyacea .. (p. 195) Verticordiidae, Poromyidae,
                       Cuspidariidae

CLASS CEPHALOPODA
I. *SUB-CLASS NAUTILOIDEA*
   14 'orders', 75 families (Nautilidae living)
II. *SUB-CLASS AMMONOIDEA*
    2 orders, 163 families (none living)
III. *SUB-CLASS COLEOIDEA*
   Order Decapoda
     Sub-order Belemnoidea (5 families, all extinct)
       Sepioidea
         Spirulacea .. (p. 206) Spirulidae
         Sepiacea .. (p. 206) Sepiidae, Sepiadariidae, Sepiolidae,
                              Idiosepiidae
       Teuthoidea
         Loliginacea .. (p. 58) Loliginidae
         Architeuthacea* (p. 206) Lycoteuthidae, Enoploteuthidae,
                                  Abraliidae, Octopodoteuthidae,
                                  Onycoteuthidae, Gonatidae,
                                  Architeuthidae, Histioteuthidae,
                                  Bathyteuthidae, Ommatostrephidae,
                                  Sthenoteuthidae, Thysanoteuthidae,
                                  Chiroteuthidae, Cranchiidae
                                  Lampadoteuthidae
   Order Vampyromorpha (p. 212) Vampyroteuthidae
   Order Octopoda
     Cirroteuthacea .. (p. 211) Cirroteuthidae, Opisthoteuthidae
     Bolitaenacea .. (p. 211) Bolitaenidae, Amphitretidae,
                              Vitreledonellidae
     Octopodacea .. (p. 210) Octopodidae
     Argonautacea .. (p. 211) Alloposidae, Tremoctopodidae,
                              Ocythoidae, Argonautidae

* Thiele's grouping obviously needs subdivision.

APPENDIX 2

NEOPILINA GALATHEAE (Lemche 1957)

A PAPER by Drs. Lemche and Wingstrand, published in abstract for the International Zoological Congress in London, in June 1958, gives many more details of the living monoplacophoran.

The head carries two sorts of appendage (Fig. 1c), a transverse pre-oral flap regarded as a retained velum and a pair of post-oral tentacular tufts held to have homologies with labial palps and perhaps with early cephalopod tentacles. The gills are in five pairs. Each is capable of muscular movement and bears on one side a row of elongated lamellae, those of the opposite margin being reduced. Within the gut, the radula bears V-shaped tooth rows, with one median tooth and five laterals at either side. The fourth lateral tooth bears resemblances to that of some chitons (Fig. 11B) with long denticles. The style sac is reported to contain a crystalline style rather than a faecal rod, while the stomach is filled with small particles of ooze, especially rich in radiolarians. There are six pairs of renal organs. The coelom consists of a pericardium around the heart and paired dorsal coelomic sacs. These seem to correspond with the gonad in other molluscs, but in *Neopilina* they are sterile, the gonocoele lying ventrally. The renal organs are branched into lobules and have narrow connections with the dorsal coelomic cavities. As well, the third and fourth renal organs receive in the female ducts from probably two interdigitate pairs of ovaries and in the male from two pairs of testes. These renal organs may in the male be filled with sperm. The heart has a median ventricle and the last gill is drained by a separate auricle at either side, the next pair of auricles draining all the others. The nervous system resembles that of chitons, having no ganglia except at the head end, and the pedal and pleurovisceral cords having ten pairs of cross connectives between them.

The true homologies of some of the organs and the question whether *Neopilina* is in the full sense metameric must await further study, in particular a knowledge of embryology. *Neopilina* increases in interest as fresh facts come to light, though some of the phylogenetic affinities suggested for it, especially those implying a link with Arthropoda, may not at once gain general acceptance.

APPENDIX 3

A FEW recent discoveries deserve special mention here. The evolution of the Anomiidae (p. 186) was not exhausted by the fixed posture with a calcified byssus cable. Owen and Yonge have recently described the habits of *Aenigmonia*, a small elongate-oval limpet-like mollusc creeping by means of its long, extensible foot upon mangrove leaves in Malayan estuaries. When closely examined this is found to be a true anomiid that has abandoned its byssus attachment; the lower valve is almost functionless, and the foot, which is never entirely lost in Anomiidae, can now be extruded anteriorly with the recovery of free locomotor powers.

Thompson and Slinn have added much to our knowledge of the Pleurobranchidae (p. 38) with a study of *Oscanius membranaceus*, showing its method of swimming with the broad parapodial edges of the foot, and its habit of feeding on ascidians by plunging its eversible proboscis into holes drilled in the test. (*J. mar. Biol. Ass.*, *38*, 507.)

The evolution of the earlier shelled Sacoglossa (p. 39) has produced an astonishing parallel with the lamellibranchs in the newly discovered *Tamanovalva limax*, a small mollusc about 7 mm. long living and feeding in Japanese waters on the green alga *Caulerpa*. Kawaguti and Baba have shown this species to possess a bivalved shell perfectly like that of a lamellibranch save for a short, sinistrally coiled protoconch upon the left valve. There is a single centrally inserted adductor muscle. The creeping foot, the head with eyes and tentacles, and particularly the buccal mass, with ascus sac and uniseriate radula, show all the features of a primitive sacoglossan, rather close to *Arthessa* and *Oxynoe*.

The life history of an African freshwater mussel, a member of the Mutelidae (p. 192), *Mutela bourguignati*, was recently described by Fryer (*Nature*, *183*, 1342). It shows some extraordinary adaptations and great differences from the Unionidae. The embryos shed from the maternal gill chambers show a long filamentar tentacle some 70 times the length of the young animal. Attaching to a cyprinoid fish, the embryo becomes enclosed in a non-calcified shell, tubular and sealed at either end. From the anterior end of this shell grow out two long nutritive processes, extensions of the mantle, that pierce the tissues of the host. The tube grows to a length of 3 mm., and within its distal extremity the adult mussel is eventually formed. The definitive shell valves at the distal end become calcified, feeding by ciliary means begins, and the attachment to the host is soon terminated by the young mussel parting company with the embedded stalk, and falling to the ground. It begins its independent existence at a length of about 1·5 mm.

Recent work at Plymouth by Dr. E. J. Denton and his collaborators will revive the whole question of the supposedly closed, gas-filled buoyancy chambers of cephalopod shells (p. 56). Far from being impermeable, it has been shown experimentally that the narrow spaces between the numerous shell trabeculae of *Sepia*, i.e. the much modified shell camerae, contain gas under reduced pressure and that the active entry or withdrawal of water into these spaces is under the control of the mantle epithelium lying over this part of the shell. Obviously, then, this is a buoyancy system under dynamic control, not a physiologically isolated gas-filled space. The next approach may be the re-investigation of the shell of living *Nautilus*, and the possible role of the siphuncle in the dynamics of shell buoyancy.

BIBLIOGRAPHY

* denotes reviewing papers, or works with comprehensive bibliographies.

There are two British journals devoted to research on the Mollusca: the *Proceedings of the Malacological Society of London* (1893 onwards) and the *Journal of Conchology*, published since 1874, by the Conchological Society of Great Britain and Ireland.

GENERAL REFERENCE BOOKS

1. ALDER, J., & HANCOCK, A., 1845–1855. *A monograph of the British Nudibranchiate Mollusca.* London.
2. COOKE, A. H., 1895. *Molluscs and brachiopods.* Vol. 3 in *Cambr. nat. Hist.* London.
3. ELLIS, A. E., 1926. *British snails.* London.
4. FISCHER, P. H., 1950. *Vie et moeurs des mollusques.* Paris.
5. FORBES, E., & HANLEY, S., 1853. *A history of British molluscs and their shells.* London.
6. HOFFMANN, H., 1938. 'Opisthobranchia', in *Bronn's Tierreich, III.*
7. JEFFREYS, J. G., 1862–1869. *British conchology.* London.
8. MOORE, R. C. (ed.), 1957. *Treatise on invertebrate palaeontology,* pt. L. New York. (Ammonoids.)
9. PELSENEER, P., 1906. *Mollusca.* Vol. 5 in *A treatise on zoology,* ed. E. Ray Lankester. London.
10. PIVETEAU, J., 1952. *Traité de paleontologie,* vol 2. Paris.
11. PRUVOT-FOL, ALICE, 1954. 'Opisthobranchia', in *La faune de France.* Paris.
12. SIMROTH, H., 1928. 'Pulmonata', in *Bronn's Tierreich, III* (2).
13. STEP, E., 1945. *Shell life.* London.
14. TAYLOR, J. W., 1894–1907. *Monograph of the land and freshwater Mollusca of the British Isles.* 4 vols. Leeds.
15. THIELE, J., 1931–1935. *Handbuch der systematischen Weichtierkunde,* 4 vols. Jena.
16. SWINNERTON, H. H., 1947. *Outlines of palaeontology.* London.
17. WOODWARD, B. B., 1913. *The life of the Mollusca.* London.

REFERENCE BOOKS ON SPECIAL TOPICS

18. BAER, J. G., 1952. *Ecology of animal parasites.* Chicago. (Parasitic Mollusca.)
19. CAULLERY, M., 1952. *Parasitism and symbiosis.* London. (Parasitic Mollusca.)
20. FRAENKEL, G. S., & GUNN, D. L., 1940. *Orientation of animals.* London. (Behaviour.)
21. HARDY, A. C., 1956. *The open sea.* Collins New Naturalist. London. (Larvae: Cephalopoda.)
22. HARVEY, A. N., 1940. *Living light.* Princetown. (Luminescence.)

222   BIBLIOGRAPHY

23. LANE, F., 1956. *Kingdom of the octopus.* London.
23A. SCHEER, B. T., (ed.) 1957. *Recent advances in invertebrate physiology.*
    Eugene, Oregon. (Renal function, ch. by A. W. Martin.)
24. THORPE, W. H., 1956. *Learning and instinct in animals.* Cambridge.
    (Behaviour.)
25. WARDEN, C. J., JENKINS, T. N., & WARNER, L. H., 1940. *Compara-*
    tive psychology, v. 2, Plants and invertebrates. New York.
    (Molluscan behaviour.)
26. YONGE, C. M., 1949. *The sea shore.* Collins New Naturalist. London.

PAPERS

27. AGERSBERG, H. P. K., 1923. *Quart. J. micr. Sci.,* 67, 507–592.
    (*Melibe.*)
28. ALLEN, J. A., 1954. *Quart. J. micr. Sci.,* 95, 473, 482. (*Pandora.*)
28A. ALLEN, J. A., 1958. *J. mar. Biol. Ass. U.K.,* 37, 97–112. (*Cochlodesma.*)
29. ANKEL, W. E., 1926. *Verh. Dtsch. Zool. Gesellsch. Jahresvers.,* 31,
    193–202. (Giant sperms.)
30. ANKEL, W. E., 1936. Prosobranchia in *Tierwelt d. Nord-is. Ostsee,* 9,
    1–240. (Prosobranchia.)
31. ANKEL, W. E., 1937. *Biol. Zbl.,* 57, 75–82. (Boring in *Natica.*)
32.*ATKINS, D., 1936–1943. *Quart. J. micr. Sci.,* 79–80 (pts. 1–7).
    (Bivalve gills and mantle cavity.)
33. BACCI, G., 1947. *Pubbl. Staz. Zool. Napoli.,* 21, 183–217. (Sex in
    Archaeogastropoda.)
34. BARNES, G. E., 1955. *J. Exp. Biol.,* 32, 158–174. (Adductor rhythm
    of *Anodonta.*)
35.*BERRY, E. W., 1928. *Quart. Rev. Biol.,* 3, 92–108. (Adaptations of
    fossil cephalopods.)
36.*BERRY, S. Stillmann, 1920. *Biol. Bull.,* 38, 141–195. (Luminescence
    in cephalopods.)
37. BIDDER, A. M., 1950. *Quart. J. micr. Sci.,* 91, 1–43. (Digestion in
    loliginidae.)
37A. BIDDER, A. M., 1957. *Pubbl. Staz. Zool. Napoli,* 29, 139–150. (Diges-
    tion in *Octopus* and *Sepia*).
38. BOYCOTT, A. E., 1934. *J. Ecol.,* 22, 1–38. (Habitats of British land
    snails.)
39. BOYCOTT, A. E., 1936. *J. Anim. Ecol.,* 5, 116–186. (Habits of British
    freshwater molluscs.)
40. BOYCOTT, B. B., & Young, J. Z., 1950. *Symposium—Soc. exp. Biol.,*
    4, 432–453. (Cephalopod learning.)
41. BOYCOTT, B. B., & YOUNG, J. Z., 1955. *Proc. roy. Soc. B.,* 143, 449–
    480. (Memory in *Octopus.*)
42. BOYCOTT, B. B., & YOUNG, J. Z., 1956. *Proc. zool. Soc. Lond.,* 126,
    491–547. (Shape discrimination in *Octopus.*)
43. BRUUN, A. F., 1943. *Dana Repts.,* No. 24. 44 pp. (*Spirula.*)
44. CARRIKER, M. R., 1946. *Biol. Bull. Woods hole,* 91, 88–111. (Diges-
    tion in *Lymnea.*)
45. CAIN, A. J., & SHEPPARD, P. M., 1954. *Genetics,* 39, 89–116. (Natural
    selection in *Cepaea.*)
46.*CARTER, G. S., 1931. *Biol. Rev.,* 6, 1–35. (Aerial and aquatic respira-
    tion.)

47. CHAPMAN, G., & NEWELL, G. E., 1956. *Proc. roy Soc. B.*, *145*, 564–580. (Siphonal extension in bivalves.)
48. CHEESEMAN, D. F., 1956. *Nature*, *178*, 987. (Feeding in *Ampullarius*.)
49. CHUN, C., 1910. *Wiss Ergebn. Tiefsee Exped.* '*Valdivia*', *18*, 1–402, (Oigopsida) and *ibid* (1915). (Myopsida and octopoda.)
49A. CIELAND, DOREEN M., 1954. *Proc. Malacol. Soc. Lond.*, *30*, 167–202. (*Valvata*.)
50.*COE, W. R., 1943–1944. *Quart. Rev. Biol.*, *18*, 154–164; *19*, 85–97. (Sex change.)
51. COLTON, H. S., & PENNYPACKER, M., 1934. *Amer. Nat.*, *68*, 129–136. (Self-fertilization in *Lymnaea*.)
52.*COMFORT, A., 1951. *Biol. Rev.*, *26*, 285–301. (Shell pigments.)
52A.*COMFORT, A., 1957. *Proc. Malacol. Soc. Lond.*, *32*, 219–241. (Age and growth.)
53. Conchological Society of Great Britain and Ireland, 1951. *J. Conch.*, *23*, 6–7. (British land and freshwater molluscs list.)
54. COOK, P. M., 1949. *Proc. Malacol. Soc. Lond.*, *27*, 265–271. (Ciliary feeding in *Viviparus*.)
55. COPELAND, M., 1918. *J. Exp. Zool.*, *25*, 177–228. (Chemosense in *Alectrion* and *Busycon*.)
55A. CREEK, GWENDOLINE A., 1953. *Proc. Malacol. Soc. Lond.*, *29*, 228–240. (Acme.)
56. CROFTS, DORIS R., 1929. *L.M.B.C. Memoir*, *29*. (*Haliotis*.)
57. CROFTS, DORIS R., 1937. *Phil. Trans. B.*, *228*, 219–268. (*Haliotis* development.)
58.*CROFTS, DORIS R., 1955. *Proc. Zool. Soc. Lond.*, *125*, 711–750. (Torsion.)
59. DAINTON, BARBARA H., 1954. *J. exp. Biol.*, *31*, 165–197. (Activity of slugs.)
59A. DAKIN, W. J., 1912. *L.M.B.C. Memoir*, *20* (*Buccinum*.)
60. DALL, W. H., 1895. *Proc. U.S. Nat. Mus.*, *17*, No. 1032. (Lamellibranch classification.)
61.*DELAUNAY, H., 1931. *Biol. Rev.*, *6*, 265–301. (Excretion.)
62. DODD, J. N., 1956. *J. mar. Biol. Assoc. U.K.*, *35*, 327–340. (Hermaphrodite *Patella*.)
63.*DOUVILLÉ, H., 1912. *Bull. Soc. Géol. France* (4), *12*, 419–467. (Lamellibranch classification.)
64. DREW, G. A., 1899. *Anat. Anzeig.*, *15*, 493–518. (Protobranchia.)
65. DREW, G. A., 1907. *Biol. Bull. Woods hole*, *12*, 127–138. (*Ensis*.)
66. DREW, G. A., 1919. *J. Morphol.*, *32*, 379–418. (Spermatophore of *Loligo*).
67. EALES, NELLIE B., 1921. *L.M.B.C. Memoir*, 24. (*Aplysia*.)
68. EALES, NELLIE B., 1950. *Proc. Malacol. Soc. Lond.*, *28*, 185–196. (Secondary symmetry in gastropods.)
69. EVANS, F. G. C., 1951. *J. anim. Ecol.*, *20*, 1–10. (Habits of chitons.)
70. EVANS, T. J., 1922. *Quart. J. micr. Sci.*, *66*, 439–455. (*Calma*.)
71. EVANS, T. J., 1952. *Proc. Malacol. Soc. Lond.*, *29*, 249–258. (*Alderia*.)
72. FLORKIN, M., & LOZET, F., 1949. *Arch. Internat. Physiol.*, *57*, 201–207. (Cellulose in *Helix*.)
73. FLOWER, R. H., 1955. *J. Palaeont.*, *29*, 857–867. (Fossil nautiloid trails.)
74. FORREST, J. E., 1953. *Proc. Linn. Soc. Lond.*, *164*, 225–234. (Dorid feeding.)

75. FREEMAN, R. F. H., & RIGLER, F. H., 1957. *J. mar. Biol. Ass. U.K.*, *36*, 553–567. (Osmorigulation in *Scrobicularia*.)

76. FRETTER, VERA, 1937. *Trans. roy. Soc. Edin.*, *59*, 119–164. (Digestion in chitons.)

77. FRETTER, VERA, 1939. *Proc. roy. Soc. Edin.*, *59*, 599–646. (Digestion in tectibranchs.)

78. FRETTER, VERA, 1941. *Proc. zool. Soc. Lond.*, *110* (B), 185–198. (Digestion in Sacoglossa.)

79. FRETTER, VERA, 1943. *J. mar. Biol. Ass. U.K.*, *25*, 685–720. (*Oncidiclla*.)

80.*FRETTER, VERA, 1946. *J. mar. Biol. Ass. U.K.*, *25*, 173–211; *26*, 312–351. (Genital ducts in Gastropoda.)

81. FRETTER, VERA, 1948. *J. mar. Biol. Ass. U.K.*, *27*, 597–632. (*Skeneopsis, Omalogyra, Rissoella*.)

82. FRETTER, VERA, 1951. *J. mar. Biol. Ass. U.K.*, *29*, 567–586. (*Triphora* and *Cerithiopsis*.)

83. FRETTER, VERA, 1952. *Proc. Malacol. Soc. Lond.*, *29*, 14–20. (Feeding in Cypraeacea.)

84. FRETTER, VERA, 1953. *Proc. Linn. Soc. Lond.*, *164*, 217–224. (Sperm transfer.)

85. FRETTER, VERA, 1955. *Proc. Malacol. Soc. Lond.*, *31*, 137–143. (*Balcis*.)

86. FRETTER, VERA, & GRAHAM, A., 1949. *J. mar. Biol. Ass. U.K.*, *28*, 493–532. (Pyramidellidae.)

87. FRETTER, VERA, & GRAHAM, A., 1954. *J. mar. Biol. Ass. U.K.*, *33*, 565–585. (*Actaeon*.)

88. GARSTANG, W., 1928. *Report Brit. Assoc.* (Sec. D.). (Larvae and torsion.)

89. GASCOIGNE, T., 1956. *Proc. roy. Soc. Edin.*, *63*, 129–151. (*Limapontia*.

89A.GOODHART, C. B., 1958. *J. Anim. Ecol*, *27*, 47–57. (*Cepaea* and thrushes.)

90. GRAHAM, A., 1931. *Trans. roy. Soc. Edin.*, *56*, 725–751. (*Ensis*.)

91. GRAHAM, A., 1932. *Trans. roy. Soc. Edin.*, *57*, 287–308. (Digestion in limpet.)

92. GRAHAM, A., 1934. *Proc. roy. Soc. Edin.*, *54*, 158–187. (Tellinacea.)

93. GRAHAM, A., 1938. *Proc. zool. Soc. Lond.*, *108* (A), 453–463. (*Turritella*.)

94.*GRAHAM, A., 1938. *Proc. roy. Soc. Edin.*, *59*, 267–307. (Gut in Aeoliids.)

95.*GRAHAM, A., 1939. *Proc. zool. Soc. Lond.*, *109* (B), 75–112. (Style-bearing Prosobranchs.)

96.*GRAHAM, A., 1949. *Trans. roy. Soc. Edin.*, *61*, 737–778. (Molluscan stomach.)

97. GRAHAM, A., 1955. *Proc. Malacol. Soc. Lond.*, *31*, 144–159. (Origins, feeding.)

98. GRAHAM, A., 1953. *Proc. Linn. Soc.*, *164*, 213–217. (Carnivorous prosobranchs.)

99.*HEATH, H., 1911. *Mem. Mus. Comp. Zool. Harvard College*, *44*. (Aplacophora.)

100. HENTSCHEL, J., 1933. *Wiss. Meeresuntersuch. Abt. Kiel.*, *21*, 131–158. (Chemosense in *Nassa*.)

101. HERDMAN, W. A., 1890. *Quart. J. micr. Sci.*, *31*, 41–63. (Nudibranch coloration.)

102. HOLME, N. A., 1954. *J. mar. Biol. Ass. U.K.*, *33*, 145–172. (*Ensis.*)
103. HOLMES, W., 1949. *Proc. zool. Soc. Lond.*, *110*, 17–36. (*Sepia* colour change.)
104. HOWELLS, H. H., 1942. *Quart. J. micr. Sci.*, *83*, 357–397. (Gut of *Aplysia.*)
105.*HOWES, N. H., & WELLS, G. P., 1934. *J. exp. Biol.*, *11*, 327–351. (Water relations of land pulmonates.)
106. HOYLE, W. E., 1886. *Challenger repts.* (Zoology), *44*. (Cephalopoda.)
107.*HUBENDICK, B., 1945. *Zool. Bidrag Uppsala*, *24*, 1–216. (Evolution of Basommatophora.)
108. HULBERT, G. C. E. B., & YONGE, C. M., 1937. *Nature*, *139*, 840. (Osphradium.)
109. HUNTER, W. R., 1949. *Proc. roy. Soc. Edin.*, B., *63*, 271–289. (*Saxicava.*)
110. HUNTER, W. R., 1955. *Glasgow Naturalist*, *17*, 173–183. (Jamaican Land Operculates.)
111. HUNTER, W. R., 1955. *Studies on Loch Lomond*, I (Univ. Glasgow). (Freshwater pulmonates.)
112.*IREDALE, T., 1939. *Sci. Repts. Great Barrier Reef Exped. Brit. Mus. N.H.*, *5*, 209–425. (Lamellibranch Classification.)
113. JACKSON, R. T., 1890. *Mem. Boston Soc. Nat. Hist.*, *4* (8). (Lamellibranch Classification.)
114.*JØRGENSON, C. B., 1955. *Biol. Rev.*, *30*, 391–454. (Ciliary Feeding.)
115. KELLOGG, J. L., 1915. *J. Morph.*, *26*, 625–701. (Bivalve Mantle Cavities.)
116.*KNIGHT, J. B., 1952. *Smithson. misc. Coll.*, *117*, no. 13. (Primitive Fossil Gastropods.)
117. KOHN, A. J., 1956. *Proc. Nat. Acad. Sci.*, *42*, 168–171. (Feeding in *Conus.*)
118. LAÇAZE-DUTHIERS, H., 1857. *Ann. Sci. Nat.* (4), 7. (*Dentalium.*)
119. LANKESTER, E. R., 1872. *Proc. roy. Soc.*, *21*, 70–80. (Haemoglobin in *Arca.*)
120.*LEBOUR, MARIE V., 1937. *J. mar. Biol. Ass. U.K.*, *22*, 105–166. (Prosobranch Eggs and Larvae.)
121. LEMCHE, H., 1957. *Nature*, *179*, 413–416. (*Neopilina.*)
121A.LILLY, MOLLY M., *Proc. Malacol. Soc. Lond.*, *30*, 87–109. (*Bithynia.*)
122. LISSMANN, H. W., 1945. *J. exp. Biol.*, *21*, 58–69. (Gastropod Movement.)
123. LOWY, J., 1955. *Nature*, *176*, 345. (Lamellibranch Adductor Muscle.)
124. MCGINITIE, G., 1941. *Biol. Bull. Woods Hole*, *80*, 18–25. (Bivalve Food Collecting.)
125. MILLOTT, N., 1937. *Phil. Trans. B.*, *228*, 173–217. (Feeding in Dorid *Jorunna.*)
126. MILLOTT, N. J., 1937. *J. exp. Biol.*, *14*. (Amoebocytes.)
127. MOORE, J. E. S., 1898–1899. *Quart. J. micr. Sci.*, *41*, 159–181; *42*, 155–187. (Prosobranchs of Lake Tanganyika.)
128.*MORLEY DAVIES, A., 1933. *Proc. Malacol. Soc. Lond.*, *20*, 322–326. (Lamellibranch Classification.)
129. MORRIS, MURIEL, 1950. *Proc. Linn. Soc. N.S.W.*, *75*, 70–80. (Aquiferous System in *Natica.*)
130. MORTON, J. E., 1951. *Quart. J. micr. Sci.*, *92*, 1–20. (*Struthiolaria.*)
131. MORTON, J. E., 1951. *Proc. roy. Soc. N.Z.*, *79*, 1–51. (Vermetidae)

132. MORTON, J. E., 1953. *Proc. Linn. Soc. Lond.*, *164*, 240–246. (Gastropod Stomach.)

133. MORTON, J. E., 1954. *J. mar. Biol. Ass. U.K.*, *33*, 297–312. (*Limacina*.)

134. MORTON, J. E., 1954. *Discovery Repts.*, *27*, 163–200. (Sex in *Limacina*.)

135.*MORTON, J. E., 1954. *Proc. zool. Soc. Lond.*, *125*, 127–168. (Pulmonate Evolution.)

136. MORTON, J. E., 1955. *J. mar. Biol. Ass. U.K.*, *34*, 113–149. (*Otina*.)

137.*MORTON, J. E., 1955. *Phil. Trans. B.*, *239*, 89–160. (Ellobiidae.)

138. MORTON, J. E., 1956. *J. mar. Biol. Ass. U.K.*, *35*, 563–586. (Digestion in *Lasaea*.)

139. MORTON, J. E., 1958. *Proc. Malacol. Soc. Lond.*, *34*, 1–10. (Torsion).

139A.MORTON, J. E., 1958. *J. mar. Biol. Ass. U.K.*, *37*, 000–000. (*Clione*.)

140. MORTON, J. E., & HOLME, N. A., 1955. *J. mar. Biol. Ass U.K.*, *34*, 101–112. (*Akera*.)

141. MOSELEY, H. N., 1895. *Quart. J. micr. Sci.*, *25*, 37–60. (Chiton shell receptors.)

142.*NAEF, A., 1921. Die Cephalopoden: *Flor. und. Faun. d. Golf. v. Neapel*, 35 (1). (Classification of Cephalopods.)

143.*NEEDHAM, J., 1938. *Biol. Rev.*, *13*, 225–251. (Uricotely in Gastropoda.)

144.*NEWELL, G. E., 1953., *J. mar. Biol. Ass. U.K.*, *37*, 229–266. (Orientation in *Littorina*.)

145.*ODHNER, N. H., 1932. (Opisthobranch classification.)

146. ODHNER, N. H., 1939. *Proc. Malacol. Soc. Lond.*, *23*, 231–235. (*Hedylopsis*.)

147. OLDFIELD, EILEEN, 1955. *Proc. Malac. Soc. Lond.*, *31*, 226–249. (*Lasaea* and *Turtonia*.)

148. ORTON, J. H., 1909. *Proc. roy. Soc. Lond.*, *81* (B), 468–484. (Sex in *Crepidula*.)

149. ORTON, J. H., 1912. *J. mar. Biol. Ass. U.K.*, *9*, 444–478. (Feeding in *Crepidula*.)

150.*ORTON, J. H., 1913. *J. mar. Biol. Ass. U.K.*, *10*, 283–311. (Ciliary feeding.)

151.*ORTON, J. H., 1928. *J. mar. Biol. Ass. U.K.*, *15*, 851–862. (Sex in limpets.)

152. ORTON, J. H., SOUTHWARD, A. J., & DODD, J. M., 1956. *J. mar. Biol. Ass. U.K.*, *35*, 149–176. (Sex in limpets.)

153. OWEN, G., 1953. *Quart. J. micr. Sci.*, *94*, 57–70. (Bivalve shell form.)

154. OWEN, G., 1955. *Quart. J. micr. Sci.*, *96*, 517–537. (Bivalve digestive gland.)

155. OWEN, G., 1953. *J. mar. Biol. Ass. U.K.*, *32*, 85–105. (*Isocardia*.)

156. OWEN, G., 1956. *Quart. J. micr. Sci.*, *97*, 541–568. (Gut of *Nucula*.)

157. OWEN, G., TRUEMAN, E. R., & YONGE, C. M., 1952. *Nature*, 171, 73–75. (Ligament in Bivalves.)

158. PARKER, G. H., 1911. *J. Morphol.*, *22*, 155–170. (Snail locomotion.)

159. Pelseneer, P., 1889. *Bull. Sci. France et Belgique*, *20* (3). (Lamellibranch classification.)

160. PICKEN, L. E. R., 1937. *J. exp. Biol.*, *14*, 20–34. (Excretion in *Anodonta* and *Lymnea*.)

161. PICKFORD, GRACE, 1946. *Dana Repts.*, 29, 40 pp. (*Vampyroteuthis*.)

162. POPHAM, M. L., 1940. *J. mar. Biol. Ass. U.K.*, *24*, 549–587. (Erycinacea.)

163. POTTS, F. A., 1923. *Biol. Rev.*, *I*, 1–16. (*Teredo*.)
164. POTTS, W. T. W., 1954. *J. exp. Biol.*, *31*, 614–617. (Osmoregulation in bivalves.)
165. PURCHON, R. D., 1941. *J. mar. Biol. Ass. U.K.*, *25*, 1–39. (*Xylophaga*.)
166. PURCHON, R. D., 1955. *Proc. zool. Soc. Lond.*, *124*, 859–911. (Pholadidae.)
167. PURCHON, R. D., 1956. *Proc. zool. Soc. Lond.*, *127*, 511–525; *129*, 27–60. (Bivalve stomach.)
168. QUAYLE, D. B., 1949. *Proc. Malacol. Soc. Lond.*, *28*, 31–37. (Burrowing of *Venerupis*.)
169. QUICK, H. E., 1943. *J. Conchol.*, *22*, 4–12. (Ecology of pulmonates.)
170.*REDFIELD, A. C., 1934. *Biol. Rev.*, *9*, 175–212. (Haemocyanin.)
171.*REES, W. J., and MAUL, G. E., 19. *Bull Brit. Mus. N.H.*, *3*, (6), (*Eledone*.)
172. REES, W. J., 1957. In *The living scallop*, London, pp. 15–32. (Pecten.)
173. RIDEWOOD, W. G., 1903. *Phil. Trans. B.*, *195*, 147–284. (Bivalve gills.)
174.*ROBERTSON, J. D., 1953. *J. exp. Biol.*, *30*, 277–296. (Molluscan excretion.)
175.*ROBSON, G. C., 1925. *Proc. zool. Soc. Lond.*, 1323–1356. (Deep-sea Octopoda.)
176. ROBSON, G. C., 1926. *J. exp. Biol.*, *3*, 149–160. (Parthenogenesis in *Paludestrina*.)
177 *ROBSON, G. C., 1933. *Proc. zool. Soc. Lond.*, 681–697. (*Architeuthis*.)
178. ROWETT, G. H. Q., 1946. *J. mar. Biol. Ass. U.K.*, *26*, 352–357. (*Calma*.)
179. SATO, T., 1931. *Z. vergl. Physiol.*, *14*, 763–783. (Haemoglobin in *Arca*.)
180.*SMITH, F. G. W., 1935. *Phil. Trans. B.*, *225*, 95–125. (Development of *Patella*.)
181.*SPATHE, L. F., 1933. *Biol. Rev.*, *8*, 418–462. (Evolution of fossil Cephalopoda.)
182. STRATTON, L. W., 1956. *J. Conchol.*, *24*, 111–138. (Ecology of land and freshwater snails.)
183. TAKATSUKI, S., 1934. *Quart. J. micr. Sci.*, *76*, 379–431. (Amoebocytes.)
184.*THORSON, G., 1950. *Biol. Rev.*, *25*, 1–45. (Larval ecology.)
185. TINBERGEN, L., 1939. *Arch. néerl. Physiol.*, *3*, 323–364. (Courtship of *Sepia*.)
186.*TOMPSETT, D. H., 1939. *L.M.B.C. Memoir*, *32*. (*Sepia*.)
187. TRUEMAN, A. E., 1941. *Quart. J. geol. Soc. Lond.*, *96*, 339–383. (Ammonoids.)
188. VERRILL, A. E., 1882. *Rept. U.S. Comm. Fish.* (1879), 211–260. (*Architeuthis*.)
189. WAGGE, L., 1952. *Quart. J. micr. Sci.*, *92*, 307–322. (Shell repair in *Helix*.)
190.*WATSON, H., 1925. *Annals Natal Museum*, *20*, 237–308. (Slug evolution.)
191. WELLS, G. P., 1944. *J. exp. Biol.*, *20*, 79–87. (Aestivation in *Helix*.)
192. WELLS, M. J., & WELLS, J., 1957. *J. exp. Biol.*, *34*, 131–142. (Tactile discrimination in *Octopus*.)
193.*WERNER, B., 1953. *Zool. Anz. Suppl.*, *17*, 529–546. (Ciliary feeding in Prosobranchia.)
194. WILLEY, A., 1902. *Zoological Results*, 6. (*Nautilus*.)

195. WILSON, D. P., & M. A., 1955. *J. mar. Biol. Ass. U.K.*, *35*, 291–305. (*Ianthina.*)

196. WINCKWORTH, R., 1932. *J. Conchol.*, *19*, 211. (List of British marine Mollusca.)

197. YONGE, C. M., 1926. *Trans. roy. Soc. Edin.*, *54*, 703–718. (Digestive diverticula.)

198.*YONGE, C. M., 1926. *J. mar. Biol. Ass. U.K.*, *14*, 295–386. (Digestion in *Ostrea.*)

199. YONGE, C. M., 1926. *J. Linn. Soc. Zool.*, *36*, 417. (Feeding in Thecosomata.)

200. YONGE, C. M., 1927. *Phil. Trans. B.*, *216*, 221–263. (Septibranchia.)

201.*YONGE, C. M., 1928. *Biol. Rev.*, *3*, 21–76. (Feeding mechanisms.)

202.*YONGE, C. M., 1936. *Mém. Mus. Roy. Hist. Nat. Belg.* (Z), *3*, 77–100. (Swimming in bivalves.)

203. YONGE, C. M., 1937. *Proc. Malacol. Soc. Lond.*, *22*, 333–338. (*Dentalium.*)

204. YONGE, C. M., 1937. *J. mar. Biol. Ass. U.K.*, *21*, 687–703. (*Aporrhais.*)

205.*YONGE, C. M., 1937. *Biol. Rev.*, *12*, 87–115. (Digestive systems.)

206. YONGE, C. M., 1938. *Nature*, *164*, 142–146. (Prosobranchs of Lake Tanganyika.)

207.*YONGE, C. M., 1938. *J. mar. Biol. Ass. U.K.*, *22*, 453–468. (Ciliary feeding prosobranchs.)

208.*YONGE, C. M., 1939. *Quart. J. micr. Sci.*, *81*, 367–390. (Mantle cavity of chitons.)

209.*YONGE, C. M., 1939. *Phil. Trans. B.*, *230*, 79–147. (Protobranchia.)

210.*YONGE, C. M., 1946. *J. mar. Biol. Ass. U.K.*, *26*, 358–376. (*Aloidis.*)

211.*YONGE, C. M., 1947. *Phil. Trans. B.*, *232*, 442–518. (Evolution of mantle cavity.)

212. YONGE, C. M., 1949. *Phil. Trans. B.*, *234*, 29–76. (Tellinacea.)

213. YONGE, C. M., 1952. *Univ. Calif. Publ. Zool.*, *55*, 439–449. (Lyonsiidae.)

214. YONGE, C. M., 1952. *Univ. California Publ. Zool.*, *55*, 401–407. (Burrowing in Myacea.)

215.*YONGE, C. M., 1953. *Trans. roy. Soc. Edin.*, *62*, 443–478. (Monomyarian lamellibranchs.)

216.*YONGE, C. M., 1955. *Phil. Trans. B.*, *237*, 335–374. (*Pinna* and Aviculacea.)

217.*YONGE, C. M., 1953. *Proc. zool. Soc. Lond.*, *123*, 551–561. (Tridacnidae.)

218. YONGE, C. M., 1955. *Quart. J. micr. Sci.*, *96*, 383–410. (Boring in Mytilidae.)

219. YONGE, C. M., 1957. *Pubbl. Staz. Zool. Mar. Napoli*, *29*, 151–170. (Bivalve mantle and siphons.)

220. YOUNG, J. Z., 1936. *Quart. J. micr. Sci.*, *78*, 367–386. (Epistellar body.)

221. YOUNG, J. Z., 1938. *J. exp. Biol.*, *15*, 170–185. (Giant fibres.)

222. YOUNG, J. Z., 1939. *Phil. Trans. B.*, *229*, 465–503. (Giant fibres.)

223.*YOUNG, J. Z., 1951. *Proc. roy. Soc. B.*, *139*, 18–37. (*Octopus* learning.)

Also: GRASSE, P.P. (ed.), 1960. *Traité de Zoologie*, t.5. fasc. 2.

FRETTER V. & GRAHAM A., 1962. *British Prosobranch Molluscs.* (Ray Society) London

YONGE, C. M. & WILBUR, K. (ed.), 1964. *Physiology of Mollusca.* New York

INDEX

A

Acanthodoris, 98
Achatina, 116, 131, 170
Aclididae, 177
Acmaeidae, 30, 127
Actaeon, 37, 74, 96, 131, 172
Adaptive Gills, 75
Adductor Muscles, 49, 152
Aesthetes, 147
Aestivation, 168
Akera, 41, 146, 172
Aloidis, 193
Alternative Sexuality, 134
Ambisexuality, 134
Amoebocytes, 88, 119
Amphitretus, 211
Ampullarius, 72, 100, 165
Ancylidae, 43
Anodonta, 50, 115–16, 152, 192
Anomia, 186
Aplysia, 37, 97, 118, 130, 146, 172
Aporrhais, 33
Aquiferous System, 113
Arca, 119, 152, 183
Archimollusc, 12
Architeuthis, 206
Ascus Sac, 98
Athoracophorus, 47

B

Balcis, 177
Bithynia, 117, 166
Boring, in wood and rock, 53, 194
Boring into shells, 95
Botula, 184
Branchial Septum, 83
Buccal Pump, 98–9
Buccinum, 35, 115
Buoyancy, 200
Burrowing, 34, 193
Byssus, 49, 183

C

Calcium, 119, 169
Calma, 99
Calyptraea, 32, 126
Camouflage, 39
Captacula, 22, 101
Capulus, 32, 92
Cardium, 51, 151
Carinaria, 34, 93
Carychium, 127, 163
Cassididae, 45
Cementation, 32, 191
Cepaea, 47
Cerata, 38, 98, 110
Chama, 191
Chaetoderma, 18, 65, 90, 121
Chiroteuthis, 207
Chiton, 18, 65, 89, 147
Chromatophores, 60, 156
Ciliary Feeding, 72, 74, 76
Ciliation of Gill, 23, 69, 80
Cirrothamma, 63, 211
Clathrus, 125
Clausilia, 43, 170
Clavagella, 195
Clione, 42, 97
Cnidus Sac, 98
Coiling in Nautiloids, 198
Colour Change, 60
Commensalism, 188
Consecutive Sexuality, 134
Conus, 96
Corolla, 42, 149
Courtship, 135
Cranchiidae, 208
Crepidula, 32, 126
Crystalline Style, 91
Current Fertilization, 125
Cuspidaria, 83, 106, 195
Cyprina, 188

D

Dentalium, 22, 101

229